SOLUTIONS MANUAL TO

Chemistry: A Fundamental

Overview of Essential Principles

Bassim Hamadeh, CEO and Publisher
John Remington, Senior Field Acquisitions Editor
Gem Rabanera, Project Editor
Abbey Hastings, Associate Production Editor
Jess Estrella, Senior Graphic Designer
Don Kesner, Interior Designer
Natalie Piccotti, Director of Marketing
Kassie Graves, Vice President of Editorial
Jamie Giganti, Director of Academic Publishing

ISBN: 978-1-5165-3584-2 (pbk) / 978-1-5165-3585-9 (br)

SOLUTIONS MANUAL TO

Chemistry: A Fundamental

Overview of Essential Principles

David R. Khan and Jason C. Yarbrough

TABLE OF CONTENTS

CHAPTER 1. THE BASICS OF CHEMISTRY 1

Key Concepts 1

Introduction and Scientific Method 2

Scientific Notation 3

Units of Measurement and Density 5

Uncertainty in Measurements and Significant Figures 13

Dimensional Analysis – Creating and Using Conversion Factors 17

Key Terms 18

CHAPTER 2. THE STRUCTURE OF MATTER 20

Key Concepts 20

Extensive and Intensive Properties 21

Matter: Physical and Chemical Properties and Changes 22

Classification of Matter Based on Composition 25

Foundational Chemical Laws and Atomic Theory 26

Atomic Structure 28

Introduction to the Periodic Table 35

Introduction to Chemical Bonding 39

Key Terms 41

CHAPTER 3. COMPOUNDS, FORMULAS, AND NOMENCLATURE 44

Key Concepts 44

Introduction to Ions, Ionic Bonds, and Ionic Compounds 45

Formulas and Names of Binary Ionic Compounds 49

Formulas and Names of Polyatomic Ions and Their Compounds 55

Formulas and Names of Inorganic Hydrates 59

Formulas and Names of Binary Molecular (Covalent) Compounds 59

Key Terms 61

CHAPTER 4. THE MOLE, CHEMICAL EQUATIONS, AND STOICHIOMETRY 63

Key Concepts 63

Molar Mass 64

Percent Composition 67

Determining Empirical and Molecular Formulas 70

Balancing Chemical Equations 73

Using Balancing Chemical Equations to Calculate Quantities
of Reactants and Products 74

Limiting Reactant and Percent Yield 76

Key Terms 83

CHAPTER 5. DISSOLUTION AND REACTIONS IN AQUEOUS SOLUTION 85

Key Concepts 85

Aqueous Solutions of Ionic Compounds and Predicting Solubility 86

Writing Chemical Equations for Reactions in Aqueous Solution 94

Writing Chemical Equations of Reactions in Aqueous Solution – Acid/Base
Neutralizations and Gas Evolving Reactions 96

Solution Concentration – Molarity and Dilution 101

Solution Concentration – Molality, Mole Fraction, and Mass Percent 105

Stoichiometry of Reactions in Solution 108

Colligative Properties – Raoult's Law 109

Colligative Properties – Boiling Point Elevation and Freezing Point Depression 111

Colligative Properties – Osmosis 114

Key Terms 115

CHAPTER 6. GASES 118

Key Concepts 118

Physical Properties Related to Gas Laws 119

Simple Gas Laws (Boyle's, Charles's, and Avogadro's Laws) 121

The Ideal Gas Law 126

Applications of the Ideal Gas Law 133

Mixtures of Gases and Partial Pressures 139

Real Gases and Deviations from Ideal Behavior 144

Key Terms 145

CHAPTER 7. THE QUANTUM ATOM: ATOMIC STRUCTURE AND PERIODICITY 147

Key Concepts 147

The Wave Nature of Light – Electromagnetic Radiation 148

The Particle Nature of Light 150

Atomic Spectra and the Bohr Model of the Hydrogen Atom 155

De Broglie and the Wave Property of the Electron 163

Heisenberg's Uncertainty Principle and Schrödinger's Equation 164

Electron Spin and Ground State Electron Configurations 167

Ionic Electron Configurations 170

Periodic Trends 172

Key Terms 174

CHAPTER 8. BONDING AND MOLECULAR GEOMETRY 178

Key Concepts 178

Chemical Bonds and Electronegativity 179

Lewis Theory – Lewis Symbols and Structures 180

Valence Shell Electron Pair Repulsion Theory (VSEPR) 192

Bond and Molecular Polarity 196

Valence Bond Theory 197

Molecular Orbital Theory 199

Key Terms 204

CHAPTER 9. INTERMOLECULAR FORCES AND PHASE DIAGRAMS 209

Key Concepts 209

Intermolecular Forces 210

Properties of Liquids Attributed to Intermolecular Forces 213

Phase Diagrams 217

Key Terms 219

CHAPTER 10. CHEMICAL EQUILIBRIUM 222

Key Concepts 222

Equilibrium Constant 223

Equilibrium Constant in Terms of Partial Pressure 227

Heterogeneous Equilibria – Solids and Liquids 228

Determining the Equilibrium Constant 229

The Reaction Quotient 232

Determining Equilibrium Concentrations 233

Le Châtelier's Principle 242

Solubility Product - K_{sp} 244

Key Terms 251

CHAPTER 11. ACIDS, BASES, AND BUFFERS 253

Key Concepts 253

Acids and Bases – Definitions 254

Acids and Bases – Nomenclature 255

Autoionization of Water and Scales Used to Quantify Acidity and Basicity 256

Acid and Base Titrations: A Common Laboratory Technique 260

Acid Strength 263

Base Strength 276

Buffers 288

Key Terms 304

CHAPTER 12. THERMODYNAMICS & THERMOCHEMISTRY 307

Key Concepts 307

The First Law of Thermodynamics and the Nature of Energy 308

Quantifying Heat 310

Quantifying Work 316

Enthalpy 317

Calorimetry 320

Hess's Law 321

Standard Conditions and Enthalpies of Formation 325

The Enthalpy of Bonding 327

Spontaneity, Entropy, and the Second Law of Thermodynamics 330

The Gibbs Free Energy 335

Gibbs Free Energy and Nonstandard Conditions 338

Key Terms 342

CHAPTER 13. OXIDATION-REDUCTION AND ELECTROCHEMISTRY 345

Key Concepts 345

Oxidation-Reduction (Redox) Reactions 346

Balancing Redox Reactions 349

Galvanic (Voltaic) Cells 366

Gibbs Free Energy, Equilibrium, and Cell Potential 373

Electrolysis 379

Key Terms 383

CHAPTER 14. CHEMICAL KINETICS 386

Key Concepts 386

Overview of Chemical Reaction Rates 387

Concentration Effects on Chemical Reaction Rates 391

Key Terms 400

CHAPTER 15. INTRODUCTION TO ORGANIC CHEMISTRY 402

Key Concepts 402

Hydrocarbons 403

Key Terms 416

CHAPTER 16. INTRODUCTION TO BIOCHEMISTRY 418

Key Concepts 418

Proteins and Amino Acids 419

Carbohydrates 422

Lipids 424

Nucleic Acids 426

Key Terms 429

The Basics of Chemistry

KEY CONCEPTS

- Matter
- Scientific Method
- Scientific Laws and Theories
- Scientific Notation
- Measurement, Units, and Unit Conversions
- Significant Figures
- Density

INTRODUCTION AND SCIENTIFIC METHOD

1. What is Chemistry?

    Chemistry is the study of matter, its structure, its properties, and the processes it undergoes.

2. What is the scientific method?

    The scientific method is the *systematic* acquisition of knowledge through observation and experiment.

3. What is a hypothesis?

    A hypothesis is a tentative or speculative explanation for observations. This becomes the basis for future experiment(s) and observation(s).

4. What is an observation?

    An observation is data collected with or without instrumentation. It a can be qualitative or quantitative.

5. What is a scientific law?

    A scientific law is a summary statement (or mathematical equation) which describes a set of observations and can be used to make predictions about the outcome of future events or experiments.

6. How are observations related to scientific laws?

    When specific observations are made consistently and are always the same, such a set of observations can result in the formulation of a *scientific law*.

7. What is a theory?

    A theory is a model which describes the underlying explanations of all observations. Theories are at the height of scientific knowledge. They are models of how the world works, which are supported by large bodies of experimental data and can be used to predict entirely new observations across a wide range of phenomena.

8. What is the difference between a law and a theory? Which one is more powerful?

    A theory is a model which describes the underlying explanations of all observations. A law is a summary of past observations which carries no explanation for itself or its predictions.

9. Classify each of the following as an observation, hypothesis, scientific law, or theory:
    a. A sample of dry ice sublimes at room temperature.

        Observation

    b. Two samples of water were acquired from two different sources within North America and found to contain the same ratio of Oxygen to Hydrogen according to mass.

        Observation

    c. All samples of a given compound will exhibit the same ratio of constituent elements according to mass.

        Law

d. Matter is composed of tiny indestructible particles called atoms. They combine in simple integer ratios to form compounds.

Theory

10. Classify each of the following as an observation, hypothesis, scientific law, or theory:

a. Wood is burned inside a closed system. Following this reaction, the total mass of the system was measured and found to be the same as before the reaction.

Observation

b. During chemical processes, all matter is conserved; it is neither created nor destroyed.

Law

c. The temperature of a sample of nitrogen gas is increased by a factor of two and the pressure of the gas is measured and found to be twice the original pressure.

Observation

d. The pressure of gases is directly proportional to their absolute temperature, holding all other variables constant.

Law

SCIENTIFIC NOTATION

11. Convert each of the following to scientific notation:
   a. 1101 1.101×10^{3}
   b. 0.031 3.1×10^{-2}
   c. 456 4.56×10^{2}
   d. 0.0000033456 3.3456×10^{-6}
   e. 23,901,000 2.3901×10^{7}

12. Convert each of the following to scientific notation:
   a. 2,398,800,000,000,000,000 2.3988×10^{18}
   b. 0.00000000002319 2.319×10^{-11}
   c. 1320 1.32×10^{3}
   d. 12,110,000,000,000 1.211×10^{13}
   e. 0.0000061901 6.1901×10^{-6}

13. Convert each of the following to scientific notation:
   a. 1,198,000 1.198×10^{6}
   b. 19,630,000,000 1.963×10^{10}
   c. 0.0000058897 5.8897×10^{-6}
   d. 0.0008536 8.536×10^{-4}
   e. 0.078991 7.8991×10^{-2}

14. Convert each of the following to scientific notation:
    a. 999 9.99×10^2
    b. 832210 8.3221×10^5
    c. 0.004572 4.572×10^{-3}
    d. 0.00000055598 5.5598×10^{-7}
    e. 0.00034299 3.4299×10^{-4}

15. Convert each of the following to standard notation:
    a. 2.31×10^4 23,100
    b. 2.31×10^{-4} 0.000231
    c. 3.0317×10^{10} 30,317,000,000
    d. 3.0317×10^{-10} 0.00000000030317
    e. 9.13×10^{-7} 0.000000913

16. Convert each of the following to standard notation:
    a. 4.21×10^6 4,210,000
    b. 7.343×10^{-2} 0.07343
    c. 3.339×10^{-16} 0.0000000000000003339
    d. 9.9×10^{-20} 0.000000000000000000099
    e. 9.9×10^{20} 990,000,000,000,000,000,000

17. Convert each of the following to standard notation:
    a. 6.98×10^{-5} 0.0000698
    b. 6.98×10^{-10} 0.000000000698
    c. 6.98×10^5 698,000
    d. 7.11×10^2 711
    e. 7.11×10^{-2} 0.0711

18. Convert each of the following to standard notation:
    a. 1.49×10^2 149
    b. 5.26×10^{-8} 0.0000000526
    c. 6.022×10^{23} 602,200,000,000,000,000,000,000
    d. 1.602×10^{-19} 0.0000000000000000001602
    e. 2.18×10^{-18} 0.00000000000000000218

19. Determine the greatest of each of the following pairs:
    a. 6.626×10^{-34} and 6.626×10^{-43}
    b. 2.18×10^{-18} and 6.626×10^{18}
    c. 6.626×10^{-2} and 6.626×10^{-4}
    d. 4.132×10^{10} and 4.133×10^{10}
    e. 1.21×10^3 and 1.45×10^2

20. Determine the greatest of each of the following pairs:
    a. 5.64×10^{-13} and 5.64×10^{-31}
    b. 7.12×10^{-14} and 7.12×10^{14}
    c. 3.91×10^{-7} and 3.91×10^{-4}
    d. 2.172×10^3 and 2.173×10^3
    e. 2.27×10^3 and 9.65×10^2

21. Complete the following table:

	Standard Notation	Scientific Notation
a.	12,001	1.2001×10^{4}
b.	0.000000452	4.52×10^{-7}
c.	0.000231	2.31×10^{-4}
d.	0.00000000000933	9.33×10^{-12}
e.	100	1×10^{2}

22. Complete the following table:

	Standard Notation	Scientific Notation
a.	0.0001299	1.299×10^{-4}
b.	45,200,000	4.52×10^{7}
c.	45,120,000,000	4.512×10^{10}
d.	8,571,000	8.571×10^{6}
e.	0.00001	1×10^{-5}

UNITS OF MEASUREMENT AND DENSITY

23. What is a unit of measurement?

A unit is a generally accepted *quantity* which is used to accurately and reproducibly report experimental measurements.

24. Name the base units of measurement for length, mass, volume, and time in the SI system.

Length – meter

Mass – kilogram

Volume – cubic meters

Time – seconds

25. What is meant by the term *derived unit*? Give two examples.

These are units which result from multiplication or division of simpler base units. Two such examples are volume (m^{3}) or density (g/ml).

26. What are prefix multipliers and how are they used?

    Prefix multipliers indicate multiplication by powers of 10 and are used to amplify base units into larger or smaller quantities.

27. How many nm are in 1 meter? How many meters are in 1 nm?

    $10^9 \, nm = 1 \, m$

    $1 \, nm = 10^{-9} \, m$

28. How many meters are in 1 km? How many kilometers are in 1 m?

    $10^3 \, m = 1 \, km$

    $1 \, m = 10^{-3} \, km$

29. How many deciliters are in 1 L? How many liters are in 1 dL?

    $10 \, dL = 1 \, L$

    $1 \, dL = 0.01 \, L$

30. How many picoseconds are in 1 s? How many seconds are 1 ps?

    $10^{12} \, ps = 1 \, s$

    $1 \, ps = 10^{-12} \, s$

31. Complete the following:
    a. 1.20×10^{12} m = __1.20__ Tm

    $$(1.20 \times 10^{12} \, m) \times \frac{1 \, Tm}{10^{12} \, m} = 1.20 \, Tm$$

    b. 1.20×10^{-12} g = __1.20__ pg

    $$(1.20 \times 10^{-12} \, g) \times \frac{10^{12} \, pm}{1 \, m} = 1.20 \, pg$$

    c. 3.2 L = __3.2×10^3__ ml

    $$(3.2 \, L) \times \frac{10^3 \, ml}{1 \, L} = 3.2 \times 10^3 \, ml$$

    d. 8.0 mg = __0.80__ cg

    $$(8.0 \, mg) \times \frac{1 \, g}{10^3 \, mg} \times \frac{10^2 \, cg}{1 \, g} = 0.80 \, cg$$

32. Complete the following:
    a. 4.61×10^4 m = __4.61×10^6__ cm
    b. 7.56×10^{-7} g = __7.56×10^{-4}__ mg
    c. 9.3 L = __9.3×10^{12}__ pl
    d. 31.56 mg = __3.156×10^{-5}__ kg

33. Convert 2.135 L into the following units:
    a. ml – 2.135×10^{3} ml
    b. ML – 2.135×10^{-6} ML
    c. kL – 2.135×10^{-3} kL
    d. nL – 2.135×10^{9} nL
    e. pL – 2.135×10^{12} pL

34. What is the volume, in m^{3}, of an object with the following dimensions? What is this same volume in dm^{3}? What is this volume in L?
    Length = 1.0 m
    Width = 3.0 m
    Height = 7.0 m

    $Volume = 1.0\ m \times 3.0\ m \times 7.0\ m = 21\ m^{3}$

    $$21\ m^{3} \times \left(\frac{10\ dm}{1\ m}\right)^{3} = 2.1 \times 10^{4}\ dm^{3}$$

    $$21\ m^{3} \times \left(\frac{100\ cm}{1\ m}\right)^{3} \times \frac{1\ ml}{1\ cm^{3}} \times \frac{1\ L}{1000\ ml} = 2.1 \times 10^{4}\ L$$

35. What is the volume, in cm^{3}, of an object with the following dimensions? What is this same volume in m^{3}? What is this volume in L?
    Length = 29 cm
    Width = 312 cm
    Height = 78 cm

    $Volume = 29\ cm \times 312\ cm \times 78\ cm = 705{,}744\ cm^{3} = 7.1 \times 10^{5}\ cm^{3}$

    $$705{,}744\ cm^{3} \times \left(\frac{1\ m}{100\ cm}\right)^{3} = 0.705744\ m^{3} = 7.1 \times 10^{-1}\ m^{3}$$

    $$705{,}744\ cm^{3} \times \frac{1\ ml}{1\ cm^{3}} \times \frac{1\ L}{1000\ ml} = 705.744\ L = 7.1 \times 10^{2}\ L$$

36. If a room measures 3 m by 5 m by 6 m, what is the volume of the room in m^{3}, dm^{3}, cm^{3}, L, and ml?

    $Volume = 3\ m \times 5\ m \times 6\ m = 90\ m^{3}$

    $$90\ m^{3} \times \left(\frac{10\ dm}{1\ m}\right)^{3} = 9 \times 10^{4}\ dm^{3}$$

    $$90\ m^{3} \times \left(\frac{100\ cm}{1\ m}\right)^{3} = 9 \times 10^{7}\ cm^{3}$$

37. Area: Complete the following conversions:

   a. $1 \, s^2 = \underline{\hspace{1.5cm}} \, ms^2$

   $$1 \, s^2 \times \left(\frac{1000 \, ms}{1 \, s}\right)^2 = 1{,}000{,}000 \, ms^2 = 1 \times 10^6 \, ms^2$$

   b. $5.6 \, cm^2 = \underline{\hspace{1.5cm}} \, mm^2$

   $$5.6 \, cm^2 \times \left(\frac{10 \, mm}{1 \, cm}\right)^2 = 560 \, mm^2 = 5.6 \times 10^2 \, mm^2$$

   c. $4.8 \, mm^2 = \underline{\hspace{1.5cm}} \, m^2$

   $$4.8 \, mm^2 \times \left(\frac{1 \, m}{1000 \, mm}\right)^2 = 0.0000048 \, m^2 = 4.8 \times 10^{-6} \, m^2$$

   d. $78.2 \, pm^2 = \underline{\hspace{1.5cm}} \, nm^2$

   $$78.2 \, pm^2 \times \left(\frac{1 \, nm}{1000 \, pm}\right)^2 = 0.0000782 \, nm^2 = 7.82 \times 10^{-5} \, nm^2$$

   e. $21.78 \, km^2 = \underline{\hspace{1.5cm}} \, Tm^2$

   $$21.78 \, km^2 \times \left(\frac{1 \, Tm}{10^9 \, km}\right)^2 = 2.178 \times 10^{-17} \, Tm^2$$

38. Area: Complete the following conversions:

   a. $4.91 \times 10^4 \, ft^2 = \underline{\hspace{1.5cm}} \, yd^2$

   $$(4.91 \times 10^4 \, ft^2) \times \left(\frac{1 \, yd}{3 \, ft}\right)^2 = 5.46 \times 10^3 \, yd^2$$

   b. $2.89 \times 10^{-2} \, m^2 = \underline{\hspace{1.5cm}} \, cm^2$

   $$(2.89 \times 10^{-2} \, m^2) \times \left(\frac{100 \, cm}{1 \, m}\right)^2 = 2.89 \times 10^2 \, cm^2$$

   c. $1.99 \, dm^2 = \underline{\hspace{1.5cm}} \, mm^2$

   $$(1.99 \, dm^2) \times \left(\frac{m}{10 \, dm}\right)^2 \times \left(\frac{100 \, cm}{m}\right)^2 = 1.99 \times 10^2 \, cm^2$$

   d. $7.32 \, Mm^2 = \underline{\hspace{1.5cm}} \, m^2$

   $$(7.32 \, Mm^2) \times \left(\frac{10^6 \, m}{1 \, Mm}\right)^2 = 7.32 \times 10^{12} \, m^2$$

   e. $8.112 \, nm^2 = \underline{\hspace{1.5cm}} \, \mu m^2$

   $$(8.112 \, nm^2) \times \left(\frac{1 \, m}{10^9 \, nm}\right)^2 \times \left(\frac{10^6 \, \mu m}{1 \, m}\right)^2 = 8.112 \times 10^{-6} \, \mu m^2$$

39. Volume: Complete the following conversions:

    a. $4.91 \times 10^4 \, \text{dm}^3 = \underline{\hspace{2cm}} \, \text{L}$

    $$(4.91 \times 10^4 \, dm^3) \times \frac{1 \, L}{1 \, dm^3} = 4.91 \times 10^4 \, L$$

    b. $4.53 \times 10^{-6} \, \text{m}^3 = \underline{\hspace{2cm}} \, \text{mm}^3$

    $$4.53 \times 10^{-6} \, m^3 \times \left(\frac{10^3 \, mm}{1 \, m} \right)^3 = 4.53 \times 10^3 \, mm^3$$

    c. $1.99 \, \text{cm}^3 = \underline{\hspace{2cm}} \, \text{mL}$

    $$1.99 \, cm^3 \times \frac{1 \, ml}{1 \, cm^3} = 1.99 \, mL$$

    d. $7.39 \, \text{Mm}^3 = \underline{\hspace{2cm}} \, \text{m}^3$

    $$7.39 \, Mm^3 \times \left(\frac{10^6 \, m}{1 \, Mm} \right)^3 = 7.39 \times 10^{18} \, m^3$$

    e. $4.333 \, \text{nm}^3 = \underline{\hspace{2cm}} \, \mu\text{m}^3$

    $$4.333 \, nm^3 \times \left(\frac{1 \, m}{10^9 \, nm} \right)^3 \times \left(\frac{10^6 \, \mu m}{1 \, m} \right)^3 = 4.333 \times 10^{-9} \, m^3$$

40. Volume: Complete the following conversions:

    a. $6.22 \, \text{km}^3 = \underline{\hspace{2cm}} \, \text{Mm}^3$

    $$6.22 \, km^3 \times \left(\frac{10^3 \, m}{1 \, km} \right)^3 \times \left(\frac{1 \, Mm}{10^6 \, m} \right)^3 = 6.22 \times 10^{-9} \, Mm^3$$

    b. $9.1 \times 10^3 \, \text{mm}^3 = \underline{\hspace{2cm}} \, \text{cm}^3$

    $$9.1 \times 10^3 \, mm^3 \times \left(\frac{1 \, m}{10^3 \, mm} \right)^3 \times \left(\frac{100 \, cm}{1 \, m} \right)^3 = 9.1 \, cm^3$$

    c. $9.1 \times 10^3 \, \text{cm}^3 = \underline{\hspace{2cm}} \, \text{mm}^3$

    $$9.1 \times 10^3 \, cm^3 \times \left(\frac{1 \, m}{10^2 \, cm} \right)^3 \times \left(\frac{10^3 \, mm}{1 \, m} \right)^3 = 9.1 \times 10^6 \, mm^3$$

    d. $6.42 \, \text{m}^3 = \underline{\hspace{2cm}} \, \text{cm}^3$

    $$6.42 \, m^3 \times \left(\frac{10^2 \, cm}{1 \, m} \right)^3 = 6.42 \times 10^6 \, cm^3$$

e. $6.112 \text{ pm}^3 =$ _____ mm^3

$$6.112 \text{ pm}^3 \times \left(\frac{1 \text{ m}}{10^{12} \text{ pm}}\right)^3 \times \left(\frac{10^3 \text{ mm}}{1 \text{ m}}\right)^3 = 6.112 \times 10^{-27} \text{ mm}^3$$

41. If a sample has a mass of 1.356 g and occupies a volume of 1.775 ml, what is its density in g/ml?

$$d = \frac{1.356 \text{ g}}{1.775 \text{ ml}} = 0.7639 \text{ g/ml}$$

42. If a sample of lithium is cut into a cube with each side being 2.00 cm in length, what is the density of lithium if the sample weighs 4.32 g?

$$d = \frac{4.32 \text{ g}}{(2.00 \text{ cm} \times 2.00 \text{ cm} \times 2.00 \text{ cm})\left(\frac{1 \text{ ml}}{1 \text{ cm}^3}\right)} = 0.540 \text{ g/ml}$$

43. If a sample has a mass of 4.13 g and occupies a volume of 3.780 ml, what is its density in g/ml?

$$d = \frac{4.13 \text{ g}}{3.780 \text{ ml}} = 1.09 \text{ g/ml}$$

44. A sample of magnesium has a volume of 4.94 ml. If the sample weighs 8.596 g, what is its density?

$$d = \frac{8.596 \text{ g}}{4.94 \text{ ml}} = 1.74 \text{ g/ml}$$

45. A metal ball has a radius of 0.751 cm. If the ball weighs 15.897 g, what is the density of the ball? Based on the data in Table 1.5, what is the identity of the metal?

$$volume = \frac{4}{3}\pi r^3 = \frac{4}{3}\pi (0.751 \text{ cm})^3 = 1.774224 \text{ cm}^3$$

$$d = \frac{mass}{volume} = \frac{15.897 \text{ g}}{1.774224 \text{ ml}} = 8.96 \text{ g/ml}; \text{ Copper}$$

46. An unknown solid compound has a mass of 54.84 g. When submerged in water in a graduated cylinder, the volume was displaced from 28.77 ml to 34.89 ml. What is the density of the sample?

$$volume = 34.89 \text{ ml} - 28.77 \text{ ml} = 6.12 \text{ ml}$$

$$d = \frac{mass}{volume} = \frac{54.84 \text{ g}}{6.12 \text{ ml}} = 8.96 \text{ g/ml}$$

47. An unknown solid compound has a mass of 13.2 g. When submerged in water in a graduated cylinder, the volume was displaced from 10.00 ml to 22.34 ml. What is the density of the sample?

volume = 22.34 *ml* − 10.00 *ml* = 12.34 *ml*

$$d = \frac{mass}{volume} = \frac{13.2\ g}{12.34\ ml} = 1.07\ g/ml$$

48. An unknown solid compound has a mass of 7.82 g. If the sample displaces 3.11 ml of water in a graduated cylinder, what is the sample's mass?

$$d = \frac{mass}{volume} = \frac{7.82\ g}{3.11\ ml} = 2.51\ g/ml$$

49. An unknown sample was submerged in a quantity of water contained in a graduated cylinder. Upon submersion, the water level rose from an initial volume of 12.50 ml to a final volume of 17.37 ml. If the sample's mass was measured to be 22.3 g, what is its density?

volume = 17.37 *ml* − 12.50 *ml* = 4.87 *ml*

$$d = \frac{mass}{volume} = \frac{22.3\ g}{4.87\ ml} = 4.58\ g/ml$$

50. An unknown sample was submerged in a quantity of water contained in a graduated cylinder. Upon submersion, the water level rose from an initial volume of 14.30 ml to a final volume of 17.57 ml. If the sample's mass was measured to be 12.50 g, what is its density?

volume = 17.57 *ml* − 14.30 *ml* = 3.27 *ml*

$$d = \frac{mass}{volume} = \frac{12.50\ g}{3.27\ ml} = 3.82\ g/ml$$

51. An unknown sample was submerged in a quantity of water contained in a graduated cylinder. Upon submersion, the water level rose from an initial volume of 42.71 ml to a final volume of 44.49 ml. If the sample's mass was measured to be 20.114 g, what is its density?

volume = 44.49 *ml* − 42.71 *ml* = 1.78 *ml*

$$d = \frac{mass}{volume} = \frac{20.114\ g}{1.78\ ml} = 11.3\ g/ml$$

52. An unknown metal sample was weighed and found to have a mass of 22.587 g. The sample was then placed in a graduated cylinder containing water with a volume of 18.91 ml. Upon submersion of the sample, the water level rose to 21.43 ml. Based on this, calculate the density of the sample and use Table 1.5 to identify the metal.

$volume = 21.43 \; ml - 18.91 \; ml = 2.52 \; ml$

$d = \dfrac{mass}{volume} = \dfrac{22.587 \; g}{2.52 \; ml} = 8.96 \; g/ml;$ Copper

53. An unknown sample was weighed and found to have a mass of 74.76 g. The sample was then placed in a graduated cylinder containing water with a volume of 39.66 ml. Upon submersion of the sample, the water level rose to 46.78 ml. Based on this, calculate the density of the sample and use Table 1.5 to identify the metal.

$volume = 46.78 \; ml - 39.66 \; ml = 7.12 \; ml$

$d = \dfrac{mass}{volume} = \dfrac{74.76 \; g}{7.12 \; ml} = 10.5 \; g/ml;$ Silver

54. An unknown sample was weighed and found to have a mass of 3.402 g. The sample was then placed in a graduated cylinder containing water with a volume of 32.10 ml. Upon submersion of the sample, the water level rose to 33.36 ml. Based on this, calculate the density of the sample and use Table 1.5 to identify the metal.

$volume = 33.36 \; ml - 32.10 \; ml = 1.26 \; ml$

$d = \dfrac{mass}{volume} = \dfrac{3.402 \; g}{1.26 \; ml} = 2.70 \; g/ml;$ Aluminum

55. Convert the following temperatures to the Kelvin Scale:
   a. 0°F

   $$K = \dfrac{(0°F - 32)}{1.8} + 273.15 = 255 \; K$$

   b. 0°C

   $$K = 0°C + 273 = 273 \; K$$

   c. 45.0°C

   $$K = 45.0°C + 273.15 = 318.2 \; K$$

   d. 212°F

   $$K = \dfrac{(212°F - 32)}{1.8} + 273.15 = 373 \; K$$

   e. 250°C

   $$K = 250°C + 273.15 = 523 \; K$$

56. Convert the following temperatures into the Celsius Scale:
    a. 32°F

    $$C = \frac{(32°F - 32)}{1.8} = 0°C$$

    b. 500 K

    $$C = 500\ K - 273.15 = 227°C$$

    c. 250 K

    $$C = 250\ K - 273.15 = -23°C$$

    d. 120°F

    $$C = \frac{(120°F - 32)}{1.8} = 49°C$$

    e. 95°F

    $$C = \frac{(95°F - 32)}{1.8} = 35°C$$

UNCERTAINTY IN MEASUREMENTS AND SIGNIFICANT FIGURES

57. Determine the number of significant figures in the following:
    a. 1.000 nm – 4 significant figures
    b. 100 nm – 1 significant figure
    c. 403100 L – 4 significant figures
    d. 91303 ml – 5 significant figures
    e. 9.1303 ml – 5 significant figures

58. Determine the number of significant figures in the following:
    a. 0.500 ml – 3 significant figures
    b. 9.1300 L – 5 significant figures
    c. 1001 balloons – Infinite significant figures – this is an exact number.
    d. 403°C – 3 significant figures
    e. 403.0°C – 4 significant figures
    f. 4.1×10^4 mm – 2 significant figures

59. Determine the number of significant figures in the following:
    a. 4.012×10^{-6} m – 4 significant figures
    b. 7.0123 m – 5 significant figures
    c. 0.0002341 L – 4 significant figures
    d. 0.004200 ml – 4 significant figures
    e. 100100 mi – 4 significant figures

60. Determine the number of significant figures in the following:
    a. 2.100 L – 4 significant figures
    b. 2.100 mL – 4 significant figures
    c. 2,100 L – 2 significant figures
    d. 2,100.00 L – 6 significant figures
    e. 0.0021000 mL – 5 significant figures

61. Which of the following are exact numbers?
    a. The ball was dropped 23.2 feet. – 3 significant figures
    b. There are 7 students in class. – Infinite significant figures – this is an exact number.
    c. The radius of a circle is the diameter divided by 2. – Infinite significant figures – this is an exact number.
    d. There are 12 inches in 1 foot. – Infinite significant figures - this is an exact number.
    e. The table is 12.5 feet long. – 3 significant figures

    b., c., and d. are exact numbers.

62. Which of the following are exact numbers?
    a. During a trip an automobile travels at an average speed of 23 mph – 2 significant figures
    b. 12 = 1 dozen – Infinite significant figures – this is an exact number.
    c. The mass of a coin is 4.31 g. – 3 significant figures
    d. There are 7 pencils in my briefcase. – Infinite significant figures – this is an exact number.
    e. It is 32.25 km to the next town. – 4 significant figures

    b., and d. are exact numbers.

63. Write 1,278,342 to 3 significant figures.

    1,280,000

64. Write 0.087217005 to 4 significant figures.

    0.08722

65. Write 2000 to 2 significant figures. (Hint: You may have to use scientific notation.)

    2.0×10^{3}

66. Write each of the following to 4 significant figures:
    a. 1

        1.000

    b. 10

        10.00

    c. 123

        123.0

    d. 1230001

        1.230×10^{6}

 e. 2101.799

  2,102

 f. 0.0221945

  0.02219

 g. 2,222,999

  2,223,000

 h. 7.901296430

  7.901

67. Perform the following calculation to the correct number of significant figures:

 $4.5 + 3.19 + 0.000321 =$

 Since the last significant digit for 4.5 is in the tenths place, this will be the position of the last significant digit in the result: 7.690321 = **7.7**

68. Perform the following calculation to the correct number of significant figures:

 $4.5 - 3.19 =$

 Since the last significant digit for 4.5 is in the tenths place, this will be the position of the last significant digit in the result: 1.31 = **1.3**

69. Perform the following calculation to the correct number of significant figures:

 $(3.98)(9.2134) =$

 Since 3.98 has the fewest significant digits (3), the result will also have 3 significant digits: 36.66933 = **36.7**

70. Perform the following calculation to the correct number of significant figures:

 $4.32 \div 67.009 = 0.0645$

71. Perform the following calculations to the correct number of significant figures:

 a. $53.23 - 1.0 = 52.2$

 b. $21.2241 + 7.23 + (4.321 \times 10^{-8}) = 28.45$

 c. $1.93001 + 2.403 + 6.0000 = 10.333$

 d. $77.88 + 88.1 - 10.0000 = 156.0$

72. Perform the following calculations to the correct number of significant figures:

 a. $9.0000 + 10.0000 - 1.00 = 18.00$

 b. $(2.0 \times 10^{5}) + 111 + 222 = 2.0 \times 10^{5}$

 c. $23.321 + 1,000 - 10.25 = 1,000$

 d. $32.78 - 16.11124 - 6.234 = 10.43$

73. Perform the following calculations to the correct number of significant figures:

   a. $5 \times 1000 = 5000$

   b. $5.32 \div 21.311 \times 120 = 30.$

   c. $66.21 \times 2.3 \times 9.5 = 1,400$

   d. $12345 \div 1 = 10,000$

74. Perform the following calculations to the correct number of significant figures:

   a. $(4.7 \times 10^4) \times 2.398 = 110,000$

   b. $8.129 \div 4.07 \times 6.231 = 12.4$

   c. $3.4037 \div (1.82 \times 10^{-3}) \div 5.001 = 374$

   d. $100.0 \div 2.10 \times 1,000,000 = 5 \times 10^7$

75. Explain the correct order of mathematical operations when carrying out calculations involving measured numbers.

   Calculations should be carried out in the following order of mathematical operations:

   1. **Parentheses** – all operations in parentheses should be carried out first and the resulting number of significant figures determined for the resulting values.

   2. **Exponents** – all exponential notations should be executed.

   3. **Multiplication/Division** – All multiplication and division should be carried out following any operations in parentheses or exponential terms.

   4. **Addition/Subtraction**

   At each step, the last significant figure should be determined in the resulting terms. This allows appropriate application of the rules regarding significant figures to be applied at each step of the process.

76. Perform the following calculations to the correct number of significant figures:

   a. $4.57 \times \dfrac{4.113}{(12.89 + 1.9975)} + 12.095 = 4.57 \times \dfrac{4.113}{14.8875} + 12.095 = 13.36$

   b. $(12.43 + 2.10001) + (3.776 - 1.2015) = 14.53001 + 2.5745 = 17.10$

   c. $6.109 \times \dfrac{(9.531 - 4.23)}{(894.2 - 892.109)} + 10.2387 = 6.109 \times \dfrac{5.301}{2.091} + 10.2387 = 26$

   d. $4.1 \div 1.064 \times (4.21 - 6.321) = -8.1$

77. Perform the following calculations to the correct number of significant figures:

   a. $7.019 + 42.1 \div 3.9000 = 17.8$

   b. $9.927 \times \dfrac{4.0000}{2.0} + 11.1 = 31$

   c. $1.1 \times 5.890 \div (10.1 + 9.013) = 0.34$

   d. $\dfrac{(7.01 - 2.5)}{(8.09991 \times 1.0)} \times (11.0021 + 4.1) = 8.4$

DIMENSIONAL ANALYSIS – CREATING AND USING CONVERSION FACTORS

78. If the density of a sample is 0.8901 g/ml, what is the mass of the sample if it displaces 4.12 ml of water in a graduated cylinder?

Since the sample displaces 4.12 ml of water, we know this is the volume of the sample. Therefore, we can use density as a conversion factor to determine its mass.

$$4.12 \ ml \times \frac{0.8901 \ g}{1 \ ml} = 3.67 \ g$$

79. The density of acetone (nail polish remover) is 0.7845 g/ml. What is the mass in kg of a sample with a volume of 2.73 L?

$$2.73 \ L \times \frac{1000 \ ml}{1 \ L} \times \frac{0.7845 \ g}{1 \ ml} \times \frac{1 \ kg}{1000 \ g} = 2.14 \ kg$$

80. The density of isopropyl alcohol is 0.7860 g/ml. What is the mass of a sample (in grams) if its volume is 1.12 ml?

$$1.12 \ ml \times \frac{0.7860 \ g}{1 \ ml} = 0.880 \ g$$

81. The density of water is 1.00 g/ml. If a 3.0 L container is full of water, what is the mass of the water in the container?

$$3.0 \ L \times \frac{1000 \ ml}{1 \ L} \times \frac{1.00 \ g}{1 \ ml} = 3.0 \times 10^{3} \ g$$

82. If a certain area is defined by a rectangle with a length of 7.31 miles and a width of 3.48 miles, what is this area in square meters?

$$(7.31 \ mi \times 3.48 \ mi) \times \left(\frac{1 \ km}{0.62137 \ mi.} \right)^{2} \times \left(\frac{1000 \ m}{1 \ km} \right)^{2} = 6.59 \times 10^{7} \ m^{2}$$

83. If a backyard pool is 8.0 m long, 4.0 m wide, and has an average depth of 2.0 m (from the water level to the bottom), how many gallons of water are required to fill the pool? (Hint: 1 gal. = 3.785 L)

$$(8.0 \ m \times 4.0 \ m \times 2.0 \ m) \times \left(\frac{10 \ dm}{1 \ m} \right)^{3} \times \frac{1 \ L}{1 \ dm^{3}} \times \frac{1 \ gal}{3.785 \ L} = 17{,}000 \ gallons$$

84. How many inches are in 1 Tm? (Hint: 2.54 cm = 1 in)

$$1 \ Tm \times \frac{10^{12} \ m}{1 \ Tm} \times \frac{100 \ cm}{1 \ m} \times \frac{1 \ in.}{2.54 \ cm} = 3.94 \times 10^{13} \ in.$$

85. How many cm are in 1 foot? (Hint: 2.54 cm = 1 in.)

$$1\,ft. \times \frac{12\,in.}{1\,ft.} \times \frac{2.54\,cm}{1\,in.} = 30.5\,cm$$

86. If a container weighs 111.34 g empty and is then filled with water, weighed again, and found to weigh 611.76 g when full, what volume can the container hold?

First you need to recall that the density of water is 1.00 g/ml. Then you must deduce the weight of the water alone. This weight is determined by calculating the difference in weight between the empty and full container.

$$(611.76\,g - 111.34\,g) \times \frac{1\,ml}{1.00\,g} = 500.42\,ml$$

This is an approximately ½ L-container

KEY TERMS

Absolute zero The temperature at which there is no thermal energy at all. As such, the point 0 Kelvin (0 K) is the lowest possible temperature reading on the Kelvin scale.

Celsius One of the three main temperature scales. In the Celsius scale, pure water freezes at 0°C and boils at 100°C. The Celsius scale is of practical convenience because its units and reference point are all based on the freezing and boiling points of pure water.

Chemistry The study of matter, its structure, its properties, and the processes it undergoes.

Conversion factor A ratio constructed from a mathematic equality which can be used to inter-convert between different units of measurement.

Density The quantitative relation between the mass of a substance and its volume. It is a measure of how much matter is contained in a given unit of volume for a particular substance.

Derived units *Units* are quantities. As such, they can be multiplied and divided like any other algebraic quantity. The results of applying mathematical operations to *units*, is the formation of new units. These are sometimes referred to as *derived units*.

Dimensional analysis A method which relies on the construction and use of *conversion factors* to convert from one set of units to another in the expression of a given quantity.

Experiment A scientific procedure carried out under controlled conditions to test a theory, law, or hypothesis.

Fahrenheit One of the three main temperature scales. In the Fahrenheit scale, saturated salt water freezes at 0°F and pure water boils at 212°F.

Gram The base unit of the measurement for mass in the metric system.

Hypothesis A tentative or speculative explanation for observations. This becomes the basis for future experiment(s) and observation(s).

Imperial system The most common system of measurement in the United States. This system includes familiar units such as the pound (lb), the mile (mi), yards (yds), feet (ft), inches (in), quarts (qt), and gallons (gal).

International system (SI) The official system of measurement for most of the world. The SI system is based on the *metric system*.

Kelvin One of the three main temperature scales. The Kelvin scale is unique in that its zero point is the coldest possible temperature, *absolute zero*.

Liter A unit of volume in the metric system. The liter is defined as 1 cubic decimeter (dm^3).

Mass The measure of how much matter an object contains. More accurately, it is the quantitative measure of how much matter makes up a sample.

Matter (from the Latin word, materia, meaning material) is defined as anything that has mass and occupies space.

Meter The base unit in the metric and SI systems for length. 1 meter is equal to 3.28 feet.

Metric system A base-10 system of measurement. The metric system is the basis for the SI system and employs prefix multipliers to amplify or diminish base units of measurement by powers of 10.

Observation An observation may be *qualitative* and as simple as noting some phenomenon observed by the naked eye. It may also be *quantitative* in nature, requiring tools or instruments in order to be recorded and understood.

Prefix multipliers A prefix multiplier is applied to a unit and either multiplies or divides it by some power of 10. For example, 1 centimeter is 1/100 of a meter.

Scientific law A summary statement (or mathematical equation) which describes a set of observations and can be used to make predictions about the outcome of future events or experiments.

Scientific method The systematic acquisition of knowledge through observation and experiment.

Scientific notation A system in which numbers are expressed as products of a coefficient between 1 and 10 multiplied by powers of ten.

Significant figures Those digits in a measured or calculated number which are meaningful.

Temperature The measure of the average kinetic energy of the molecules or particles that make up a sample.

Theory A model which describes the underlying explanations of all observations. Theories are the height of scientific knowledge. They are models of how the world works, which are supported by large bodies of experimental data and can be used to predict entirely new observations across a wide range of phenomena.

Unit of measurement A generally accepted *quantity* which is used to accurately and reproducibly report experimental measurements.

Volume The measure of how much space a sample of matter occupies.

CHAPTER 2

The Structure of Matter

KEY CONCEPTS

- Classification of Matter According to Composition
- Classification of Matter According to Physical State
- Chemical and Physical Changes and Properties
- Elements and Atomic Theory
- Atomic Structure
- Isotopes and Atomic Mass
- The Periodic Table

EXTENSIVE AND INTENSIVE PROPERTIES

1. What are extensive properties?

    Extensive properties are dependent upon the amount of the substance present, such as mass and volume.

2. What are intensive properties?

    Intensive properties are independent of the amount of substance present.

3. Which of the following is an example of an extensive property?
    a. Volume
    b. Boiling Point
    c. Density
    d. Freezing Point

    Volume

4. Which of the following is an example of an extensive property?
    a. Solubility
    b. Weight
    c. Density
    d. Freezing Point

    Weight

5. Which of the following is an example of an intensive property?
    a. Mass
    b. Weight
    c. Melting Point
    d. Volume

    Melting Point

6. Which of the following is an example of an intensive property?
    a. Length
    b. Density
    c. Weight
    d. Mass

    Density

7. Mass is an (extensive/intensive) property.

8. Density is an (extensive/intensive) property.

9. Color is an (extensive/intensive) property.

10. Volume is an (extensive/intensive) property.

11. Flammability is an (extensive/intensive) property.

12. The charge of an atom is an (extensive/intensive) property.

13. Classify each of the following as an extensive or intensive property:
    a. Length- Extensive
    b. Mass- Extensive
    c. Malleability- Intensive
    d. Solubility- Intensive

14. Classify each of the following as an extensive or intensive property:
    a. Freezing Point- Intensive
    b. Temperature- Intensive
    c. Conductivity- Intensive
    d. Weight- Extensive

15. Categorize the items below as having either extensive or intensive properties:
    a. Mass of a tea cup- Extensive
    b. Volume of coffee in a mug- Extensive
    c. Color of a balloon- Intensive
    d. Circumference of a baseball- Extensive

16. Categorize the items below as having either extensive or intensive properties:
    a. Temperature of liquid mercury- Intensive
    b. Height of a person- Extensive
    c. Boiling point of a substance- Intensive
    d. The melting point of a substance- Intensive

MATTER: PHYSICAL AND CHEMICAL PROPERTIES AND CHANGES

17. What is the definition of matter?

    Matter is defined as anything that has mass and occupies space.

18. What are the three states of matter discussed in this chapter?

    The three states of matter discussed in this chapter are solid, liquid, and gas.

19. What are the characteristics that are exhibited by solids?

    Solids have a definite shape, definite volume and are not fluid or compressible.

20. What are the characteristics that are exhibited by liquids?

    Liquids have an indefinite shape, definite volume and are fluid and incompressible.

21. What are the characteristics that are exhibited by gases?

    Gases have an indefinite shape, indefinite volume and are fluid and compressible.

22. What is a physical property?

    A physical property can be observed or measured. Some examples of physical properties are color, density, boiling point, and melting point.

23. What is a chemical property?

A chemical property refers to the ability of a substance to form new substances. Examples of chemical properties can include flammability and pH.

24. Which of the following is an example of a physical property?
    a. Corrosiveness
    b. Toxicity
    c. Flammability
    d. Boiling Point

    Boiling Point

25. Which of the following is an example of a physical property?
    a. Density
    b. pH
    c. Flammability
    d. Toxicity

    Density

26. Which of the following is an example of a chemical property?
    a. Color
    b. Melting Point
    c. Density
    d. pH

    pH

27. Which of the following is an example of a chemical property?
    a. Corrosiveness
    b. Boiling point
    c. Texture
    d. Color

    Corrosiveness

28. What is a physical change?

A physical change occurs when a substance goes from one state to the next without altering the chemical composition of the substance.

29. What is a chemical change?

A chemical change occurs when a reaction results in the formation of a new substance.

30. Classify the following as either a chemical or physical change:
    a. The melting of ice into liquid water- Physical Change
    b. The rusting of iron- Chemical Change
    c. Sugar dissolving in water- Physical Change
    d. The burning of propane for heat- Chemical Change

31. Classify the following as either a chemical or physical change:
    a. The evaporation of rubbing alcohol- Physical Change
    b. The brewing of tea- Physical Change
    c. A match igniting a firework- Chemical Change
    d. The burning of coal- Chemical Change

32. Which of the following is an example of a chemical change?
    a. Boiling of water
    b. Rusting of iron
    c. Evaporation of alcohol
    d. Dissolving of sugar in water

    Rusting of iron

33. Which of the following is an example of a chemical change?
    a. A metal surface becomes dull due to continued abrasion
    b. Copper metal turns green with prolonged exposure to air
    c. Boiling water
    d. Breaking a block of aluminum into smaller pieces

    Copper metal turns green with prolonged exposure to air

34. Which of the following is an example of a physical change?
    a. The melting of ice into liquid water
    b. Burning wood
    c. Tarnishing of jewelry
    d. Baking a cake

    The melting of ice into liquid water

35. Which if the following is an example of a physical change?
    a. Shaping clay into a ball
    b. The souring of milk
    c. Combustion of butane
    d. Rusting of iron

    Shaping clay into a ball

36. A match igniting a firework is an example of a (physical/chemical) change.

37. Breaking a glass bottle is an example of a (physical/chemical) change.

38. Shredding paper is an example of a (physical/chemical) change.

39. Cooking an egg is an example of a (physical/chemical) change.

40. Bubbles forming when hydrogen peroxide is applied to a cut is an example of a (chemical/physical) change?

41. Combining vinegar and baking soda to produce carbon dioxide gas is an example of a (chemical/physical) change.

CLASSIFICATION OF MATTER BASED ON COMPOSITION

42. What is a pure substance? Give an example.

A pure substance is a sample of matter which cannot be separated or divided into simpler components by physical means. Pure water would be a good example of a pure substance.

43. What is a compound? Give an example.

A compound is a substance composed of two or more elements that are joined together in fixed, definite proportions. Table salt (or NaCl) is a good example of a compound.

44. What is a mixture?

A mixture of substances is composed of two or more components such that it has variable composition.

45. What is a homogeneous mixture? What is a heterogeneous mixture?

A homogeneous mixture is the same or uniform throughout. A heterogeneous mixture is not uniform throughout, and it varies in its composition when comparing one region to the next.

46. Soil is an example of a (homogeneous/**heterogeneous**) mixture.

47. A dilute solution of hydrochloric acid is an example of a (**homogeneous**/heterogeneous) mixture.

48. Wet sand from the beach is a (homogeneous/**heterogeneous**) mixture.

49. Italian vinaigrette salad dressing is a (homogeneous/**heterogeneous**) mixture.

50. Sweetened tea is a (**homogeneous**/heterogeneous) mixture.

51. Mouthwash is a (**homogeneous**/heterogeneous) mixture.

52. Beef stew is a (homogeneous/**heterogeneous**) mixture.

53. What is distillation?

Distillation can involve the separation of two or more liquids that have different boiling points. This technique can also be used to separate a liquid from a solid.

54. What is centrifugation?

Centrifugation involves the application of centripetal force, for example using a centrifuge, to allow for heavier substances to settle as sediment at the bottom of a mixture while lighter substances remain on the top. This is a common technique used for separating the various components that make up human blood.

55. What is filtration

Filtration is a separation technique in which a solid can be separated from a liquid by simply pouring a solid/liquid mixture through filter paper which captures the solid while the liquid flows through the paper into a new container.

56. Label each of the following as either a pure substance or a mixture:
    a. Dilute solution of hydrochloric acid Mixture, homogeneous
    b. Distilled water Pure Substance, Compound
    c. Carbon monoxide Pure Substance, Compound

57. Label each of the following as either a pure substance or a mixture:
    a. Vinegar Mixture, homogeneous
    b. Coffee Mixture, homogeneous
    c. Gold Pure Substance, Element

FOUNDATIONAL CHEMICAL LAWS AND ATOMIC THEORY

58. Define the law of conservation of mass.

    The law of conservation of mass states that the total mass of substances involved in a chemical reaction does not change, and thus matter is not created nor destroyed during the reaction.

59. If a 6.32-g sample composed of copper and chlorine was decomposed back to its constituent elements and 2.99 g of Copper was recovered, what was the mass of the Chlorine gas generated during this chemical reaction?

$$CuCl_2 \rightarrow Cu + Cl_2$$

$M_{Cl} = Total\ Mass - M_{Cu}$

$M_{Cl} = 6.32\ g - 2.99\ g =$ **3.33 g Chlorine**

60. 1.234 g of butane was burned (reacted with 4.416 g of oxygen) to form carbon dioxide and water. If 3.737 g of CO_2 is generated from this chemical reaction, what mass of water must have been formed?

$$C_4H_{10} + O_2 \rightarrow CO_2 + H_2O$$

| Butane | Oxygen | Carbon Dioxide | Water |

$Total\ Mass = M_{But} + M_{O_2}$

$M_W = Total\ Mass - M_{CO_2} = M_{Butane} + M_{O_2} - M_{CO_2}$

$M_W = 1.234\ g + 4.416\ g - 3.737\ g =$ **1.913 g Water**

61. Define the law of definite composition.

    The law of definite composition states that all samples of a particular compound are composed of the same elements with the same proportions of constituent elements, no matter what their source or how they were prepared.

62. Two samples of a compound composed of barium and chlorine are analyzed in the lab. Sample 1 contains 0.341 g of chlorine and 0.659 g of barium. If sample 2 has 0.511 g of chlorine, then what is the mass of barium in sample 2? (Hint: Use the law of definite composition to solve the problem.)

    The mass ratio of barium to chlorine must always be the same from sample to sample according to the law of definite composition. Therefore,

$$\frac{M_{Ba}}{M_{Cl}} = \frac{0.659\ g}{0.341\ g} = \frac{?}{0.511\ g}$$

$$\boldsymbol{M_{Ba} = 0.988\ g}$$

63. There are two samples of a compound which is composed of only copper and chlorine. Sample 1 has a mass of 2.00 g and sample 2 has a mass of 1.55 g. It is found that 1.055 g of sample 1 is due to chlorine and therefore the copper composes the remaining 0.945 g of the sample. According to the Law of Definite Composition, what are the masses of the copper and chlorine in sample 2?

The mass ratio of copper to chlorine must always be the same from sample to sample according to the law of definite composition. Therefore,

If in sample 2: $M_{Cu} + M_{Cl} = 1.55\ g$ Then: $M_{Cu} = 1.55\ g - M_{Cl}$

1. $\dfrac{M_{Cu}}{M_{Cl}} = \dfrac{0.945\ g}{1.055\ g}$

2. $\dfrac{1.55\ g - M_{Cl}}{M_{Cl}} = \dfrac{0.945\ g}{1.055\ g}$

3. $\dfrac{1.55\ g}{M_{Cl}} - 1 = \dfrac{0.945\ g}{1.055\ g}$

4. $M_{Cl} = \dfrac{1.55\ g}{\left(\dfrac{0.945\ g}{1.055\ g} + 1\right)} = 0.818$

5. $M_{Cu} = 1.55\ g - M_{Cl} = 1.55\ g - 0.818\ g = 0.732\ g$

$$\boldsymbol{M_{Cu} = 0.732\ g;\quad M_{Cl} = 0.818\ g}$$

64. There are two samples of a compound which is composed of only iron and oxygen. Sample 1 has a mass of 2.74 g and sample 2 has a mass of 1.00 g. It is found that 2.130 g of sample 1 is due to iron and therefore the oxygen composes the remaining 0.610 g of the sample. According to the Law of Definite Composition, what are the masses of the iron and oxygen in sample 2?

The mass ratio of iron to oxygen must always be the same from sample to sample according to the Law of Definite Composition. Therefore,

If in sample 2: $M_{Fe} + M_O = 1.00\ g$ Then: $M_{Fe} = 1.00\ g - M_O$

1. $\dfrac{M_{Fe}}{M_O} = \dfrac{2.130\ g}{0.610\ g}$

2. $\dfrac{1.00\ g - M_O}{M_O} = \dfrac{2.130\ g}{0.610\ g}$

3. $\dfrac{1.00\ g}{M_0} - 1 = \dfrac{2.130\ g}{0.610\ g}$

4. $M_0 = \dfrac{1.00\ g}{\left(\dfrac{2.130\ g}{0.610\ g} + 1\right)} = 0.223\ g$

5. $M_{Fe} = 1.00\ g - M_0 = 1.00\ g - 0.223\ g = 0.777\ g$

$M_{Fe} = 0.777\ g; \quad M_{Cl} = 0.223\ g$

65. Define the law of multiple proportions.

The law of multiple proportions states that if two elements—we will call them element 1 and element 2 for the purposes of this definition—react to form two different compounds, then the different masses of element 2 that combine with a fixed amount of element 1 can be expressed as a ratio of small whole numbers.

66. A certain mass of carbon reacts with 6.80 grams of oxygen to form carbon monoxide. According to the law of multiple proportions, how many grams of oxygen would react with the same mass of carbon to form carbon dioxide?

If 6.80 g of oxygen react with a certain amount of carbon in carbon monoxide, then it would require twice that amount in carbon dioxide for the same amount of carbon. Thus, $6.80 \times 2 = 13.6$ g of oxygen.

ATOMIC STRUCTURE

67. Marie Curie and coworkers suggested that atoms emitted some kind of very unique rays when they disintegrate, which she termed *radioactivity*.

68. What are cathode rays?

Cathode rays are streams of electrons.

69. When referring to electrons and protons in an atom, explain why is it appropriate to deal in unit-less, relative charges of +1 and −1 for protons and electrons respectively?

The electric charge of an electron is -1.602×10^{-19} Coulombs and that of a proton is $+1.602 \times 10^{-19}$ Coulombs. Because these two electric charges are precisely equal in magnitude but opposite in sign, they balance with each other within the atomic structure at a ratio of precisely 1 to 1. That is to say, 1 electron exactly balances with 1 proton and there are no other charged particles in an atom. Owing to this, we simply refer to the charge as either a positive or negative whole-number multiple of the quantity, 1.602×10^{-19} Coulombs. So if there is a charge of +3 on an Aluminum ion, this is implicitly understood to mean $(+3) \times (1.602 \times 10^{-19}$ C).

70. For each of the following elements, determine the number of protons, neutrons, and electrons:

a. $^{20}_{10}Ne$ - 10 protons (atomic number), 10 neutrons (mass number is 20, so 20 − 10 protons = 10 neutrons), 10 electrons (to balance the 10 protons for neutral neon).

b. $^{12}_{6}C$ - 6 protons (atomic number), 6 neutrons (mass number is 12, so 12 − 6 protons = 6 neutrons), 6 electrons (to balance the 6 protons for neutral carbon).

c. $^{190}_{76}Os$ - 76 protons (atomic number), 114 neutrons (mass number is 190, so 190 – 76 protons = 114 neutrons), 76 electrons (to balance the 76 protons for neutral osmium).

d. $^{40}_{20}Ca$ - 20 protons (atomic number), 20 neutrons (mass number is 40, so 40 – 20 protons = 20 neutrons), 20 electrons (to balance the 20 protons for neutral calcium).

71. For each of the following elements, determine the number of protons, neutrons, and electrons:

a. $^{207}_{82}Pb$ - 82 protons (atomic number), 125 neutrons (mass number is 207, so 207 – 82 protons = 125 neutrons), 82 electrons (to balance the 82 protons for neutral lead).

b. $^{16}_{8}O$ - 8 protons (atomic number), 8 neutrons (mass number is 16, so 16 – 8 protons = 8 neutrons), 8 electrons (to balance the 8 protons for neutral oxygen).

c. $^{9}_{4}Be$ - 4 protons (atomic number), 5 neutrons (mass number is 9, so 9 – 4 protons = 5 neutrons), 4 electrons (to balance the 4 protons for neutral beryllium).

d. $^{80}_{35}Br$ - 35 protons (atomic number), 45 neutrons (mass number is 80, so 80-35 protons = 45 neutrons), 35 electrons (to balance the 35 protons for neutral bromine).

72. Complete the following table:

Symbol	Number of Protons	Number of Neutrons	Number of Electrons	Atomic Number	Mass Number
$^{13}_{6}C$	6	7	6	6	13
$^{14}_{7}N$	7	7	7	7	14
$^{35}_{17}Cl$	17	18	17	17	35
$^{127}_{53}I$	53	74	53	53	127
$^{24}_{12}Mg$	12	12	12	12	24

73. What is the number of protons, neutrons, and electrons for an isotope of tantalum (Ta) with a mass number of 181?

Number of Protons = 73

Number of Neutrons = 181 – 73 = 108

Number of Electrons = 73

74. What is the number of protons, neutrons, and electrons for an isotope of zinc (Zn) with a mass number of 65?

Number of Protons = 30

Number of Neutrons = 65 – 30 = 35

Number of Electrons = 30

75. What is the number of protons, neutrons, and electrons for an isotope of nickel (Ni) with a mass number of 58?

Number of Protons = 28

Number of Neutrons = 58 − 28 = 30

Number of Electrons = 28

76. What is the number of protons, neutrons, and electrons for an isotope of rubidium (Rb) with a mass number of 85?

Number of Protons = 37

Number of Neutrons = 85 − 37 = 48

Number of Electrons = 37

77. What is the number of protons, neutrons, and electrons for an isotope of gallium (Ga) with a mass number of 71?

Number of Protons = 31

Number of Neutrons = 71 − 31 = 40

Number of Electrons = 31

78. What is the number of protons, neutrons, and electrons for an isotope of tin (Sn) with a mass number of 122?

Number of Protons = 50

Number of Neutrons = 122 − 50 = 72

Number of Electrons = 50

79. What is the number of protons, neutrons, and electrons for an isotope of indium (In) with a mass number of 115?

Number of Protons = 49

Number of Neutrons = 115 − 49 = 66

Number of Electrons = 49

80. What is the number of protons, neutrons, and electrons for an isotope of krypton (Kr) with a mass number of 83?

Number of Protons = 36

Number of Neutrons = 83 − 36 = 47

Number of Electrons = 36

81. How many protons and neutrons are present in $^{45}_{21}Sc$?

Number of Protons = 21

Number of Neutrons = 45 − 21 = 24

82. How many protons and neutrons are present in $^{19}_{9}F$?

Number of Protons = 9

Number of Neutrons = 19 − 9 = 10

83. How many protons and neutrons are present in $^{11}_{5}B$?

Number of Protons = 5

Number of Neutrons = 11 − 5 = 6

84. What is the atomic number, mass number, and electron count for an isotope of barium (Ba) with 76 neutrons?

Atomic Number = 56

Mass Number = 56 + 76 = 132

Number of Electrons = 56

85. What is the atomic number, mass number, and electron count for an isotope of copper (Cu) with 36 neutrons?

Atomic Number = 29

Mass Number = 29 + 36 = 65

Number of Electrons = 29

86. What is the atomic number, mass number, and electron count for an isotope of selenium (Se) with 48 neutrons?

Atomic Number = 34

Mass Number = 34 + 48 = 82

Number of Electrons = 34

87. Below is a list of scientists (left column) and their major contributions to science (right column). Match the scientist with the scientific contribution for which they are famously known.

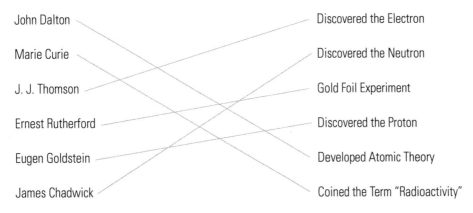

John Dalton	Discovered the Electron
Marie Curie	Discovered the Neutron
J. J. Thomson	Gold Foil Experiment
Ernest Rutherford	Discovered the Proton
Eugen Goldstein	Developed Atomic Theory
James Chadwick	Coined the Term "Radioactivity"

88. *Isotopes* are atoms that have the same atomic number, but different mass numbers.

89. Which of the following is an isotope of $^{20}_{11}X$?

    a. $^{24}_{12}X$

    b. $^{22}_{11}X$

    c. $^{27}_{13}X$

    d. $^{20}_{10}X$

$^{22}_{11}X$ (protons define the element and therefore do not change between isotopes).

90. Which of the following is an isotope of $^{20}_{10}X$?

    a. $^{24}_{12}X$

    b. $^{22}_{11}X$

    c. $^{27}_{13}X$

    d. $^{22}_{10}X$

$^{22}_{10}X$ (protons define the element and therefore do not change between isotopes).

91. There are two naturally occurring isotopes for potassium: ^{39}K with a mass of 38.96 amu and a percent abundance of 93.26% and ^{41}K with a mass of 40.96 amu and a percent abundance of 6.73%. Calculate the atomic mass of potassium.

$$AM_K = \sum_i \left(\frac{IA\%}{100\ \%} \right)(Mass_i)$$

$$AM_K = \left(\frac{93.26\%}{100\%} \right)(38.96\ amu) + \left(\frac{6.73\%}{100\%} \right)(40.96\ amu) = \textbf{39.09 amu}$$

92. There are three naturally occurring isotopes for magnesium: ^{24}Mg with a mass of 23.99 amu and a percent abundance of 78.99%, ^{25}Mg with a mass of 24.99 amu and a percent abundance of 10.00%, and ^{26}Mg with a mass of 25.98 amu and a percent abundance of 11.01%. Calculate the atomic mass of magnesium.

$$AM_{Mg} = \sum_i \left(\frac{IA\%}{100\ \%} \right)(Mass_i)$$

$$AM_{Mg} = \left(\frac{78.99\%}{100\%} \right)(23.99\ amu) + \left(\frac{10.00\%}{100\%} \right)(24.99\ amu) + \left(\frac{11.01\%}{100\%} \right)(25.98\ amu) = \textbf{24.31 amu}$$

93. Bromine has two naturally occurring isotopes: ^{79}Br and ^{81}Br. ^{79}Br has an isotope abundance of 50.69% and ^{81}Br has a mass of 80.916 amu and an isotope abundance of 49.31%. What is the mass (in amu) of ^{79}Br?

$$AM_{Br} = \sum_i \left(\frac{IA\%}{100\%} \right)(Mass_i)$$

1. $79.904 \ amu = \left(\frac{50.69\%}{100\%} \right)m_{79} + \left(\frac{49.31\%}{100\%} \right)(80.916 \ amu)$

2. $79.904 - (0.4931)(80.916) = (0.5069)m_{79}$

3. $m_{79} = \dfrac{79.904 - (0.4931)(80.916)}{0.5069} = \mathbf{78.920 \ amu}$

94. Chlorine has two naturally occurring isotopes, ^{35}Cl and ^{37}Cl. ^{35}Cl has a mass of 34.969 amu and ^{37}Cl has a mass of 36.966 amu. What is the isotope abundance (%) of each of these two isotopes?

$$AM_{Cl} = \sum_i \left(\frac{IA\%}{100\%} \right)(Mass_i) \qquad\qquad 100\% = IA_{35} + IA_{37}$$

1. $35.453 \ amu = \left(\dfrac{100 - IA_{37}}{100\%} \right)(34.969 \ amu) + \left(\dfrac{IA_{37}}{100\%} \right)(36.966 \ amu)$

2. $35.453 \ amu = (1 - IA_{37})(34.969 \ amu) + (IA_{37})(36.966 \ amu)$

3. $35.453 \ amu = 34.969 \ amu - 34.969 \ IA_{37} + 36.966 \ IA_{37}$

4. $35.453 \ amu - 34.969 \ amu = 1.997 \ IA_{37}$

5. $0.484 \ amu = 1.997 \ IA_{37}$

6. $IA_{37} = \dfrac{0.484 \ amu}{1.997 \ amu} = 0.2424 \ \rightarrow \ IA_{37} = \mathbf{24.24\%}$

7. $IA_{35} = 100\% - 24.24\% = \mathbf{75.76\%}$

95. Silicon has three naturally occurring isotopes. ^{28}Si has a mass of 27.98 amu and an isotope abundance of 92.23%. ^{29}Si has a mass of 28.98 amu and an isotope abundance of 4.68%. ^{30}Si has an isotope abundance of 3.09%. What is the mass of the ^{30}Si isotope?

$$AM_{Si} = \sum_i \left(\frac{IA\%}{100\%} \right)(Mass_i)$$

1. $28.086 \ amu = \left(\dfrac{92.23\%}{100\%} \right)m_{28} + \left(\dfrac{4.68\%}{100\%} \right)m_{29} + \left(\dfrac{3.09\%}{100\%} \right)m_{30}$

2. $28.086 \ amu = (0.9223)(27.98 \ amu) + (0.0468)(28.98 \ amu) + (0.0309)\left(m_{30} \right)$

3. $(0.0309)\left(m_{30} \right) = 28.086 \ amu - (0.9223)(27.98 \ amu) - (0.0468)(28.98 \ amu)$

4. $m_{30} = \dfrac{28.086 \ amu - (0.9223)(27.98 \ amu) - (0.0468)(28.98 \ amu)}{0.0309} = \mathbf{29.90 \ amu}$

96. Silver has two naturally occurring isotopes with isotopic masses of 106.905 amu and 108.905 amu. What is the percentage abundance of each isotope?

$$AM_{Ag} = \sum_i \left(\frac{IA\%}{100\%} \right)(Mass_i) = \sum_i (IA_i)(Mass_i)$$

$$IA_{107} + IA_{109} = 1 \qquad\qquad \text{Therfore: } IA_{109} = 1 - IA_{107}$$

1. $107.868 \; amu = \sum_i (IA_i)(Mass_i) = (IA_{107})(m_{107}) + (IA_{109})(m_{109})$

2. $107.868 \; amu = (IA_{107})(106.905 \; amu) + (1 - IA_{107})(108.905 \; amu)$

3. $107.868 \; amu = 108.905 \; amu + (106.905 \; amu - 108.905 \; amu)IA_{107}$

4. $107.868 \; amu - 108.905 \; amu = (-2.000 \; amu)IA_{107}$

5. $IA_{107} = \dfrac{107.868 \; amu - 108.905 \; amu}{-2.000 \; amu} = 0.5185$

6. $IA_{109} = 1 - IA_{107} = 1 - 0.5185 = 0.4815$

$IA_{107} = 51.85\%$; $\qquad\qquad$ **$IA_{109} = 48.15\%$**

97. Copper has two naturally occurring isotopes: ^{63}Cu with a mass of 62.9296 amu and ^{65}Cu with a mass of 64.9278 amu. Which of these isotopes is present in the greatest natural isotope abundance?

Since the atomic mass of copper is 63.546 amu, the isotope whose mass is closest to the atomic mass is the one with the greatest natural abundance.

$$AM_{Cu} - M_{63} = |63.546 - 62.9296| = 0.6164 \; amu$$

$$AM_{Cu} - M_{65} = |63.546 - 64.9278| = 1.3818 \; amu$$

In this case it is ^{63}Cu that has the greatest natural abundance.

98. Oxygen has an atomic mass of 15.9994 amu. Additionally, there are three naturally occurring isotopes of oxygen: ^{16}O with a mass of 15.995 amu, ^{17}O with a mass of 16.999 amu, and ^{18}O with a mass of 17.999 amu. If ^{17}O has an isotope abundance of 0.037%, what are the natural isotope abundances of the other two isotopes of oxygen?

First, if: $1 = IA_{16} + IA_{17} + IA_{18}$

Then: $1 = IA_{16} + \left(\dfrac{0.037\%}{100\%} \right) + IA_{18} = IA_{16} + (0.00037) + IA_{18}$

$1 - 0.00037 = IA_{16} + IA_{18}$

$IA_{18} = 0.99963 - IA_{16}$

Second: $AM_0 = \sum_i \left(\dfrac{IA\%}{100\%} \right) (Mass_i) = \sum_i (IA_i)(Mass_i)$

Therefore:

1. $15.9994 \ amu = IA_{16}(15.995 \ amu) + (0.00037)(16.999 \ amu) + IA_{18}(17.999 \ amu)$

2. $15.9994 \ amu - (0.00629 \ amu) = IA_{16}(15.995 \ amu) + (0.99963 - IA_{16})(17.999 \ amu)$

3. $15.9931 \ amu = 17.99234 \ amu + (15.995 - 17.999) \ IA_{16}$

4. $15.9931 \ amu - 17.99234 \ amu = (15.995 \ amu - 17.999 \ amu) \ IA_{16}$

5. $IA_{16} = \dfrac{15.9931 \ amu - 17.99234 \ amu}{15.995 \ amu - 17.999 \ amu} = 0.997625$

6. $IA_{18} = 0.99963 - IA_{16} = 0.002005$

    $\mathbf{IA_{16} = 99.763\%}$ $\qquad\qquad \mathbf{IA_{18} = 0.2005\%}$

INTRODUCTION TO THE PERIODIC TABLE

99. Based on periodic law, you would expect _____ to have similar chemical and physical properties as sodium.
    a. beryllium
    b. magnesium
    c. potassium
    d. strontium

    potassium

100. Based on periodic law, you would expect _____ to have similar chemical and physical properties as magnesium.
    a. lithium
    b. calcium
    c. rubidium
    d. cesium

    calcium

101. Based on periodic law, you would expect _____ to have similar chemical and physical properties as fluorine.
    a. sulfur
    b. oxygen
    c. selenium
    d. chlorine

    chlorine

102. Based on periodic law, you would expect _____ to have similar chemical and physical properties as bromine.
    a. sodium
    b. beryllium
    c. fluorine
    d. argon

    fluorine

103. _____ is an example of a metal.
    a. sulfur
    b. arsenic
    c. aluminum
    d. silicon

    aluminum

104. _____ is an example of a nonmetal.
    a. boron
    b. carbon
    c. silver
    d. beryllium

    carbon

105. _____ is an example of a metalloid.
    a. phosphorus
    b. zinc
    c. iodine
    d. arsenic

    arsenic

106. _____ is an example of a transition metal.
    a. iron
    b. lithium
    c. neon
    d. calcium

    iron

107. _____ is an example of an element present in the lanthanide series.
    a. carbon
    b. lithium
    c. europium
    d. sulfur

    europium

108. _____ is an example of an element present in the actinide series.
    a. mendelevium
    b. lithium

   c. oxygen

   d. chlorine

     mendelevium

109. The halogens appear in group _____.
   a. 1A
   b. 2A
   c. 7A
   d. 8A

     7A

110. The alkali metals appear in group _____.
   a. 1A
   b. 2A
   c. 7A
   d. 8A

     1A

111. The noble gases appear in group _____.
   a. 1A
   b. 2A
   c. 7A
   d. 8A

     8A

112. The alkaline earth metals gases appear in group _____.
   a. 1A
   b. 2A
   c. 7A
   d. 8A

     2A

113. Below is a list of elements (left column) and groups (right column) of various elements present on the periodic table. Match each element to its group as it would appear on the periodic table.

Potassium	Alkaline Earth Metals
Strontium	Halogens
Tungsten	Transition Metals
Arsenic	Noble Gases
Bromine	Alkali Metals
Argon	Metalloid

114. Below is a list of elements (left column) and groups (right column) of various atoms present on the periodic table. Match each element to its group as it would appear on the periodic table.

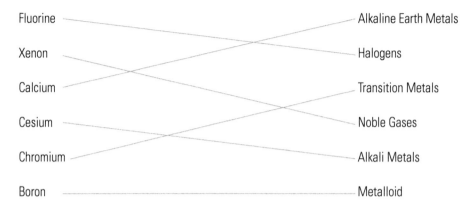

Fluorine — Alkaline Earth Metals

Xenon — Halogens

Calcium — Transition Metals

Cesium — Noble Gases

Chromium — Alkali Metals

Boron — Metalloid

115. Below is a list of the name (left column) and the symbol (right column) of various elements present on the periodic table. Match the name to its symbol.

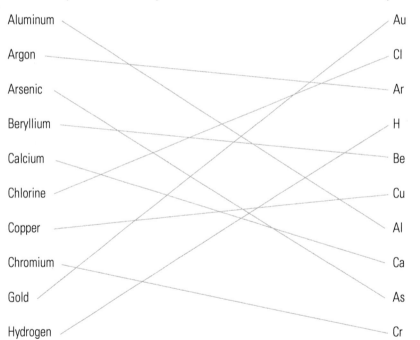

Aluminum — Au

Argon — Cl

Arsenic — Ar

Beryllium — H

Calcium — Be

Chlorine — Cu

Copper — Al

Chromium — Ca

Gold — As

Hydrogen — Cr

116. Below is a list of the name (left column) and the symbol (right column) of various elements present on the periodic table. Match the name to its symbol.

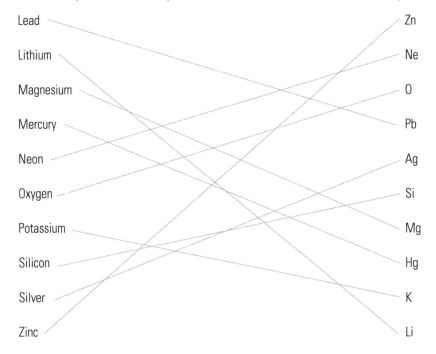

Lead	Zn
Lithium	Ne
Magnesium	O
Mercury	Pb
Neon	Ag
Oxygen	Si
Potassium	Mg
Silicon	Hg
Silver	K
Zinc	Li

INTRODUCTION TO CHEMICAL BONDING

117. What is a chemical bond?

Chemical bonds are the forces that hold atoms together.

118. What is an ionic bond?

Ionic bonds are formed when electrons are transferred from one element to another. These bonds are typically formed between metals and nonmetals.

119. What is a covalent bond?

Covalent bonds arise when elements share electrons. This is usually between two nonmetals.

120. In an ionic bond, metals tend to ___lose___ electrons and have a ___positive___ charge and are called ___cations___, while nonmetals tend to ___gain___ electrons and have a negative___ charge and are called ___anions___.

121. _____ is an example of an ionic compound.
    a. SO_2
    b. CO
    c. $BaCl_2$
    d. CO_2

    $BaCl_2$

122. _____ is an example of an ionic compound.
    a. CCl_4
    b. $FeBr_3$
    c. CS_2
    d. PCl_3

    $FeBr_3$

123. _____ is an example of a covalent compound.
    a. KCl
    b. $FeBr_3$
    c. $MgCl_2$
    d. PCl_3

    PCl_3

124. Is the bond formed in the compound NaCl ionic or covalent? If the bond is ionic, then identify the cation and anion, as well as the charges of the elements involved in the compound.

    The bond is ionic as it is formed between a metal and a nonmetal. In this compound Na^+ is the cation and Cl^- is the anion.

125. Is the bond formed in the compound H_2O ionic or covalent? If the bond is ionic, then identify the cation and anion, as well as the charges of the elements involved in the compound.

    The bond is covalent as it is being formed between two nonmetals.

126. Is the bond formed in the compound $CaCl_2$ ionic or covalent? If the bond is ionic, then identify the cation and anion, as well as the charges of the elements involved in the compound.

    This bond is ionic as it is formed between a metal and a nonmetal. In this compound Ca^{2+} is the cation and Cl^- is the anion.

127. The following ionic compounds contain transition metals that have variable charges. Based on what you know about ionic bonding, label the correct charges for the following ions in the compound:
    a. $PbCl_2$ (Pb^{2+}, Cl^-)
    b. Cu_2O (Cu^+, O^{2-})
    c. FeO (Fe^{2+}, O^{2-})
    d. Fe_2O_3 (Fe^{3+}, O^{2-})

128. The following ionic compounds contain transition metals that have variable charges. Based on what you know about ionic bonding, label the correct charges for the following ions in the compound:
    a. $CoBr_2$ (Co^{2+}, Br^-)
    b. SnO (Sn^{2+}, O^{2-})
    c. Co_2O_3 (Co^{3+}, O^{2-})
    d. HgO (Hg^{2+}, O^{2-})

KEY TERMS

Actinide Series   The elements with atomic numbers 89 through103 (actinium through lawrencium). These are located in a part of the periodic table referred to as the "*f*-block".

Alkali metals   The elements that appear in group 1A. These are very reactive and are located in the "*s*-block".

Alkaline earth metals   The elements that appear in group 2A. These are located in the "*s*-block".

Anions   Charged particles that exhibit a "negative" electric charge.

Anode   The positively charged electrode in a cathode ray tube.

Atomic mass   The mass of one atom of an element expressed in atomic mass units (*amu*).

Atomic mass unit   A unit of mass defined as 1/12 of the mass of an atom of carbon-12. Atomic mass units are the standard unit of measurement used to report atomic masses and formula masses.

Atomic number   The number of protons that are contained in the nucleus of an atom. It is this number that defines an atom as being of a particular element.

Cathode   The negatively charged electrode in a cathode ray tube.

Cathode ray tube   An evacuated glass tube equipped with two electrodes which are used to create an electron beam. J.J. Thomson used cathode ray tubes to discover the electron.

Cathode rays   Streams of electrons that can be observed in a cathode ray tube.

Cations   Charged particles that exhibit a positive electric charge.

Centrifugation   (Sometimes referred to as "spinning down samples") The application of centripetal force, for example using a centrifuge, to allow for heavier substances to settle as sediment at the bottom of a mixture while lighter substances remain on the top.

Chemical bonds   The forces that hold atoms together in a compound. These arise from the electrostatic forces between protons and electrons.

Chemical change   Changes which involve altering the composition of matter in such a way that different substances (products) are formed.

Chemical property   Any quality or attribute of a substance which can only be observed through a change in chemical identity. In other words, chemical properties are those properties manifested through chemical reactions.

Compounds   Substances composed of two or more elements that are joined together in fixed, definite proportions.

Covalent bonds   Chemical bonds characterized by the sharing of electrons between two atoms.

Distillation   The separation of two or more liquids that have different boiling points. In this technique, the liquid with the lowest boiling point can be boiled off from the mixture of liquids to the gas phase and then travel through a cooled condenser which will return the substance back to the liquid phase in a separate container from the original mixture.

Electrons   Low-mass particles present in all atoms that are the negatively charged constituents of cathode rays. They generally reside in the "electron cloud" around the nucleus of an atom.

Electrostatic forces   Electrical charges give rise to *electrostatic forces*, which can either be repulsive or attractive forces. Thus, two positive charges would repel each other, and the same would be true for two negative charges. Particles which exhibit electric charges of opposite sign will realize an attractive electrostatic force.

Element   The fundamental constituents of matter that cannot be broken down into simpler substances by chemical means. The elements are distinguished by the structure of the atomic nucleus, specifically by the atomic number.

Extensive properties   Properties which are dependent on the size of the sample in question.

Filtration   Another separation technique in which a solid can be separated from a liquid by simply pouring a solid/liquid mixture through filter paper (or other "liquid-permeable" barrier) which captures the solid while the liquid flows through the paper into a new container.

Groups (also referred to as **families**)   Elements of similar chemical and physical properties as described in the periodic law, arranged in vertical columns on the periodic table.

Halogens   Elements in group 7A (17) of the periodic table and are among the most reactive elements on the periodic table.

Heterogeneous mixture   A mixture that is not uniform throughout a given sample; it varies in its composition when comparing one region of the sample to the next.

Homogeneous mixture   A mixture that is characterized by having a composition which is the same or uniform throughout a given sample.

Intensive properties   Properties which are not dependent on the size of the sample in question.

Ion   A charged particle.

Ionic bond   Chemical bonds characterized by the complete transfer of one or more electrons from one atom to another.

Isotope abundance   The fraction (often reported as a percentage) of all naturally occurring atoms of a given element, which can be attributed to a single isotope.

Isotopes   Atoms that have the same atomic number but different mass numbers. In other words, atoms of the same element with different numbers of neutrons (resulting in different masses).

Lanthanide series   The elements with atomic numbers 57 through 71 (lanthanum through lutetium). These are located in a part of the periodic referred to as the "*f*-block".

Law of definite composition   All samples of a particular compound are composed of the same elements with the same proportions by mass, no matter what their source or how they were prepared.

Law of mass conservation   The total mass of the substances involved in a chemical reaction does not change, and thus matter is not created nor destroyed during the reaction.

Law of multiple proportions   If two elements (we will call them element 1 and element 2 for the purposes of this definition) react to form two different compounds, then the two masses of element 2 that combine with a fixed mass of element 1 in each of the two compounds can be expressed as a ratio of small whole numbers.

Main group elements   Elements in groups 1A, 2A, 3A, 4A, 5A, 6A, 7A and 8A (1, 2, 13, 14, 15, 16, 17 and 18).

Mass number   The total sum of the number of protons and neutrons in the nucleus of an atom of a given isotope.

Matter   Anything that has mass and occupies volume.

Metalloids   Elements which reside between the metals and nonmetals on the periodic table and exhibit properties of both metals and nonmetals.

Metals   Elements which reside on the left side of the periodic table. They are solid (except mercury), opaque, shiny, electrically conductive, thermally conductive, malleable, and ductile.

Mixture   Substances composed of two or more components such that they can be separated by physical means and have variable composition from one sample to the next.

Neutrons   Heavy, non-charged subatomic particles present in the nucleus of atoms.

Noble gases   These gases are located in group 8A and are practically inert or unreactive.

Nonmetals   Elements which reside on the upper right corner of the periodic table. They are found in all three states of matter (solid, liquid, and gas), are poor conductors of electricity, are poor conductors of heat, and their solids are brittle.

Periodic law   If the chemical elements are presented in order of increasing relative mass, their chemical and physical properties recur at various intervals in a cyclical manner.

Periods   The horizontal rows of the periodic table are referred to as periods.

Physical change   Changes which do not involve altering the composition of matter in such a way that different substances (products) are formed.

Physical properties   Any quality or attribute of a substance which is not observed through a change in chemical identity. In other words, physical properties are those properties manifested through physical changes only.

Protons   Heavy, positively charged particles which are present in the nucleus of atoms.

Pure substances   A sample of matter which cannot be separated or divided into simpler components by physical means. Put another way, a pure substance is composed of only one component (either an element or compound).

Radioactivity   The phenomenon exhibited by certain elements in which they spontaneously emit radiation (in the form of both particles and electromagnetic waves) resulting from changes in the nuclei of atoms.

Transition elements   The elements which are located in groups 1B–8B (groups 3–12) on the periodic table. These are characterized by partially filled d-orbital subshells.

CHAPTER
3

Compounds, Formulas, and Nomenclature

KEY CONCEPTS

- Atoms, Ions, and Compounds

- Chemical Bonds – Ionic Bonding and Covalent Bonding

- Names and Formulas of Binary Ionic Compounds Containing Metals of Invariable Charge

- Names and Formulas of Binary Ionic Compounds Containing Metals of Variable Charge

- Names and Formulas of Ionic Compounds Containing Polyatomic Ions

- Names and Formulas of Binary Molecular Compounds

INTRODUCTION TO IONS, IONIC BONDS, AND IONIC COMPOUNDS

1. What is an ion?

    An ion is a charged particle. It can consist of one or more atoms wherein there exists an imbalance in the numbers of electrons and protons. Ions form when either an atom or molecule loses or gains electrons.

2. What is a cation?

    A cation is a positively charged ion. Cations are characterized as having fewer electrons than protons in the nuclei of the atoms which comprise the ion.

3. What is an anion?

    An anion is a negatively charged ion. Anions are characterized as having more electrons than protons in the nuclei of the atoms which comprise the ion.

4. What is meant by the term monatomic ion?

    A monatomic ion is one composed of only one atom.

5. What is meant by the term polyatomic ion?

    A polyatomic ion is composed of more than one atom.

6. What is meant by the term binary compound?

    A binary compound is a compound which is composed of only two elements.

7. Explain how ionic bonds form?

    When metals react with nonmetals, there is an innate tendency for the metal to lose one or more electrons. When this happens the nonmetal has a tendency to gain one or more electrons. This exchange of electrons from the metal to the nonmetal results in the formation of two ions, a cation and an anion. The electrostatic attraction between ions of opposite charge is the basis for the chemical bond formed in this fashion.

8. Why are ionic compounds neutral even though they are composed of charged ions?

    Ions which comprise ionic compounds will naturally do so in fixed ratios such that all electric charge is balanced.

9. What is the charge on a monatomic ion with 55 protons and 54 electrons?

    # protons – # electrons = charge

    $55 - 54 = +\mathbf{1}$

10. What is the charge on a monatomic ion with 15 protons and 18 electrons?

    $15 - 18 = -\mathbf{3}$

11. What is the charge on a monatomic ion with 8 protons and 10 electrons?

    $8 - 10 = -\mathbf{2}$

12. What is the charge on a monatomic ion with 20 protons and 18 electrons?

    $20 - 18 = +2$

13. Give the number of protons and electrons for the following:

    a. Al^{3+}

        Atomic number = **13**

        Charge = Atomic number − # electrons

        $+3 = 13 - \#e$

        $\#e = 10$

    b. Br^-

        Atomic number = **35**

        Charge = Atomic number − # electrons

        $-1 = 35 - \#e$

        $\#e = 36$

    c. S^{2-}

        Atomic number = **16**

        Charge = Atomic number − # electrons

        $-2 = 16 - \#e$

        $\#e = 18$

    d. Fe^{3+}

        Atomic number = **26**

        Charge = Atomic number − # electrons

        $+3 = 26 - \#e$

        $\#e = 23$

14. Give the number of protons and electrons for the following:

    a. Fe^{2+}

        26 protons; 24 electrons

    b. F^-

        9 protons; 10 electrons

    c. N^{3-}

        7 protons; 10 electrons

d. Ba^{2+}

56 protons; 54 electrons

15. Give the number of protons and electrons for the following:
    a. Na^+

    11 protons; 10 electrons

    b. Se^{2-}

    34 protons; 36 electrons

    c. Sr^{2+}

    38 protons; 36 electrons

    d. Pb^{4+}

    82 protons; 78 electrons

16. Give the number of protons and electrons for the following:
    a. Mg^{2+}

    12 protons; 10 electrons

    b. Ca^{2+}

    20 protons; 18 electrons

    c. P^{3-}

    15 protons; 18 electrons

    d. Pb^{2+}

    82 protons; 80 electrons

17. Name and predict the charge on the following ions:
    a. H

    Hydrogen, H^+

    b. Li

    Lithium, Li^+

    c. O

    Oxide, O^{2-}

    d. F

    Fluoride, F^-

18. Name and predict the charge on the following ions:
    a. N

        Nitride, N^{3-}

    b. Be

        Beryllium, Be^{2+}

    c. Ba

        Barium, Ba^{2+}

    d. Cs

        Cesium, Cs^{+}

19. Name and predict the charge on the following ions:
    a. Cl

        Chloride, Cl^{-}

    b. S

        Sulfide, S^{2-}

    c. P

        Phosphide, P^{3-}

    d. Br

        Bromide, Br^{-}

20. Name and predict the charge on the following ions:
    a. Se

        Selenide, Se^{2-}

    b. I

        Iodide, I^{-}

    c. Rb

        Rubidium, Rb^{+}

    d. Sr

        Strontium, Sr^{2+}

21. Name and predict the charge on the following ions:
    a. Mg

        Magnesium, Mg^{2+}

b. Na

Sodium, Na$^+$

c. Ca

Calcium, Ca^{2+}

d. Al

Aluminum, Al^{3+}

FORMULAS AND NAMES OF BINARY IONIC COMPOUNDS

22. Explain what is meant by the term formula unit.

Ionic compounds do not form molecules comprised of a specific number of atoms, as is the case with molecular compounds. Because ionic compounds are composed of 3-D arrays of cations and anions, they are represented by formulas in which subscripts indicate the lowest, whole-number "ratio" of the different ions which compose a given compound.

23. Name the binary ionic compounds composed of the following pairs of elements:
    a. Aluminum and sulfur

    Aluminum sulfide

    b. Magnesium and selenium

    Magnesium selenide

    c. Aluminum and oxygen

    Aluminum oxide

    d. Sodium and nitrogen

    Sodium nitride

24. Name the binary ionic compounds composed of the following pairs of elements:
    a. Potassium and chlorine

    Potassium chloride

    b. Strontium and phosphorus

    Strontium phosphide

    c. Cesium and fluorine

    Cesium fluoride

    d. Potassium and iodine

    Potassium iodide

25. Name the binary ionic compounds composed of the following pairs of elements:
    a. Rubidium and oxygen

    Rubidium oxide

    b. Calcium and bromine

    Calcium bromide

    c. Aluminum and nitrogen

    Aluminum nitride

    d. Sodium and iodine

    Sodium iodide

26. Name the binary ionic compounds composed of the following pairs of elements:
    a. Sodium and selenium

    Sodium selenide

    b. Potassium and sulfur

    Potassium sulfide

    c. Barium and fluorine

    Barium fluoride

    d. Lithium and oxygen

    Lithium oxide

27. Write the formulas of binary ionic compounds composed of the following pairs of elements:
    a. Aluminum and chlorine

    $AlCl_3$

    b. Calcium and selenium

    $CaSe$

    c. Aluminum and bromine

    $AlBr_3$

    d. Silver and nitrogen

    Ag_3N

28. Write the formulas of binary ionic compounds composed of the following pairs of elements:
    a. Chlorine and zinc

    $ZnCl_2$

b.   Phosphorus and scandium

   ScP

c.   Fluorine and silver

   AgF

d.   Barium and iodine

   BaI_2

29. Write the formulas of binary ionic compounds composed of the following pairs of elements:

   a.   Oxygen and silver

   Ag_2O

   b.   Calcium and sulfur

   CaS

   c.   Zinc and sulfur

   ZnS

   d.   Scandium and oxygen

   Sc_2O_3

30. Write the formulas of binary ionic compounds composed of the following pairs of elements:

   a.   Sodium and iodine

   NaI

   b.   Silver and sulfur

   Ag_2S

   c.   Barium and fluorine

   BaF_2

   d.   Zinc and oxygen

   ZnO

31. Write the names of the following binary ionic compounds:

   a. Cr_2S_3

   Chromium can form more than one ion, so we must determine its charge:

   $(2)(x) + (3)(-2) = 0$

   $x = +3$

   Chromium(III) sulfide

   b. $CuCl_2$

      Copper can form more than one ion, so we must determine its charge:

      $(1)(x) + (2)(-1) = 0$

      $x = +2$

      Copper(II) chloride

   c. Cr_3N_2

      Chromium can form more than one ion, so we must determine its charge:

      $(3)(x) + (2)(-3) = 0$

      $x = +2$

      Chromium(II) nitride

   d. NiF_2

      Nickel can form more than one ion, so we must determine its charge:

      $(1)(x) + (2)(-1) = 0$

      $x = +2$

      Nickel(II) fluoride

32. Write the names of the following binary ionic compounds:

   a. FeS

      Iron(II) sulfide

   b. $FeCl_3$

      Iron(III) chloride

   c. Co_3N_2

      Cobalt(II) nitride

   d. CoI_3

      Cobalt(III) iodide

33. Write the names of the following binary ionic compounds:

   a. Fe_3P_2

      Iron(II) phosphide

   b. PbS_2

      Lead(IV) sulfide

c. $PbCl_2$

Lead(II) chloride

d. CoI_2

Cobalt(II) iodide

34. Write the names of the following binary ionic compounds:

a. Hg_2Cl_2

Mercury(I) chloride

b. SnO_2

Tin(IV) oxide

c. CrS

Chromium(II) sulfide

d. Cu_3P

Copper(I) phosphide

35. Write the formulas of the following compounds:

a. Sodium sulfide

Write the symbol of the cation and anion:

No need to reduce subscripts. **Na_2S**

b. Barium nitride

Write the symbol of the cation and anion:

No need to reduce subscripts. **Ba_3N_2**

c. Cesium oxide

Write the symbol of the cation and anion:

No need to reduce subscripts. **Cs_2O**

d. Aluminum fluoride

Write the symbol of the cation and anion:

Al^{3+} F^-

Al_1F_3

No need to reduce subscripts. **AlF_3**

36. Write the formulas of the following compounds:
    a. Tin(II) oxide

    SnO

    b. Lead(IV) phosphide

    Pb_3P_4

    c. Nickel (II) chloride

    $NiCl_2$

    d. Manganese(IV) oxide

    MnO_2

37. Write the formulas of the following compounds:
    a. Aluminum iodide

    AlI_3

    b. Cobalt(III) selenide

    Co_2Se_3

    c. Zinc oxide

    ZnO

    d. Scandium chloride

    $ScCl_3$

38. Write the formulas of the following compounds:
    a. Lithium oxide

    Li_2O

    b. Iron(II) phosphide

    Fe_3P_2

    c. Potassium nitride

    K_3N

    d. Copper(II) sulfite

    CuS

FORMULAS AND NAMES OF POLYATOMIC IONS AND THEIR COMPOUNDS

39. Name the following compounds:

    a. $Cr_2(SO_4)_3$

       Chromium can form more than one ion, so we must determine its charge:

       $(2)(x)+(3)(-2) = 0$

       $x = +3$

       Chromium(III) sulfate

    b. $Al(NO_3)_3$

       Aluminum nitrate

    c. $Ba(OH)_2$

       Barium hydroxide

    d. Na_2O_2

       Sodium peroxide

40. Name the following compounds:

    a. $CsMnO_4$

       Cesium permanganate

    b. $FePO_4$

       Iron(III) phosphate

    c. Cu_2SO_4

       Copper(I) sulfate

    d. NH_4Cl

       Ammonium chloride

41. Name the following compounds:

    a. $Sc_2(SO_4)_3$

       Scandium sulfate

    b. $NaOH$

       Sodium hydroxide

    c. K_3PO_4

       Potassium phosphate

    d. Cu_2SO_3

       Copper(I) sulfite

42. Name the following compounds:
    a. $NiCO_3$

    Nickel(II) carbonate

    b. K_2HPO_4

    Potassium hydrogen phosphate

    c. $Na_2Cr_2O_7$

    Sodium dichromate

    d. NH_4NO_2

    Ammonium nitrite

43. Name the following compounds:
    a. $Al_2(CrO_4)_3$

    Aluminum chromate

    b. $Fe_3(PO_4)_2$

    Iron(II) phosphate

    c. $Fe(NO_3)_2$

    Iron(II) nitrate

    d. $Cr(C_2H_3O_2)_2$

    Chromium(II) acetate

44. Write the formulas for the following compounds:
    a. Strontium iodide

    SrI_2

    b. Aluminum hydroxide

    $Al(OH)_3$

    c. Potassium hypochlorite

    $KClO$

    d. Silver carbonate

    Ag_2CO_3

45. Write the formulas for the following compounds:
    a. Copper(I) permanganate

    $CuMnO_4$

    b. Cesium chlorate

    $CsClO_3$

    c. Rubidium nitrate

       $RbNO_3$

    d. Sodium hydrogen sulfite

       $NaHSO_3$

46. Write the formulas for the following compounds:
    a. Magnesium phosphate

       $Mg_3(PO_4)_2$

    b. Iron(III) chromate

       $Fe_2(CrO_4)_3$

    c. Ammonium sulfate

       $(NH_4)_2SO_4$

    d. Calcium hydrogen phosphate

       $CaHPO_4$

47. Write the formulas for the following compounds:
    a. Copper(I) cyanide

       $CuCN$

    b. Strontium chlorite

       $Sr(ClO_2)_2$

    c. Lead(II) carbonate

       $PbCO_3$

    d. Tin(II) fluoride

       SnF_2

48. Write the formulas for the following compounds:
    a. Calcium carbonate

       $CaCO_3$

    b. Ammonium bromide

       NH_4Br

    c. Cobalt(II) acetate

       $Co(C_2H_3O_2)_2$

    d. Lithium chromate

       Li_2CrO_4

49. Write the formula for the compounds that form from calcium and the following anions:

    a. Phosphate

    $Ca_3(PO_4)_2$

    b. Cyanide

    $Ca(CN)_2$

    c. Peroxide

    CaO_2

    d. Dichromate

    $CaCr_2O_7$

50. Write the formulas for the compounds that form from aluminum and the following anions:

    a. Dihydrogen phosphate

    $Al(H_2PO_4)_3$

    b. Hydrogen phosphate

    $Al_2(HPO_4)_3$

    c. Phosphate

    $AlPO_4$

    d. Nitrate

    $Al(NO_3)_3$

51. Write the formulas for the compounds that form from potassium and the following anions:

    a. Permanganate

    $KMnO_4$

    b. Acetate

    $KC_2H_3O_2$

    c. Dichromate

    $K_2Cr_2O_7$

    d. Carbonate

    K_2CO_3

52. Write the formulas for the compounds that form from iron(III) and the following anions:

   a. Nitrite

$$Fe(NO_2)_3$$

   b. Sulfate

$$Fe_2(SO_4)_3$$

   c. Perchlorate

$$Fe(ClO_4)_3$$

   d. Hydrogen sulfite

$$Fe(HSO_3)_3$$

FORMULAS AND NAMES OF INORGANIC HYDRATES

53. Write the formula of Copper(II) sulfate pentahydrate.

Since the word "hydrate" is modified by the prefix "penta-" in this case we know that there are five water molecules in this formula:

$$CuSO_4 \cdot 5H_2O$$

54. Write the formula of Iron(III) phosphate dihydrate.

$$FePO_4 \cdot 2H_2O$$

55. Write the name of $MgSO_4 \cdot 7H_2O$.

Magnesium sulfate heptahydrate

56. Write the name of $NaC_2H_3O_2 \cdot 3H_2O$.

Sodium acetate trihydrate

FORMULAS AND NAMES OF BINARY MOLECULAR (COVALENT) COMPOUNDS

57. Name the following compounds:

   a. CO_2

Carbon dioxide

   b. NF_3

Nitrogen trifluoride

c. PCl_3

Phosphorus trichloride

d. N_2O_4

Dinitrogen tetroxide

58. Name the following compounds:

a. N_2O

Dinitrogen monoxide

b. S_2F_4

Disulfur tetrafluoride

c. PF_5

Phosphorus pentafluoride

d. SO_3

Sulfur trioxide

59. Write the names of the following compounds:

a. XeF_4

Xenon tetrafluoride

b. BBr_3

Boron tribromide

c. CBr_4

Carbon tetrabromide

d. P_2S_5

Diphosphorus pentasulfide

60. Write the formulas of the following compounds:

a. Diboron dichloride

B_2Cl_2

b. Diiodine pentoxide

I_2O_5

c. Carbon tetrachloride

CCl_4

d. Nitrogen trifluoride

NF_3

61. Write the formulas of the following compounds:
    a. Tetraphosphorus decasulfide

    P_4S_{10}

    b. Dinitrogen trioxide

    N_2O_3

    c. Dinitrogen pentoxide

    N_2O_5

    d. Sulfur dioxide

    SO_2

62. SO_2 is called sulfur dioxide but MgO_2 is simply called magnesium oxide. Why?

    Magnesium oxide is an ionic compound. Ionic compounds do not form discrete molecules and therefore their formulas represent lowest whole-number ratios of ions. As such there is no need to indicate any particular number associated with the magnesium or oxide ions because their charges are fixed and so is the ratio of magnesium and oxide ions. Molecular compounds exist as discrete molecules with specific numbers of atoms of each type of element.

63. Are molecules present in a sample of CaF_2? Why or why not?

    No, CaF_2 is an ionic compound. Ions do not form molecules. Rather, they exist as 3-dimensional, crystalline arrays of ions.

64. Are Ions present in PCl_3? Why or why not?

    No, PCl_3 is a molecular compound. There is no need for complete transfer of electrons between elements and concomitant ion formation when forming covalent bonds. Covalent bonds form through the "sharing" of pairs of electrons.

KEY TERMS

Anhydrous   This term means "without water" and is applied to compounds in order to indicate the compound is dry. For example, if we were to vigorously heat the compound nickel(II) sulfate hexahydrate ($NiSO_4 \cdot 6H_2O$), this would drive off all of the waters of hydration leaving us with what would be termed, *Anhydrous* nickel(II) sulfate ($NiSO_4$).

Anion   A charged particle that exhibits a negative electric charge.

Binary compound   A compound which is composed of only two elements.

Cation   A charged particle that exhibits a positive electric charge.

Chemical bonds   The forces that hold atoms (elements) together, allowing for the formation of chemical *compounds*.

Covalent bonds   Bonds that are characterized by the sharing of electrons between two atoms.

Covalent compound   Compounds which result from the formation of covalent bonds. These compounds are composed of nonmetals bonded to nonmetals.

Diatomic molecular element   Elements which, in their elemental state, exist as molecules consisting of two atoms of the element in question.

Formula   A notation which makes use of elemental symbols to indicate the various elements which compose a given compound along with corresponding numeric subscripts which indicate the exact or relative number of each type of element or ion respectively.

Formula unit   A formula which expresses the relative numbers (smallest whole-number ratio) of the types of elements or ions contained in an *ionic* compound.

Hydrate   Ionic compounds which contain a specific number of water molecules within each formula unit.

Ion   A charged particle.

Ionic bond   Bonds which form through the complete transfer of one or more electrons from a metal to a nonmetal. When this occurs, the resulting ions are then bonded together by virtue of the electrostatic attraction which exists between particles of opposite charge.

Ionic compound   Compounds which result from the formation of ionic bonds. These compounds are composed of metals bonded to nonmetals.

Main group element   Elements in groups 1A, 2A, 3A, 4A, 5A, 6A, 7A, and 8A (1, 2, 13, 14, 15, 16, 17, and 18).

Metal of invariable charge   Metals which only form one ion. In other words, metals which only adopt a single specific charge when in its ionic form.

Metals of variable charge   Metals which can form more than one ion. In other words, metals which adopt different relative electric charges when forming ions.

Molecular compound   Synonymous with "covalent compound." These are compounds which result from the formation of covalent bonds. These compounds are composed of nonmetals bonded to nonmetals.

Molecular element   Elements which, in their elemental state, exist as molecules consisting of multiple atoms of the element in question.

Molecular formula   Makes use of the symbols of the elements comprising a molecule along with numeric subscripts to indicate the exact number of atoms of each element contained within a molecule of a given covalent compound.

Molecules   Discrete collections of two or more atoms held together by covalent chemical bonds.

Monatomic ion   Ions composed of only a single atom.

Polyatomic ion   Ions composed of two or more atoms covalently bonded together.

The Mole, Chemical Equations, and Stoichiometry

KEY CONCEPTS

- Avogadro's Number and the Mole

- Molar Mass and Percent Composition

- Calculating Empirical and Molecular Formulas

- Balancing Chemical Equations

- Stoichiometry – Determining Limiting Reagents, Theoretical Yields, and Percent Yields

MOLAR MASS

1. What is molar mass?

    The molar mass is the mass of one mole of that species expressed in grams, which can either be an element (either monoatomic or molecular) or a compound.

2. Determine the molar mass of each of the following elements:
    a. Sulfur (From the periodic table we get $32.07 \frac{grams}{mol}$)

    b. Zinc (From the periodic table we get $65.39 \frac{grams}{mol}$)

    c. Oxygen (From the periodic table we get $16.00 \frac{grams}{mol}$)

    d. Strontium (From the periodic table we get $87.62 \frac{grams}{mol}$)

3. Determine the molar mass of each of the following elements:
    a. Bromine (From the periodic table we get $79.90 \frac{grams}{mol}$)

    b. Fluorine (From the periodic table we get $19.00 \frac{grams}{mol}$)

    c. Iron (From the periodic table we get $55.85 \frac{grams}{mol}$)

    d. Barium (From the periodic table we get $137.33 \frac{grams}{mol}$)

4. How many carbon, hydrogen, and oxygen atoms are in C_4H_9OH?

    There are four carbon atoms, ten hydrogen atoms, and one oxygen atom in C_4H_9OH.

5. How many aluminum, oxygen, and hydrogen atoms are in $Al(OH)_3$?

    There is one aluminum atom and there are three oxygen and three hydrogen atoms in $Al(OH)_3$.

6. Determine the molar mass of each of the following:
    a. Cu_2S $(2 \times 63.55) + (1 \times 32.07) = 159.2 \frac{grams}{mol}$

    b. CO $(1 \times 12.01) + (1 \times 16.00) = 28.01 \frac{grams}{mol}$

    c. Fe_2O_3 $(2 \times 55.85) + (3 \times 16.00) = 159.7 \frac{grams}{mol}$

    d. C_6H_6 $(6 \times 12.01) + (6 \times 1.01) = 78.12 \frac{grams}{mol}$

7. Determine the molar mass of each of the following:
    a. H_2O $(2 \times 1.01) + (1 \times 16.00) = 18.02 \frac{grams}{mol}$

    b. CO_2 $(1 \times 12.01) + (2 \times 16.00) = 44.01 \frac{grams}{mol}$

    c. Na_2SO_4 $(2 \times 22.99) + (1 \times 32.07) + (4 \times 16.00) = 142.05 \frac{grams}{mol}$

    d. $Al(OH)_3$ $(1 \times 26.98) + (3 \times 16.00) + (3 \times 1.01) = 78.01 \frac{grams}{mol}$

8. What is Avogadro's number?

    Avogadro's number is 6.022×10^{23}. This number represents the amount of entities (or things) in one mol, which is the SI unit for the amount of a substance.

9. How do we calculate the number of mols of a particular substance if given the number of grams?

    We use the molecular weight of that substance with grams on the bottom and mols on the top. That is:

    $$\text{\# of mols} = \text{mass (grams)} \times \frac{1 \text{ mol}}{\text{\# of grams}}$$

10. How do we calculate the number of grams of a particular substance if given the number of mols?

    We use the molecular weight of that substance with grams on the top and mols on the bottom. That is:

    $$\text{mass (grams)} = \text{\# of mols} \times \frac{\text{\# of grams}}{1 \text{ mol}}$$

11. How do we calculate the number of entities of a particular substance if given the number of mols?

    We use Avogadro's number (6.022×10^{23} entities/mol), with 6.022×10^{23} entities on the top and 1 mol on the bottom. That is:

    $$\text{\# of entities} = \text{\# of mols} \times \frac{6.022 \times 10^{23} \text{ entities}}{1 \text{ mol}}$$

12. How do we calculate the number of mols of a particular substance if given the number of entities?

    We use Avogadro's number (6.022×10^{23} entities/mol), with 6.022×10^{23} entities on the bottom and 1 mol on the top. That is:

    $$\text{\# of mols} = \text{\# of entities} \times \frac{1 \text{ mol}}{6.022 \times 10^{23} \text{ entities}}$$

13. How many mols are in 11.89 g of $NaNO_3$?

    $$11.89 \text{ g } NaNO_3 \times \frac{1 \text{ mol } NaNO_3}{85.00 \text{ g } NaNO_3} = 0.1399 \text{ mols } NaNO_3$$

14. How many mols are in 23.38 g of Na_2SO_4?

    $$23.38 \text{ g } Na_2SO_4 \times \frac{1 \text{ mol } Na_2SO_4}{142.05 \text{ g } Na_2SO_4} = 0.1646 \text{ mols } Na_2SO_4$$

15. How many mols are in 5.48 g of C_6H_6?

    $$5.48 \text{ g } C_6H_6 \times \frac{1 \text{ mol } C_6H_6}{78.12 \text{ g } C_6H_6} = 0.0701 \text{ mols } C_6H_6$$

16. What is the mass of 1.743 mols of Fe_3O_4?

$$1.743 \ mols \ Fe_3O_4 \times \frac{231.6 \ g \ Fe_3O_4}{1 \ mol \ Fe_3O_4} = 403.7 \ g \ Fe_3O_4$$

17. What is the mass of 0.9368 mols of Cu_2S?

$$0.9368 \ mols \ Cu_2S \times \frac{159.2 \ g \ Cu_2S}{1 \ mol \ Cu_2S} = 149.1 \ g \ Cu_2S$$

18. What is the mass of 0.1639 mols of $CuSO_4$?

$$0.1639 \ mols \ CuSO_4 \times \frac{159.62 \ g \ CuSO_4}{1 \ mol \ CuSO_4} = 26.16 \ g \ CuSO_4$$

19. How many SF_6 molecules are in 1.35 mols of SF_6?

$$1.35 \ mols \ SF_6 \times \frac{6.022 \times 10^{23} \ molecules \ SF_6}{1 \ mol \ SF_6} = 8.13 \times 10^{23} \ molecules \ SF_6$$

20. How many C_3H_8 molecules are in 0.9832 mols of C_3H_8?

$$0.9832 \ mols \ C_3H_8 \times \frac{6.022 \times 10^{23} \ molecules \ C_3H_8}{1 \ mol \ C_3H_8} = 5.921 \times 10^{23} \ molecules \ C_3H_8$$

21. How many C_5H_{12} molecules are in 4.295 mols of C_5H_{12}?

$$4.295 \ mols \ C_5H_{12} \times \frac{6.022 \times 10^{23} \ molecules \ C_5H_{12}}{1 \ mol \ C_5H_{12}} = 2.586 \times 10^{24} \ molecules \ C_5H_{12}$$

22. How many mols of boron trifluoride is equivalent to 3.285×10^{24} molecules of boron trifluoride?

$$3.285 \times 10^{24} \ molecules \ BF_3 \times \frac{1 \ mol \ BF_3}{6.022 \times 10^{23} \ molecules \ BF_3} = 5.455 \ mols \ BF_3$$

23. How many mols of nitrogen monoxide is equivalent to 7.93×10^{25} molecules of nitrogen monoxide?

$$7.93 \times 10^{25} \ molecules \ NO \times \frac{1 \ mol \ NO}{6.022 \times 10^{23} \ molecules \ NO} = 132 \ mols \ NO$$

24. How many mols of C_6H_{14} is equivalent to 9.84×10^{17} molecules of C_6H_{14}?

$$9.84 \times 10^{17} \ molecules \ C_6H_{14} \times \frac{1 \ mol \ C_6H_{14}}{6.022 \times 10^{23} \ molecules \ C_6H_{14}} = 1.63 \times 10^{-6} \ mols \ C_6H_{14}$$

25. How many octane (C_8H_{18}) molecules are in 12.72 kg of octane?

$$12.72 \; kg \; C_8H_{18} \times \frac{1000 \; g \; C_8H_{18}}{1 \; kg \; C_8H_{18}} \times \frac{1 \; mol \; C_8H_{18}}{114.26 \; g} \times \frac{6.022 \times 10^{23} \; molecules \; C_8H_{18}}{1 \; mol \; C_8H_{18}}$$

$$= 6.704 \times 10^{25} \; molecules \; C_8H_{18}$$

26. Ethylene glycol is commonly used in antifreeze mixtures. What is the mass (kg) of 4.28×10^{25} molecules of ethylene glycol ($C_2H_6O_2$)?

$$4.28 \times 10^{25} \; molecules \; C_2H_6O_2 \times \frac{1 \; mol \; C_2H_6O_2}{6.022 \times 10^{23} \; molecules \; C_2H_6O_2} \times \frac{62.08 \; g \; C_2H_6O_2}{1 \; mol \; C_2H_6O_2} \times \frac{1 \; kg}{1000 \; g}$$

$$= 4.41 \; kg \; C_2H_6O_2$$

PERCENT COMPOSITION

27. What is percent composition and how is it calculated?

Percent composition takes into account how much of each element is present in a given molecule as a percentage. Percentages are calculated based on mass percent, so the total mass of a given element (in the numerator) as compared to the molecular mass as a whole (in the denominator).

28. What is the mass percent of carbon in each of the following hydrocarbons?
    a. CH_4

$$\frac{12.01}{12.01 + (1.01 \times 4)} \times 100 = 74.83\%$$

    b. C_2H_6

$$\frac{(12.01 \times 2)}{(12.01 \times 2) + (1.01 \times 6)} \times 100 = 79.85\%$$

    c. C_3H_8

$$\frac{(12.01 \times 3)}{(12.01 \times 3) + (1.01 \times 8)} \times 100 = 81.68\%$$

    d. C_4H_{10}

$$\frac{(12.01 \times 4)}{(12.01 \times 4) + (1.01 \times 10)} \times 100 = 82.63\%$$

29. What is the mass percent of Cl in $C_2Cl_4F_2$?

$$\frac{(35.45 \times 4)}{(12.01 \times 2) + (35.45 \times 4) + (19.00 \times 2)} \times 100 = 69.57\%$$

30. What is the mass percent of Br in $SnBr_2Cl_2$?

$$\frac{(79.90 \times 2)}{(118.71) + (79.90 \times 2) + (35.45 \times 2)} \times 100 = 45.73\%$$

31. What is the mass percent of O in $Al_2(SO_4)_3$?

$$\frac{(16.00 \times 12)}{(26.98 \times 2) + (32.07 \times 3) + (16.00 \times 12)} \times 100 = 56.11\%$$

32. Calculate the mass percent of each element in HNO_3.

    Mass % for hydrogen:

$$\frac{(1.01)}{(1.01) + (14.01) + (16.00 \times 3)} \times 100 = 1.60\%$$

    Mass % for nitrogen:

$$\frac{(14.01)}{(1.01) + (14.01) + (16.00 \times 3)} \times 100 = 22.23\%$$

    Mass % for oxygen:

$$\frac{(16.00 \times 3)}{(1.01) + (14.01) + (16.00 \times 3)} \times 100 = 76.17\%$$

    Now, let's make sure that these percentages add up to 100%:

    $1.60\% + 22.23\% + 76.17\% = 100.00\%$

33. Caffeine ($C_8H_{10}N_4O_2$) is a central nervous system stimulant, and is currently one of the world's most widely consumed drugs. Calculate the mass percent of each element in caffeine.

    Mass % for carbon:

$$\frac{(12.01 \times 8)}{(12.01 \times 8) + (1.01 \times 10) + (14.01 \times 4) + (16.00 \times 2)} \times 100 = 49.47\%$$

    Mass % for hydrogen:

$$\frac{(1.01 \times 10)}{(12.01 \times 8) + (1.01 \times 10) + (14.01 \times 4) + (16.00 \times 2)} \times 100 = 5.20\%$$

    Mass % for nitrogen:

$$\frac{(14.01 \times 4)}{(12.01 \times 8) + (1.01 \times 10) + (14.01 \times 4) + (16.00 \times 2)} \times 100 = 28.85\%$$

Mass % for oxygen:

$$\frac{(16.00 \times 2)}{(12.01 \times 8) + (1.01 \times 10) + (14.01 \times 4) + (16.00 \times 2)} \times 100 = 16.48\%$$

Now, let's make sure that these percentages add up to 100%:

$49.47\% + 5.20\% + 28.85\% + 16.48\% = 100.00\%$

34. What is the mass of lead in 20.0 grams of PbS?

$Molar\ Mass\ of\ Pb = 207.2\ \dfrac{g}{mol}$

$Molar\ Mass\ of\ PbS = 239.3\ \dfrac{g}{mol}$

Thus,

$20.0\ g\ PbS \times \dfrac{207.2\ g\ Pb}{239.3\ g\ PbS} = 17.3\ grams\ of\ lead$

We could also calculate the percent lead in PbS $\left(\dfrac{207.2}{239.3} \times 100 = 86.59\% \right)$, and then simply take 86.59% of 20.0 grams and get 17.3 grams of lead.

35. What is the mass of copper in 10.0 grams of CuS?

$Molar\ Mass\ of\ Cu = 63.55\ \dfrac{g}{mol}$

$Molar\ Mass\ of\ CuS = 95.62\ \dfrac{g}{mol}$

Thus,

$10.0\ g\ CuS \times \dfrac{63.55\ g\ Cu}{95.62\ g\ CuS} = 6.65\ grams\ of\ copper$

We could also calculate the percent copper in CuS $\left(\dfrac{63.55}{95.62} \times 100 = 66.46\% \right)$, and then simply take 66.46% of 10.0 grams and get 6.65 grams Cu.

36. If you want to obtain 15.0 grams of iron from iron (III) oxide, what mass of iron (III) oxide must you use?

First, let's find the mass percent of iron in Fe_2O_3:

$$\frac{(55.85 \times 2)}{(55.85 \times 2) + (16.00 \times 3)} \times 100 = 69.94\%\ Fe\ in\ Fe_2O_3.$$

Thus,

$0.6994 \times x = 15.0$ *grams, solve for* x

$x = 21.4$ *grams of* Fe_2O_3 *is needed in order to obtain* 15.0 *grams of iron*

DETERMINING EMPIRICAL AND MOLECULAR FORMULAS

37. What does an empirical formula tell us?

The empirical formula is the simplest possible whole-number ratio of atoms in a given molecule.

38. What does a molecular formula tell us?

While the empirical formula tells us the simplest possible whole-number ratio of atoms in a given molecule, the molecular formula tells us the exact number of atoms present in the molecule.

39. Based on what you know about empirical and molecular formulas, fill in the missing spaces in the chart below.

Empirical Formula	Molecular Formula	Molar Mass (g/mol)
C_4H_9	C_8H_{18}	114.26
C_3H_8	C_3H_8	44.11
CH_3	C_2H_6	30.08
C_5H_{11}	$C_{10}H_{22}$	142.32

40. Based on what you know about empirical and molecular formulas, fill in the missing spaces in the chart below.

Empirical Formula	Molecular Formula	Molar Mass (g/mol)
C_5H_{12}	C_5H_{12}	72.17
C_3H_7	C_6H_{14}	86.20
C_2H_5	C_4H_{10}	58.14
C_7H_{16}	C_7H_{16}	100.23

41. The empirical formula for succinic acid is $C_2H_3O_2$. Knowing that succinic acid has a molar mass of 118.10 g/mol, what is its molecular formula?

If we calculate the empirical formula molar mass of $C_2H_3O_2$, we would get the following:

$$(2 \times 12.01) + (3 \times 1.01) + (2 \times 16.00) = 59.05 \ g/mol$$

Since the molar mass of succinic acid is twice this amount, we multiply everything in the empirical formula by 2. Thus, we have $C_4H_6O_4$ as the molecular formula for succinic acid.

42. The empirical formula for glucose is CH_2O. Knowing that glucose has a molar mass of 180.18 g/mol, what is its molecular formula?

    If we calculate the empirical formula molar mass of CH_2O, we would get the following:

    $$(1 \times 12.01) + (2 \times 1.01) + (1 \times 16.00) = 30.03 \ g/mol$$

    Since the molar mass of glucose is 6 times this amount, we multiply everything in the empirical formula by 6. Thus, we have $C_6H_{12}O_6$ as the molecular formula for glucose.

43. The pseudoformula for malic acid is $C_1H_{1.5}O_{1.25}$. What is the empirical formula for malic acid? Knowing that malic acid has a molar mass of 134.10 g/mol, what is its molecular formula?

    Since we need whole numbers in the empirical formula for subscripts, we must first multiply everything in the pseudoformula by 4 to give us $C_4H_6O_5$. Now, we calculate the empirical formula molar mass of $C_4H_6O_5$:

    $$(4 \times 12.01) + (6 \times 1.01) + (5 \times 16.00) = 134.10 \ g/mol$$

    Since this mass is equal to the molar mass of malic acid, the empirical formula is also its molecular formula $(C_4H_6O_5)$.

44. Nicotine is highly addictive stimulant drug that can be found in the tobacco plant *Nicotiana tabacum*, and is commonly used in cigarettes. It is 74.1% carbon, 8.60% hydrogen, and 17.3% nitrogen and has a molar mass of 162.26 g/mol. What are the empirical and molecular formulas of nicotine?

    First, we assume a 100 gram sample. Thus, we can convert all of the percentages to grams. From there, we can calculate the number of mols of each element from grams using the atomic weights of each atom present in the molecule.

    Thus,

    $$74.1 \ g \ C \times \frac{1 \ mol \ C}{12.01 \ g \ C} = 6.17 \ mols \ C$$

    $$8.60 \ g \ H \times \frac{1 \ mol \ H}{1.01 \ g \ H} = 8.51 \ mols \ H$$

    $$17.3 \ g \ N \times \frac{1 \ mol \ N}{14.01 \ g \ N} = 1.23 \ mols \ N$$

    Next, we write a pseudoformula:

    $C_{6.17}H_{8.51}N_{1.23}$

    Now we divide all of the subscripts by the smallest number (1.23 in this case). So, now we get:

    $C_5H_7N_1$, so our empirical formula is C_5H_7N.

Now if we add up the empirical formula molar mass of C_5H_7N, we get 81.13 g/mol. However, in the question it states that the molar mass of nicotine is 162.26 g/mol. We then must simply multiply everything in the empirical formula by 2 to get our molecular formula. Thus, $C_{10}H_{14}N_2$ is our molecular formula for nicotine.

45. Warfarin is an anticoagulant drug that can be given to patients in order to prevent blood clots in veins or arteries. This can have the effect of reducing the risk of stroke, heart attack, or other serious medical conditions. Warfarin is known to be 74.0% carbon, 5.24% hydrogen, and 20.7% oxygen and has a molar mass of 308.35 g/mol. What are the empirical and molecular formulas of warfarin?

First, we assume a 100 gram sample. Thus, we can convert all of the percentages to grams. From there, we can calculate the number of mols of each element from grams using the atomic weights of each atom present in the molecule.

Thus,

$$74.0 \ g \ C \times \frac{1 \ mol \ C}{12.01 \ g \ C} = 6.16 \ mols \ C$$

$$5.24 \ g \ H \times \frac{1 \ mol \ H}{1.01 \ g \ H} = 5.19 \ mols \ H$$

$$20.7 \ g \ O \times \frac{1 \ mol \ O}{16.00 \ g \ O} = 1.30 \ mols \ O$$

Next, we write a pseudoformula:

$C_{6.16}H_{5.19}O_{1.30}$

Now we divide all of the subscripts by the smallest number (1.30 in this case). So, now we get:

$C_{4.75}H_4O_1$. Since we do not have all whole numbers, we now multiply everything in the formula by 4 to get our empirical formula for warfarin as $C_{19}H_{16}O_4$.

Now if we add up the empirical formula molar mass of $C_{19}H_{16}O_4$, we get 308.35 g/mol. Since this mass is equal to the molar mass of warfarin, the empirical formula is also its molecular formula ($C_{19}H_{16}O_4$).

46. Most of us have visited the dentist to get work done on our teeth and have been treated with the local anesthetic Novocain. Novocain is 66.1% carbon, 8.55% hydrogen, 11.9% nitrogen, and 13.5% oxygen and has a molar mass of 236.35 g/mol. What are the empirical and molecular formulas of Novocain?

First, we assume a 100 gram sample. Thus, we can convert all of the percentages to grams. From there, we can calculate the number of mols of each element from grams using the atomic weights of each atom present in the molecule.

Thus,

$$66.1 \ g \ C \times \frac{1 \ mol \ C}{12.01 \ g \ C} = 5.50 \ mols \ C$$

$$8.55 \ g \ H \times \frac{1 \ mol \ H}{1.01 \ g \ H} = 8.47 \ mols \ H$$

$$11.9 \ g \ N \times \frac{1 \ mol \ N}{14.01 \ g \ N} = 0.849 \ mols \ N$$

$$13.5 \ g \ O \times \frac{1 \ mol \ O}{16.00 \ g \ O} = 0.844 \ mols \ O$$

Next, we write a pseudoformula:

$C_{5.50}H_{8.47}N_{0.849}O_{0.844}$

Now we divide all of the subscripts by the smallest number (0.844 in this case). So, now we get:

$C_{6.5}H_{10}N_{1}O_{1}$. Since we do not have all whole numbers, we now multiply everything in the formula by 2 to get our empirical formula for Novocain as $C_{13}H_{20}N_{2}O_{2}$.

Now if we add up the empirical formula molar mass of $C_{13}H_{20}N_{2}O_{2}$, we get 236.35 g/mol. Since this mass is equal to the molar mass of Novocain, the empirical formula is also its molecular formula ($C_{13}H_{20}N_{2}O_{2}$).

BALANCING CHEMICAL EQUATIONS

47. Why is a balanced chemical equation important?

A balanced chemical equation is important because it provides not only the molecular formulas of both the reactants and products as well as their respective physical states, but it also allows for quantitative studies of chemical reactions.

48. In a chemical equation, the notation "(l)" means that the substance is a liquid.

49. In a chemical equation, the notation "(aq)" means that the substance is dissolved in water.

50. In a chemical equation, the notation "(s)" means that the substance is a solid.

51. In a chemical equation, the notation "(g)" means that the substance is a gas.

52. When N_2 (g) reacts with H_2 (g), it produces ammonia NH_3 (g). Write a balanced equation for this reaction.

$$N_2(g) + 3H_2(g) \rightarrow 2NH_3 \ (g)$$

53. When solid aluminum chloride reacts with liquid water it produces solid aluminum hydroxide and aqueous hydrochloric acid (HCl). Write a balanced chemical equation for this reaction.

$$AlCl_3(s) + 3H_2O\ (l) \rightarrow Al(OH)_3(s) + 3HCl\ (aq)$$

54. The complete combustion of gaseous methane (CH_4) in the presence of oxygen produces carbon dioxide gas and water vapor. Write a balanced chemical equation for this reaction.

$$CH_4\ (g) + 2O_2\ (g) \rightarrow CO_2\ (g) + 2H_2O\ (g)$$

55. When solid nickel (II) carbonate reacts with aqueous nitric acid (HNO_3), it produces aqueous nickel (II) nitrate, carbon dioxide gas, and liquid water. Write a balanced chemical equation for this reaction.

$$NiCO_3\ (s) + 2HNO_3\ (aq) \rightarrow Ni(NO_3)_2\ (aq) + CO_2(g) + H_2O\ (l)$$

56. During alcohol production, aqueous ethyl alcohol (C_2H_5OH) is formed along with gaseous carbon dioxide when solid sucrose ($C_{12}H_{22}O_{11}$) undergoes fermentation by yeasts in the presence of liquid water. Write a balanced chemical equation for this reaction.

$$C_{12}H_{22}O_{11}(s) + H_2O(l) \rightarrow 4C_2H_5OH(aq) + 4CO_2(g)$$

USING BALANCING CHEMICAL EQUATIONS TO CALCULATE QUANTITIES OF REACTANTS AND PRODUCTS

57. From the balanced chemical equation in question #52, what is the stoichiometric ratio between N_2 and H_2?

The stoichiometric ratio between N_2 and H_2 is 1 mol N_2/3 mol H_2.

58. From the balanced chemical equation in question #52, what is the stoichiometric ratio between N_2 and NH_3?

The stoichiometric ratio between N_2 and NH_3 is 1 mol N_2/2 mol NH_3.

59. From the balanced chemical equation in question #52, what is the stoichiometric ratio between H_2 and NH_3?

The stoichiometric ratio between H_2 and NH_3 is 3 mol H_2/2 mol NH_3.

60. Consider the following balanced chemical equation:

$$H_2\ (g) + Cl_2\ (g) \rightarrow 2HCl\ (g)$$

a. How much HCl (mols) can be produced from 0.136 mols of H_2 (assume excess of Cl_2)?

$$0.136\ mols\ H_2 \times \frac{2\ mols\ HCl}{1\ mol\ H_2} = 0.272\ mols\ HCl$$

b. How much Cl_2 (mols) is required to completely react with 0.827 mols of H_2?

$$0.827\ mols\ H_2 \times \frac{1\ mol\ Cl_2}{1\ mol\ H_2} = 0.827\ mols\ Cl_2$$

c. How much HCl (grams) can be produced from 5.85 grams of H_2 (assume excess of Cl_2)?

$$5.85\ grams\ H_2 \times \frac{1\ mol\ H_2}{2.02\ grams\ H_2} \times \frac{2\ mols\ HCl}{1\ mol\ H_2} \times \frac{36.46\ grams\ HCl}{1\ mol\ HCl} = 211\ grams\ HCl$$

d. How much Cl_2 (grams) is required to completely react with 2.42 grams of H_2?

$$2.42\ grams\ H_2 \times \frac{1\ mol\ H_2}{2.02\ grams\ H_2} \times \frac{1\ mol\ Cl_2}{1\ mol\ H_2} \times \frac{70.90\ grams\ Cl_2}{1\ mol\ Cl_2} = 84.9\ grams\ Cl_2$$

61. Aqueous cobalt (III) nitrate reacts with aqueous ammonium sulfide to produce solid cobalt (III) sulfide and aqueous ammonium nitrate.

First, we should write out the equation and balance:

$$2Co(NO_3)_3\ (aq) + 3(NH_4)_2S\ (aq) \rightarrow Co_2S_3\ (s) + 6NH_4NO_3\ (aq)$$

a. How much cobalt (III) sulfide (mols) can be produced from 2.94 mols of cobalt (III) nitrate (assume excess of ammonium sulfide)?

$$2.94\ mols\ Co(NO_3)_3 \times \frac{1\ mol\ Co_2S_3}{2\ mols\ Co(NO_3)_3} = 1.47\ mols\ Co_2S_3$$

b. How much ammonium sulfide (mols) is required to completely react with 0.941 mols of cobalt (III) nitrate?

$$0.941\ mols\ Co(NO_3)_3 \times \frac{3\ mols\ (NH_4)_2S}{2\ mols\ Co(NO_3)_3} = 1.41\ mols\ (NH_4)_2S$$

c. How much cobalt (III) sulfide (grams) can be produced from 3.76 grams of cobalt (III) nitrate (assume excess of ammonium sulfide)?

$$3.76\ grams\ Co(NO_3)_3 \times \frac{1\ mol\ Co(NO_3)_3}{244.96\ grams\ Co(NO_3)_3} \times \frac{1\ mol\ Co_2S_3}{2\ mols\ Co(NO_3)_3} \times \frac{214.04\ grams\ Co_2S_3}{1\ mol\ Co_2S_3}$$

$$= 1.64\ grams\ Co_2S_3$$

d. How much ammonium sulfide (grams) is required to completely react with 7.92 grams of cobalt (III) nitrate?

$$7.92 \text{ grams } Co(NO_3)_3 \times \frac{1 \text{ mol } Co(NO_3)_3}{244.96 \text{ grams } Co(NO_3)_3} \times \frac{3 \text{ mols } (NH_4)_2S}{2 \text{ mols } Co(NO_3)_3} \times \frac{68.16 \text{ grams } (NH_4)_2S}{1 \text{ mol } (NH_4)_2S}$$

$$= 3.31 \text{ grams } (NH_4)_2S$$

LIMITING REACTANT AND PERCENT YIELD

62. What is the limiting reactant and why does the reaction stop once this particular reactant has been consumed?

The limiting reactant is the reactant that is depleted first, thus the reaction stops regardless of whether or not other reactants remain.

63. What is the excess reactant?

The excess reactant is leftover following the depletion of the limiting reactant. The reaction stops following depletion of the limiting reactant, because while the excess reactant remains, it has nothing to react with in order to generate more of the products for that given chemical reaction.

64. How do we calculate percent yield?

Percent yield is the actual yield divided by the theoretical yield and multiplied by 100 to give a percent. Thus, we have:

$$Percent \ Yield = \frac{Actual \ Yield}{Theoretical \ Yield} \times 100$$

65. Given that you have 8.00 grams of each reactant in the balanced chemical equations below, which one is the limiting reactant and how much product of interest (in **BOLD**) is produced (mols) assuming the limiting reactant is completely consumed?

a. $Fe_2O_3 \ (s) + 3CO \ (g) \rightarrow \textbf{2Fe} \ (s) + 3CO_2 \ (g)$

$$8.00 \text{ grams } Fe_2O_3 \times \frac{1 \text{ mol } Fe_2O_3}{159.70 \text{ grams } Fe_2O_3} \times \frac{2 \text{ mols } Fe}{1 \text{ mols } Fe_2O_3} = 0.100 \text{ mols } Fe \text{ potentially produced}$$

$$8.00 \text{ grams } CO \times \frac{1 \text{ mol } CO}{28.01 \text{ grams } CO} \times \frac{2 \text{ mols } Fe}{3 \text{ mols } CO} = 0.190 \text{ mols } Fe \text{ potentially produced}$$

Thus, Fe_2O_3 is the limiting reactant with 0.100 mols (smaller number) of Fe produced.

b. $4HCl \ (aq) + O_2 \ (g) \rightarrow 2H_2O \ (l) + \textbf{2Cl}_2 \ (g)$

$$8.00 \text{ grams } HCl \times \frac{1 \text{ mol } HCl}{36.46 \text{ grams } HCl} \times \frac{2 \text{ mols } Cl_2}{4 \text{ mols } HCl} = 0.110 \text{ mols } Cl_2 \text{ potentially produced}$$

$$8.00 \text{ grams } O_2 \times \frac{1 \text{ mol } O_2}{32.00 \text{ grams } O_2} \times \frac{2 \text{ mols } Cl_2}{1 \text{ mol } O_2} = 0.500 \text{ mols } Cl_2 \text{ potentially produced}$$

Thus, HCl is the limiting reactant with 0.110 mols (smaller number) of Cl_2 produced.

c. $2NaOH\ (aq) + CO_2\ (g) \rightarrow \mathbf{Na_2CO_3}\ (aq) + H_2O\ (l)$

$$8.00\ grams\ NaOH \times \frac{1\ mol\ NaOH}{40.00\ grams\ NaOH} \times \frac{1\ mol\ Na_2CO_3}{2\ mols\ NaOH} = 0.100\ mols\ Na_2CO_3\ potentially\ produced$$

$$8.00\ grams\ CO_2 \times \frac{1\ mol\ CO_2}{44.01\ grams\ CO_2} \times \frac{1\ mol\ Na_2CO_3}{1\ mol\ CO_2} = 0.182\ mols\ Na_2CO_3\ potentially\ produced$$

Thus, NaOH is the limiting reactant with 0.100 mols (smaller number) of Na_2CO_3 produced.

d. $C_3H_8\ (g) + 5O_2\ (g) \rightarrow \mathbf{3CO_2}\ (g) + 4H_2O\ (g)$

$$8.00\ grams\ C_3H_8 \times \frac{1\ mol\ C_3H_8}{44.11\ grams\ C_3H_8} \times \frac{3\ mols\ CO_2}{1\ mol\ C_3H_8} = 0.544\ mols\ CO_2\ potentially\ produced$$

$$8.00\ grams\ O_2 \times \frac{1\ mol\ O_2}{32.00\ grams\ O_2} \times \frac{3\ mols\ CO_2}{5\ mols\ O_2} = 0.150\ mols\ CO_2\ potentially\ produced$$

Thus, O_2 is the limiting reactant with 0.150 mols (smaller number) of CO_2 produced.

66. Given that you have 8.00 grams of each reactant in the balanced chemical equations below, which one is the limiting reactant and how much product of interest (in **BOLD**) is produced (mols) assuming the limiting reactant is completely consumed?

a. $Ca(OH)_2\ (aq) + 2HBr\ (aq) \rightarrow \mathbf{CaBr_2}\ (aq) + 2H_2O\ (l)$

$$8.00\ grams\ Ca(OH)_2 \times \frac{1\ mol\ Ca(OH)_2}{74.10\ grams\ Ca(OH)_2} \times \frac{1\ mol\ CaBr_2}{1\ mol\ Ca(OH)_2}$$
$$= 1.08 \times 10^{-1}\ mols\ CaBr_2\ potentially\ produced$$

$$8.00\ grams\ HBr \times \frac{1\ mol\ HBr}{80.91\ grams\ HBr} \times \frac{1\ mol\ CaBr_2}{2\ mols\ HBr} = 4.94 \times 10^{-2}\ mols\ CaBr_2\ potentially\ produced$$

Thus, HBr is the limiting reactant with 4.94×10^{-2} mols (smaller number) of $CaBr_2$ produced.

b. $SiO_2\ (s) + 2C\ (s) \rightarrow \mathbf{Si}\ (s) + 2CO\ (g)$

$$8.00\ grams\ SiO_2 \times \frac{1\ mol\ SiO_2}{60.09\ grams\ SiO_2} \times \frac{1\ mol\ Si}{1\ mol\ SiO_2} = 0.133\ mols\ Si\ potentially\ produced$$

$$8.00\ grams\ C \times \frac{1\ mol\ C}{12.01\ grams\ C} \times \frac{1\ mol\ Si}{2\ mols\ C} = 0.333\ mols\ Si\ potentially\ produced$$

Thus, SiO_2 is the limiting reactant with 0.133 mols (smaller number) of Si produced.

c. $Na_2S\ (aq) + Cu(NO_3)_2\ (aq) \rightarrow 2NaNO_3\ (aq) + \textbf{CuS}\ (s)$

$$8.00\ grams\ Na_2S \times \frac{1\ mol\ Na_2S}{78.05\ grams\ Na_2S} \times \frac{1\ mol\ CuS}{1\ mol\ Na_2S} = 1.02 \times 10^{-1}\ mols\ CuS\ potentially\ produce$$

$$8.00\ grams\ Cu(NO_3)_2 \times \frac{1\ mol\ Cu(NO_3)_2}{187.57\ grams\ Cu(NO_3)_2} \times \frac{1\ mol\ CuS}{1\ mol\ Cu(NO_3)_2}$$
$$= 4.27 \times 10^{-2}\ mols\ CuS\ potentially\ produced$$

Thus, $Cu(NO_3)_2$ is the limiting reactant with 4.27×10^{-2} mols (smaller number) of CuS produced.

d. $CH_4\ (g) + H_2O\ (g) \rightarrow CO\ (g) + \textbf{3H}_2\ (g)$

$$8.00\ grams\ CH_4 \times \frac{1\ mol\ CH_4}{16.05\ grams\ CH_4} \times \frac{3\ mols\ H_2}{1\ mol\ CH_4} = 1.50\ mols\ H_2\ potentially\ produced$$

$$8.00\ grams\ H_2O \times \frac{1\ mol\ H_2O}{18.02\ grams\ H_2O} \times \frac{3\ mols\ H_2}{1\ mol\ H_2O} = 1.33\ mols\ H_2\ potentially\ produced$$

Thus, H_2O is the limiting reactant with 1.33 mols (smaller number) of H_2 produced.

67. Based on your answers from question # 65, predict how much product of interest (in **BOLD**) is produced in grams assuming that all of the limiting reactant is consumed.

a. What is the mass of **Fe** produced (grams) in this chemical reaction?

From question #65 a.), we know that 0.100 mols of Fe are produced following the complete consumption of the limiting reactant Fe_2O_3. Therefore,

$$0.100\ mols\ Fe \times \frac{55.85\ grams\ Fe}{1\ mol\ Fe} = 5.59\ grams\ Fe\ produced$$

b. What is the mass of **Cl**$_2$ produced (grams) in this chemical reaction?

From question #65 b.), we know that 0.110 mols of Cl_2 are produced following the complete consumption of the limiting reactant HCl. Therefore,

$$0.110\ mols\ Cl_2 \times \frac{70.90\ grams\ Cl_2}{1\ mol\ Cl_2} = 7.80\ grams\ Cl_2\ produced$$

c. What is the mass of **Na**$_2$**CO**$_3$ produced (grams) in this chemical reaction?

From question #65 c.), we know that 0.100 mols of Na_2CO_3 are produced following the complete consumption of the limiting reactant NaOH. Therefore,

$$0.100\ mols\ Na_2CO_3 \times \frac{105.99\ grams\ Na_2CO_3}{1\ mol\ Na_2CO_3} = 10.6\ grams\ Na_2CO_3\ produced$$

d. What is the mass of **CO₂** produced (grams) in this chemical reaction?

From question #65 d.), we know that 0.150 mols of CO_2 are produced following the complete consumption of the limiting reactant O_2. Therefore,

$$0.150 \; mols \; CO_2 \times \frac{44.01 \; grams \; CO_2}{1 \; mol \; CO_2} = 6.60 \; grams \; CO_2 \; produced$$

68. Based on your answers from question # 66, predict how much product of interest (in **BOLD**) is produced in grams (assuming that all of the limiting reactant is consumed).

a. What is the mass of **CaBr₂** produced (grams) in this chemical reaction?

From question #66 a., we know that 4.94×10^{-2} mols of $CaBr_2$ are produced following the complete consumption of the limiting reactant HBr. Therefore,

$$4.94 \times 10^{-2} \; mols \; CaBr_2 \times \frac{199.88 \; grams \; CaBr_2}{1 \; mol \; CaBr_2} = 9.87 \; grams \; CaBr_2 \; produced$$

b. What is the mass of **Si** produced (grams) in this chemical reaction?

From question #66 b., we know that 0.133 mols of Si are produced following the complete consumption of the limiting reactant SiO_2. Therefore,

$$0.133 \; mols \; Si \times \frac{28.09 \; grams \; Si}{1 \; mol \; Si} = 3.74 \; grams \; Si \; produced$$

c. What is the mass of **CuS** produced (grams) in this chemical reaction?

From question #66 c., we know that 4.27×10^{-2} mols of CuS are produced following the complete consumption of the limiting reactant $Cu(NO_3)_2$. Therefore,

$$4.27 \times 10^{-2} \; mols \; CuS \times \frac{95.62 \; grams \; CuS}{1 \; mol \; CuS} = 4.08 \; grams \; CuS \; produced$$

d. What is the mass of **H₂** produced (grams) in this chemical reaction?

From question #66 d., we know that 1.33 mols of H_2 are produced following the complete consumption of the limiting reactant H_2O. Therefore,

$$1.33 \; mols \; H_2 \times \frac{2.02 \; grams \; H_2}{1 \; mol \; H_2} = 2.69 \; grams \; H_2 \; produced$$

69. Sodium fluoride is a common additive to toothpaste and is known to help improve dental health by strengthening the enamel on the surface of teeth, as well as preventing the formation of cavities. The chemical synthesis of sodium fluoride is illustrated below in the following balanced chemical equation:

$$2Na \; (s) + F_2 \; (g) \rightarrow 2NaF \; (s)$$

If 15.5 grams of both sodium and fluorine are used, how much sodium fluoride can be produced (grams)? What is the limiting and excess reactant? What is the percent yield if we have an experimentally derived actual yield of 23.4 grams of sodium fluoride produced?

$$15.5 \text{ grams } Na \times \frac{1 \text{ mol } Na}{22.99 \text{ grams } Na} \times \frac{2 \text{ mols } NaF}{2 \text{ mols } Na} = 0.674 \text{ mols } NaF$$

$$15.5 \text{ grams } F_2 \times \frac{1 \text{ mol } F_2}{38.00 \text{ grams } F_2} \times \frac{2 \text{ mols } NaF}{1 \text{ mol } F_2} = 0.816 \text{ mols } NaF$$

Thus, Na is our limiting reactant (smaller number), and F_2 is the excess reactant. Therefore,

$$0.674 \text{ mols } NaF \times \frac{41.99 \text{ grams } NaF}{1 \text{ mol } NaF} = 28.3 \text{ grams } NaF \text{ (theoretical yield)}$$

$$Percent \text{ } yield = \frac{23.4 \text{ grams } NaF}{28.3 \text{ grams } NaF} \times 100 = 82.7\%$$

70. Scrap aluminum can be treated with chlorine gas to yield aluminum chloride according to the following balanced chemical equation:

$$2Al \ (s) + 3Cl_2 \ (g) \rightarrow 2AlCl_3 \ (s)$$

If 13.2 grams of scrap aluminum and 16.3 grams of chlorine gas are combined in the reaction, how much aluminum chloride can be produced (grams)? What is the limiting and excess reactant? What is the percent yield if we have an experimentally derived actual yield of 16.2 grams of aluminum chloride produced?

$$13.2 \text{ grams } Al \times \frac{1 \text{ mol } Al}{26.98 \text{ grams } Al} \times \frac{2 \text{ mols } AlCl_3}{2 \text{ mols } Al} = 0.489 \text{ mols } AlCl_3$$

$$16.3 \text{ grams } Cl_2 \times \frac{1 \text{ mol } Cl_2}{70.90 \text{ grams } Cl_2} \times \frac{2 \text{ mols } AlCl_3}{3 \text{ mols } Cl_2} = 0.153 \text{ mols } AlCl_3$$

Thus, Cl_2 is our limiting reactant (smaller number), and Al is the excess reactant. Therefore,

$$0.153 \text{ mols } AlCl_3 \times \frac{133.33 \text{ grams } AlCl_3}{1 \text{ mol } AlCl_3} = 20.4 \text{ grams } AlCl_3 \text{ (theoretical yield)}$$

$$Percent \text{ } yield = \frac{16.2 \text{ grams } AlCl_3}{20.4 \text{ grams } AlCl_3} \times 100 = 79.4\%$$

71. Consider the reaction between iron (III) oxide and carbon monoxide according to the following balanced chemical equation:

$$Fe_2O_3 \ (s) + 3CO \ (g) \rightarrow 2Fe \ (s) + 3CO_2 \ (g)$$

If 45.1 grams of iron (III) oxide and 19.3 grams of carbon monoxide are combined in the reaction, how much iron metal can be produced (grams)? What is the limiting and excess reactant? What is the percent yield if we have an experimentally derived actual yield of 19.8 grams of iron metal produced?

$$45.1 \text{ grams } Fe_2O_3 \times \frac{1 \text{ mol } Fe_2O_3}{159.7 \text{ grams } Fe_2O_3} \times \frac{2 \text{ mols } Fe}{1 \text{ mol } Fe_2O_3} = 0.565 \text{ mols } Fe$$

$$19.3 \text{ grams } CO \times \frac{1 \text{ mol } CO}{28.01 \text{ grams } CO} \times \frac{2 \text{ mols } Fe}{3 \text{ mols } CO} = 0.459 \text{ mols } Fe$$

Thus, CO is our limiting reactant (smaller number), and Fe_2O_3 is the excess reactant. Therefore,

$$0.459 \text{ mols } Fe \times \frac{55.85 \text{ grams } Fe}{1 \text{ mol } Fe} = 25.6 \text{ grams } Fe \text{ (theoretical yield)}$$

$$Percent \; yield = \frac{19.8 \text{ grams } Fe}{25.6 \text{ grams } Fe} \times 100 = 77.\,3\%$$

72. Aspirin ($C_9H_8O_4$) is a medication that can be taken in order to manage pain, fever, and inflammation. It can be produced by the reaction of salicylic acid ($C_7H_6O_3$) and acetic anhydride ($C_4H_6O_3$) as depicted in the following balanced chemical equation:

$$C_7H_6O_3 \, (s) + C_4H_6O_3 \, (l) \rightarrow C_9H_8O_4 \, (s) + CH_3CO_2H \, (l)$$

If 20.0 grams of both salicylic acid and acetic anhydride are used to produce aspirin, how much aspirin can be produced (grams)? What is the limiting and excess reactant? What is the percent yield if we have an experimentally derived actual yield of 19.4 grams of aspirin produced?

$$20.0 \text{ grams } C_7H_6O_3 \times \frac{1 \text{ mol } C_7H_6O_3}{138.13 \text{ grams } C_7H_6O_3} \times \frac{1 \text{ mol } C_9H_8O_4}{1 \text{ mol } C_7H_6O_3} = 0.145 \text{ mols } C_9H_8O_4$$

$$20.0 \text{ grams } C_4H_6O_3 \times \frac{1 \text{ mol } C_4H_6O_3}{102.10 \text{ grams } C_4H_6O_3} \times \frac{1 \text{ mol } C_9H_8O_4}{1 \text{ mol } C_4H_6O_3} = 0.196 \text{ mols } C_9H_8O_4$$

Thus, $C_7H_6O_3$ is our limiting reactant (smaller number), and $C_4H_6O_3$ is the excess reactant. Therefore,

$$0.145 \text{ mols } C_9H_8O_4 \times \frac{180.17 \text{ grams } C_9H_8O_4}{1 \text{ mol } C_9H_8O_4} = 26.1 \text{ grams } C_9H_8O_4 \text{ (theoretical yield)}$$

$$Percent \; yield = \frac{19.4 \text{ grams } C_9H_8O_4}{26.1 \text{ grams } C_9H_8O_4} \times 100 = 74.3\%$$

73. From the given information in question #69, how much (grams) of the excess reactant remains following the chemical reaction (assume complete consumption of the limiting reactant)?

$$2Na \ (s) + F_2 \ (g) \rightarrow 2NaF \ (s)$$

From question #69, we know that 0.674 mols of product were formed from the complete consumption of the limiting reactant (Na), making F_2 the excess reactant. Thus,

$$0.674 \ mols \ NaF \times \frac{1 \ mol \ F_2}{2 \ mols \ NaF} = 0.337 \ mols \ F_2 \ were \ used \ in \ the \ reaction$$

$$0.337 \ mols \ F_2 \times \frac{38.00 \ grams \ F_2}{1 \ mol \ F_2} = 12.8 \ grams \ F_2 \ used \ in \ the \ reaction$$

Therefore, 15.5 grams F_2 − 12.8 grams F_2 = 2.70 grams (7.11×10^{-2} mols) F_2 remaining following the complete consumption of the limiting reactant (Na) in this reaction.

74. From the given information in question #70, how much (grams) of the excess reactant remains following the chemical reaction (assume complete consumption of the limiting reactant?

$$2Al \ (s) + 3Cl_2 \ (g) \rightarrow 2AlCl_3 \ (s)$$

From question #70, we know that 0.153 mols of product were formed from the complete consumption of the limiting reactant (Cl_2), making Al the excess reactant. Thus,

$$0.153 \ mols \ AlCl_3 \times \frac{2 \ mols \ Al}{2 \ mols \ AlCl_3} = 0.153 \ mols \ Al \ were \ used \ in \ the \ reaction$$

$$0.153 \ mols \ Al \times \frac{26.98 \ grams \ Al}{1 \ mol \ Al} = 4.13 \ grams \ Al \ used \ in \ the \ reaction$$

Therefore, 13.2 grams Al − 4.13 grams Al = 9.07 grams (0.336 mols) Al remaining following the complete consumption of the limiting reactant (Cl_2) in this reaction.

75. From the given information in question #71, how much (grams) of the excess reactant remains following the chemical reaction (assume complete consumption of the limiting reactant?

$$Fe_2O_3 \ (s) + 3CO \ (g) \rightarrow 2Fe \ (s) + 3CO_2 \ (g)$$

From question #71, we know that 0.459 mols of product (Fe) were formed from the complete consumption of the limiting reactant (CO), making Fe_2O_3 the excess reactant. Thus,

$$0.459 \ mols \ Fe \times \frac{1 \ mol \ Fe_2O_3}{2 \ mols \ Fe} = 0.230 \ mols \ Fe_2O_3 \ were \ used \ in \ the \ reaction$$

$$0.230 \ mols \ Fe_2O_3 \times \frac{159.7 \ grams \ Fe_2O_3}{1 \ mol \ Fe_2O_3} = 36.7 \ grams \ Fe_2O_3 \ used \ in \ the \ reaction$$

Therefore, 45.1 grams Fe_2O_3 − 36.7 grams Fe_2O_3 = 8.40 grams (5.26×10^{-2} mols) Fe_2O_3 remaining following the complete consumption of the limiting reactant (CO) in this reaction.

76. From the given information in question #72, how much (grams) of the excess reactant remains following the chemical reaction (assume complete consumption of the limiting reactant?

$$C_7H_6O_3 \ (s) + C_4H_6O_3 \ (l) \rightarrow C_9H_8O_4 \ (s) + CH_3CO_2H \ (l)$$

From question #72, we know that 0.145 of product $(C_9H_8O_4)$ were formed from the complete consumption of the limiting reactant $(C_7H_6O_3)$, making $C_4H_6O_3$ the excess reactant. Thus,

$$0.145 \ mols \ C_9H_8O_4 \times \frac{1 \ mol \ C_4H_6O_3}{1 \ mol \ C_9H_8O_4} = 0.145 \ mols \ C_4H_6O_3 \ were \ used \ in \ the \ reaction$$

$$0.145 \ mols \ C_4H_6O_3 \times \frac{102.10 \ grams \ C_4H_6O_3}{1 \ mol \ C_4H_6O_3} = 14.8 \ grams \ C_4H_6O_3 \ used \ in \ the \ reaction$$

Therefore, 20.0 grams $C_4H_6O_3$ – 14.8 grams $C_4H_6O_3$ = 5.20 grams (5.09×10^{-2} mols) $C_4H_6O_3$ remaining following the complete consumption of the limiting reactant $(C_7H_6O_3)$ in this reaction.

KEY TERMS

Actual yield   The amount of product actually isolated from chemical reaction.

Avogadro's number 6.022×10^{23} is the number of chemical entities (atoms, ions, or molecules) in one mole of a substance.

Chemical equations   Equations that provide information regarding the compounds involved in a reaction as well as the physical state of each compound.

Combustion reactions   Reactions in which oxygen is a reactant with another substance and which produces oxygen containing products. These can be thought of as "burning" reactions (such as the fuel in your car), and the complete combustion of hydrocarbons involving oxygen always produces CO_2 and H_2O.

Empirical formulas   In an *empirical formula*, the subscripts represent the lowest whole-number ratio of the different atoms that make up the compound in question.

Excess reactant   Reactants in a chemical reaction which are not completely consumed.

Limiting reactant   The reactant in a chemical reaction which is depleted first.

Mass percent composition   The relative mass of an element in a given compound expressed as a percentage.

Molar mass   The mass of one mole of a given species expressed in grams/mol, which can either be an element (either monoatomic or molecular) or a compound.

Mole   The amount of a substance that contains the same number of entities as 12 grams of carbon-12 (^{12}C). As it turns out, there are 6.022×10^{23} carbon-12 atoms in exactly 12 grams.

Molecular formula   A *molecular formula* makes use of the symbols of the elements comprising a molecule along with numeric subscripts to indicate the exact number of atoms of each element contained within a molecule of a given covalent compound.

Percent yield   The actual yield in a chemical reaction, expressed as percentage of the theoretical yield.

Stoichiometric ratio   The ratio of the number of moles of a reactant or product in a chemical reaction relative to the other reactants and products.

Stoichiometry   The calculation of the relative quantities of reactants and products in chemical reactions.

Theoretical yield   The theoretical maximum obtainable yield of product, given the specific initial quantities of the reactants in a chemical reaction.

Dissolution and Reactions in Aqueous Solution

- The Polarity of Water

- The Components of a Solution and Concentration

- Calculating Concentrations in Units of Molarity, Molality, Mole Fraction, and Mass Percent

- Solubility and the Solubility Rules for Ionic Compounds

- Strong and Weak Electrolytes

- Precipitation Reactions and Gas-Evolving Reactions

- Ionic Equations

- The Colligative Properties of Solutions, Such as Vapor Pressure, Boiling Point, and Freezing Point

AQUEOUS SOLUTIONS OF IONIC COMPOUNDS AND PREDICTING SOLUBILITY

1. What is an electrolyte? What general class of compounds are electrolytes?

    An electrolyte is a compound that when dissolved in water dissociates into freely solvated ions. Such ions can act as mobile charge carriers allowing for the conduction of electric current. Soluble ionic compounds and acids are electrolytes.

2. What is a weak electrolyte? What general class of compounds are weak electrolytes?

    A weak electrolyte is a compound (an acid) that does not completely dissociate when dissolved in water. This results in a solution which is a poorer conductor of electric current than it otherwise would be.

3. Describe the mechanism of the dissolution of ionic compounds in water. How does the polarity of water play a role?

    When an ionic compound dissolves, the electrostatic interaction between the water molecules and the ions comprising the ionic solid are collectively more favorable than those between the anions and cations in the ionic compound itself. This results in "dissociation" of the ions from one another, each moving into solution surrounded by a "solvation sphere" of water molecules.

4. What is meant by the term solvated?

    Surrounded by solvent molecules.

5. Using the solubility rules, determine whether the following compounds are soluble or insoluble in water:
    a. $CaCl_2$ – Soluble
    b. Li_2SO_4 – Soluble
    c. CaS – Soluble
    d. $Fe_3(PO_4)_2$ – Insoluble

6. Using the solubility rules, determine whether the following compounds are soluble or insoluble in water:
    a. $PbSO_4$ – Insoluble
    b. $NaNO_3$ – Soluble
    c. BaS – Soluble
    d. $Pb(ClO_3)_2$ – Soluble

7. Using the solubility rules, determine whether the following compounds are soluble or insoluble in water:
    a. Hg_2Br_2 – Insoluble
    b. K_2CO_3 – Soluble
    c. $Ca(NO_3)_2$ – Soluble
    d. $BaBr_2$ – Soluble

8. Using the solubility rules, determine whether the following compounds are soluble or insoluble in water:
    a. $MgCl_2$ – Soluble
    b. $Ba(C_2H_3O_2)_2$ – Soluble
    c. Rb_2S – Insoluble
    d. $CsOH$ – Insoluble

9. Which of the following is an electrolyte? Explain your answers.
    a. $C_{12}H_{22}O_{11}$ – Nonelectrolyte. Molecular compounds are nonelectrolytes (except in the case of acids).
    b. $NaCl$ – Electrolyte. Soluble ionic compounds are electrolytes.
    c. $MgBr_2$ – Electrolyte. Soluble ionic compounds are electrolytes.
    d. $Mg(C_2H_3O_2)_2$ – Electrolyte. Soluble ionic compounds are electrolytes.

10. Which of the following is an electrolyte? Explain your answers.
    a. PCl_3 – Nonelectrolyte. Molecular compounds are nonelectrolytes (except in the case of acids).
    b. $Fe(NO_3)_3$ – Electrolyte. Soluble ionic compounds are electrolytes.
    c. $SrSO_4$ – Nonelectrolyte. Strontium sulfate is not soluble.
    d. C_3H_7OH – Nonelectrolyte. Molecular compounds are nonelectrolytes (except in the case of acids).

11. Write a balanced equation depicting the dissolution of the following compounds in water:
    a. K_2CO_3

    $$K_2CO_3(s) \xrightarrow{H_2O} 2\ K^+(aq) + CO_3^{2-}(aq)$$

    b. $Ca(NO_3)_2$

    $$Ca(NO_3)_2(s) \xrightarrow{H_2O} Ca^{2+}(aq) + 2\ NO_3^-(aq)$$

    c. $Ba(C_2H_3O_2)_2$

    $$Ba(C_2H_3O_2)_2(s) \xrightarrow{H_2O} Ba^{2+}(aq) + 2\ C_2H_3O_2^-(aq)$$

    d. Li_2SO_4

    $$Li_2SO_4(s) \xrightarrow{H_2O} 2\ Li^+(aq) + SO_4^{2-}(aq)$$

12. Write a balanced equation depicting the dissolution of the following compounds in water:
    a. $NaCl$

    $$NaCl(s) \xrightarrow{H_2O} Na^+(aq) + Cl^-(aq)$$

    b. K_2SO_4

    $$K_2SO_4(s) \xrightarrow{H_2O} 2\ K^+(aq) + SO_4^{2-}(aq)$$

c. $Mg(ClO_4)_2$

$$MgClO_4(s) \xrightarrow{H_2O} Mg^{2+}(aq) + 2\ ClO_4^-(aq)$$

d. HCl

$$HCl(g) \xrightarrow{H_2O} H^+(aq) + Cl^-(aq)$$

13. Write a balanced equation depicting the dissolution of the following compounds in water:

a. KOH

$$KOH(s) \xrightarrow{H_2O} K^+(aq) + OH^-(aq)$$

b. $(NH_4)_2CO_3$

$$(NH_4)_2CO_3(s) \xrightarrow{H_2O} 2\ NH_4^+(aq) + CO_3^{2-}(aq)$$

c. Na_2SO_4

$$Na_2SO_4(s) \xrightarrow{H_2O} 2\ Na^+(aq) + SO_4^{2-}(aq)$$

d. K_3PO_4

$$K_3PO_4(s) \xrightarrow{H_2O} 3\ K^+(aq) + PO_4^{3-}(aq)$$

14. Write a balanced equation depicting the dissolution of the following compounds in water:

a. NH_4NO_3

$$NH_4NO_3(s) \xrightarrow{H_2O} NH_3^+(aq) + NO_3^-(aq)$$

b. $NaOH$

$$NaOH(s) \xrightarrow{H_2O} Na^+(aq) + OH^-(aq)$$

c. Li_2S

$$Li_2S(s) \xrightarrow{H_2O} 2\ Li^+(aq) + S^{2-}(aq)$$

d. CsI

$$CsI(s) \xrightarrow{H_2O} Cs^+(aq) + I^-(aq)$$

15. How many total moles of ions are present in solution when the following are dissolved in water?

a. 8.00 g *NaCl*

Recall the equation for the dissolution of *NaCl*:

$$NaCl(s) \xrightarrow{H_2O} Na^+(aq) + Cl^-(aq)$$

Determine the moles of each ion formed using the balanced equation:

$$8.00 \ g \ NaCl \times \frac{1 \ mol \ NaCl}{58.44 \ g \ NaCl} \times \frac{1 \ mol \ Na^+}{1 \ mol \ NaCl} = 0.1369 \ mol \ Na^+$$

$$8.00 \ g \ NaCl \times \frac{1 \ mol \ NaCl}{58.44 \ g \ NaCl} \times \frac{1 \ mol \ Cl^-}{1 \ mol \ NaCl} = 0.1369 \ mol \ Cl^-$$

$$0.1369 \ mol \ Na^+ + 0.1369 \ mol \ Cl^- = 0.2738 \ mol \ ions$$

Therefore, we find that there are 0.2738 mols of ions in solution.

b. 8.00 g *NaOH*

Recall the equation for the dissolution of *NaOH*:

$$NaOH(s) \xrightarrow{H_2O} Na^+(aq) + OH^-(aq)$$

Determine the moles of each ion formed using the balanced equation:

$$8.00 \ g \ NaOH \times \frac{1 \ mol \ NaOH}{40.00 \ g \ NaOH} \times \frac{1 \ mol \ Na^+}{1 \ mol \ NaOH} = 0.200 \ mol \ Na^+$$

$$8.00 \ g \ NaOH \times \frac{1 \ mol \ NaOH}{40.00 \ g \ NaOH} \times \frac{1 \ mol \ OH^-}{1 \ mol \ NaOH} = 0.200 \ mol \ OH^-$$

$$0.200 \ mol \ Na^+ + 0.200 \ mol \ OH^- = 0.400 \ mol \ ions$$

Therefore, we find that there are 0.400 mols of ions in solution.

c. 10.00 g *NaCl*

Recall the equation for the dissolution of *NaCl*:

$$NaCl(s) \xrightarrow{H_2O} Na^+(aq) + Cl^-(aq)$$

Determine the moles of each ion formed using the balanced equation:

$$10.00 \text{ g } NaCl \times \frac{1 \text{ mol } NaCl}{58.44 \text{ g } NaCl} \times \frac{1 \text{ mol } Na^+}{1 \text{ mol } NaCl} = 0.1711 \text{ mol } Na^+$$

$$10.00 \text{ g } NaCl \times \frac{1 \text{ mol } NaCl}{58.44 \text{ g } NaCl} \times \frac{1 \text{ mol } Cl^-}{1 \text{ mol } NaCl} = 0.1711 \text{ mol } Cl^-$$

$$0.1711 \text{ mol } Na^+ + 0.1711 \text{ mol } Cl^- = 0.3422 \text{ mol ions}$$

Therefore, we find that there are 0.3422 mols of ions in solution.

d. 10.00 g **NaOH**

Recall the equation for the dissolution of $NaOH$:

$$NaOH(s) \xrightarrow{H_2O} Na^+(aq) + OH^-(aq)$$

Determine the moles of each ion formed using the balanced equation:

$$10.00 \text{ g } NaOH \times \frac{1 \text{ mol } NaOH}{40.00 \text{ g } NaOH} \times \frac{1 \text{ mol } Na^+}{1 \text{ mol } NaOH} = 0.250 \text{ mol } Na^+$$

$$10.00 \text{ g } NaOH \times \frac{1 \text{ mol } NaOH}{40.00 \text{ g } NaOH} \times \frac{1 \text{ mol } OH^-}{1 \text{ mol } NaOH} = 0.250 \text{ mol } OH^-$$

$$0.250 \text{ mol } Na^+ + 0.250 \text{ mol } OH^- = 0.500 \text{ mol ions}$$

Therefore, we find that there are 0.500 mols of ions in solution.

16. How many total moles of ions are present in solution when the following are dissolved in water?
    a. 4.72 g $NaC_2H_3O_2$

    Write the equation for the dissolution of $NaC_2H_3O_2$:

    $$NaC_2H_3O_2(s) \xrightarrow{H_2O} Na^+(aq) + C_2H_3O_2^-(aq)$$

    Determine the moles of each ion formed using the balanced equation:

    $$4.72 \text{ g } NaC_2H_3O_2 \times \frac{1 \text{ mol } NaC_2H_3O_2}{82.04 \text{ g } NaC_2H_3O_2} \times \frac{1 \text{ mol } Na^+}{1 \text{ mol } NaC_2H_3O_2} = 0.05753 \text{ mol } Na^+$$

$$4.72 \text{ } g \text{ } NaC_2H_3O_2 \times \frac{1 \text{ } mol \text{ } NaC_2H_3O_2}{82.04 \text{ } g \text{ } NaC_2H_3O_2} \times \frac{1 \text{ } mol \text{ } C_2H_3O_2^-}{1 \text{ } mol \text{ } NaC_2H_3O_2} = 0.05753 \text{ } mol \text{ } C_2H_3O_2^-$$

$$0.05753 \text{ } mol \text{ } Na^+ + 0.05753 \text{ } mol \text{ } C_2H_3O_2^- = 0.11506 \text{ } mol \text{ } ions$$

Therefore, we find that there are 0.11506 mols of ions in solution.

b. 1.33 g K_2SO_4

Write the equation for the dissolution of K_2SO_4:

$$K_2SO_4(s) \xrightarrow{H_2O} 2 \text{ } K^+(aq) + SO_4^{2-}(aq)$$

Determine the moles of each ion formed using the balanced equation:

$$1.33 \text{ } g \text{ } K_2SO_4 \times \frac{1 \text{ } mol \text{ } K_2SO_4}{174.27 \text{ } g \text{ } K_2SO_4} \times \frac{2 \text{ } mol \text{ } K^+}{1 \text{ } mol \text{ } K_2SO_4} = 0.01526 \text{ } mol \text{ } K^+$$

$$1.33 \text{ } g \text{ } K_2SO_4 \times \frac{1 \text{ } mol \text{ } K_2SO_4}{174.27 \text{ } g \text{ } K_2SO_4} \times \frac{1 \text{ } mol \text{ } SO_4^{2-}}{1 \text{ } mol \text{ } K_2SO_4} = 0.00763 \text{ } mol \text{ } SO_4^{2-}$$

$$0.01526 \text{ } mol \text{ } K^+ + 0.00763 \text{ } mol \text{ } SO_4^{2-} = 0.02290 \text{ } mol \text{ } ions$$

Therefore, we find that there are 0.02289 mols of ions in solution.

c. 11.34 g $Fe_2(SO_4)_3$

Write the equation for the dissolution of $Fe_2(SO_4)_3$:

$$Fe_2(SO_4)_3(s) \xrightarrow{H_2O} 2 \text{ } Fe^{3+}(aq) + 3 \text{ } SO_4^{2-}(aq)$$

Determine the moles of each ion formed using the balanced equation:

$$11.34 \text{ } g \text{ } Fe_2(SO_4)_3 \times \frac{1 \text{ } mol \text{ } Fe_2(SO_4)_3}{399.91 \text{ } g \text{ } Fe_2(SO_4)_3} \times \frac{2 \text{ } mol \text{ } Fe^{3+}}{1 \text{ } mol \text{ } Fe_2(SO_4)_3} = 0.05671 \text{ } mol \text{ } Fe^{3+}$$

$$11.34 \text{ } g \text{ } Fe_2(SO_4)_3 \times \frac{1 \text{ } mol \text{ } Fe_2(SO_4)_3}{399.91 \text{ } g \text{ } Fe_2(SO_4)_3} \times \frac{3 \text{ } mol \text{ } SO_4^{2-}}{1 \text{ } mol \text{ } Fe_2(SO_4)_3} = 0.08507 \text{ } mol \text{ } SO_4^{2-}$$

$$0.05671 \text{ } mol \text{ } Fe^{3+} + 0.08507 \text{ } mol \text{ } SO_4^{2-} = 0.14178 \text{ } mol \text{ } ions$$

Therefore, we find that there are 0.14178 mols of ions in solution.

d. 5.66 g $Pb(NO_3)_2$

Write the equation for the dissolution of $Pb(NO_3)_2$:

$$Pb(NO_3)_2(s) \xrightarrow{H_2O} Pb^{2+}(aq) + 2\ NO_3^-(aq)$$

Determine the moles of each ion formed using the balanced equation:

$$5.66\ g\ Pb(NO_3)_2 \times \frac{1\ mol\ Pb(NO_3)_2}{331.22\ g\ Pb(NO_3)_2} \times \frac{1\ mol\ Pb^{2+}}{1\ mol\ Pb(NO_3)_2} = 0.01709\ mol\ Pb^{2+}$$

$$5.66\ g\ Pb(NO_3)_2 \times \frac{1\ mol\ Pb(NO_3)_2}{331.22\ g\ Pb(NO_3)_2} \times \frac{2\ mol\ NO_3^-}{1\ mol\ Pb(NO_3)_2} = 0.03418\ mol\ NO_3^-$$

$$0.01709\ mol\ Pb^{2+} + 0.03418\ mol\ NO_3^- = 0.05127\ mol\ ions$$

Therefore, we find that there are 0.05127 mols of ions in solution.

17. How many ions are present in solution when the following are dissolved in water?
a. 47.12 g K_3PO_4

$$K_3PO_4(s) \xrightarrow{H_2O} 3\ K^+(aq) + PO_4^{3+}(aq)$$

$$47.12\ g\ K_3PO_4 \times \frac{1\ mol\ K_3PO_4}{212.27\ g\ K_3PO_4} \times \frac{3\ mol\ K^+}{1\ mol\ K_3PO_4} \times \frac{6.022 \times 10^{23}\ K^+ ions}{1\ mol\ K^+} = 4.010 \times 10^{23}\ K^+ ions$$

$$47.12\ g\ K_3PO_4 \times \frac{1\ mol\ K_3PO_4}{212.27\ g\ K_3PO_4} \times \frac{1\ mol\ PO_4^{3-}}{1\ mol\ K_3PO_4} \times \frac{6.022 \times 10^{23}\ PO_4^{3-} ions}{1\ mol\ PO_4^{3-}} = 1.3367 \times 10^{23}\ PO_4^{3-} ions$$

$$4.010 \times 10^{23}\ K^+ ions + 1.3367 \times 10^{23}\ PO_4^{3-} ions = \mathbf{5.347 \times 10^{23}}\ \textbf{ions}$$

b. 13.56 g $CuSO_4 \cdot 5H_2O$

$$CuSO_4 \cdot 5H_2O(s) \xrightarrow{H_2O} Cu^{2+}(aq) + SO_4^{2-}(aq)$$

$$13.56\ g\ CuSO_4 \cdot 5H_2O \times \frac{1\ mol\ CuSO_4 \cdot 5H_2O}{249.72\ g\ CuSO_4 \cdot 5H_2O} \times \frac{1\ mol\ Cu^{2+}}{1\ mol\ CuSO_4 \cdot 5H_2O}$$

$$\times \frac{6.022 \times 10^{23}\ Cu^{2+} ions}{1\ mol\ Cu^{2+}} = 3.270 \times 10^{22}\ Cu^{2+}\ ions$$

$$13.56 \ g \ CuSO_4 \cdot 5H_2O \times \frac{1 \ mol \ CuSO_4 \cdot 5H_2O}{249.72 \ g \ CuSO_4 \cdot 5H_2O} \times \frac{1 \ mol \ SO_4^{2-}}{1 \ mol \ CuSO_4 \cdot 5H_2O} \times \frac{6.022 \times 10^{23} \ SO_4^{2-} \ ions}{1 \ mol \ SO_4^{2-}}$$

$$= 3.270 \times 10^{22} \ SO_4^{2-} \ ions$$

$$2.909 \times 10^{22} \ Cu^{2+} \ ions + 2.909 \times 10^{22} \ SO_4^{2-} \ ions = \textbf{6.540} \times \textbf{10}^{\textbf{22}} \ \textbf{\textit{ions}}$$

c.   4.22 g Na_3PO_4

$$Na_3PO_4(s) \xrightarrow{\ H_2O\ } 3 \ Na^+ (aq) + PO_4^{3-} (aq)$$

$$4.22 \ g \ Na_3PO_4 \times \frac{1 \ mol \ Na_3PO_4}{163.94 \ g \ Na_3PO_4} \times \frac{3 \ mol \ Na^+}{1 \ mol \ Na_3PO_4} \times \frac{6.022 \times 10^{23} \ Na^+ ions}{1 \ mol \ Na^+}$$

$$= 4.650 \times 10^{22} \ Na^+ ions$$

$$4.22 \ g \ Na_3PO_4 \times \frac{1 \ mol \ Na_3PO_4}{163.94 \ g \ Na_3PO_4} \times \frac{1 \ mol \ PO_4^{3-}}{1 \ mol \ Na_3PO_4} \times \frac{6.022 \times 10^{23} \ Na^+ ions}{1 \ mol \ PO_4^{3-}}$$

$$= 1.550 \times 10^{22} \ PO_4^{3-} ions$$

$$4.650 \times 10^{22} \ Na^+ ions + 1.550 \times 10^{22} \ PO_4^{3-} ions = \textbf{6.200} \times \textbf{10}^{\textbf{22}} \ \textbf{\textit{ions}}$$

d.   6.22 g NH_4Cl

$$NH_4Cl(s) \xrightarrow{\ H_2O\ } NH_4^+ (aq) + Cl^- (aq)$$

$$6.22 \ g \ NH_4Cl \times \frac{1 \ mol \ NH_4Cl}{53.50 \ g \ NH_4Cl} \times \frac{1 \ mol \ NH_4^+}{1 \ mol \ NH_4Cl} \times \frac{6.022 \times 10^{23} \ NH_4^+ ions}{1 \ mol \ NH_4^+}$$

$$= 7.003 \times 10^{22} \ NH_4^+ ions$$

$$6.22 \ g \ NH_4Cl \times \frac{1 \ mol \ NH_4Cl}{53.50 \ g \ NH_4Cl} \times \frac{1 \ mol \ Cl^-}{1 \ mol \ NH_4Cl} \times \frac{6.022 \times 10^{23} \ Cl^- ions}{1 \ mol \ Cl^-}$$

$$= 7.003 \times 10^{22} \ Cl^- ions$$

$$7.003 \times 10^{22} \ NH_4^+ ions + 7.003 \times 10^{22} \ Cl^- ions = \textbf{1.400} \times \textbf{10}^{\textbf{23}} \ \textbf{\textit{ions}}$$

18. How many ions are present in solution when the following are dissolved in water?
    a.   5.55 g K_2SO_4

   5.754×10^{22} *ions*

b. 3.11 g $CoCl_2$

4.328×10^{22} ions

c. 3.11 g $CoCl_2 \cdot 6H_2O$

2.361×10^{22} ions

d. 2.67 g $Fe_2(SO_4)_3$

2.010×10^{22} ions

WRITING CHEMICAL EQUATIONS FOR REACTIONS IN AQUEOUS SOLUTION

19. Balance the following reactions and write the complete and net ionic equations for each one (complete with the physical state (*s, l, g, or aq*) of each ion or compound noted in the equation).

a. $Pb(NO_3)_2 + KI \rightarrow PbI_2 + KNO_3$

Determine the solubility of each ionic compound and note it with an (aq) for soluble compounds and a (s) for insoluble compounds.

$$Pb(NO_3)_2(aq) + KI(aq) \rightarrow PbI_2(s) + KNO_3(aq)$$

Balance the equation:

Molecular Equation: $Pb(NO_3)_2(aq) + 2\ KI(aq) \rightarrow PbI_2(s) + 2\ KNO_3(aq)$

Represent the soluble compounds as freely solvated ions:

Complete Ionic Equation:

$Pb^{2+}(aq) + 2\ NO_3^-(aq) + 2\ K^+(aq) + 2\ I^-(aq) \rightarrow PbI_2(s) + 2\ K^+(aq) + 2\ NO_3^-(aq)$

Remove the spectator ions:

Net Ionic Equation: $Pb^{2+}(aq) + 2\ I^-(aq) \rightarrow PbI_2(s)$

b. $NaOH + Mg(C_2H_3O_2)_2 \rightarrow NaC_2H_3O_2 + Mg(OH)_2$

Molecular Equation:

$$2\ NaOH(aq) + Mg(C_2H_3O_2)_2(aq) \rightarrow 2\ NaC_2H_3O_2(aq) + Mg(OH)_2(aq)$$

Since all possible products are soluble, there is no reaction.

20. Balance the following reactions and write the complete and net ionic equations for each one (complete with the physical state **(s, l, g, or aq)** of each ion or compound noted in the equation).

a. $Li_2S + Ca(ClO_3)_2 \rightarrow LiClO_3 + CaS$

Molecular Equation:

$$Li_2S(aq) + Ca(ClO_3)_2(aq) \rightarrow 2\ LiClO_3(aq) + CaS(s)$$

Complete Ionic Equation:

$$2\ Li^+(aq) + S^{2-}(aq) + Ca^{2+}(aq) + 2\ ClO_3^-(aq) \rightarrow CaS(s) + 2\ Li^+(aq) + 2\ ClO_3^-(aq)$$

Net Ionic Equation:

$$S^{2-}(aq) + Ca^{2+}(aq) \rightarrow CaS(s)$$

b. $Mn(NO_3)_2 + Li_3PO_4 \rightarrow Mn_3(PO_4)_2 + LiNO_3$

Molecular Equation:

$$3\ Mn(NO_3)_2(aq) + 2\ Li_3PO_4(aq) \rightarrow 6\ LiNO_3(aq) + Mn_3(PO_4)_2(s)$$

Complete Ionic Equation:

$$3\ Mn^{2+}(aq) + 6\ NO_3^-(aq) + 6\ Li^+(aq) + 2\ PO_4^{3-}(aq) \rightarrow Mn_3(PO_4)_2(s) + 6\ Li^+(aq) + 6\ NO_3^-(aq)$$

Net Ionic Equation:

$$3\ Mn^{2+}(aq) + 2\ PO_4^{3-}(aq) \rightarrow Mn_3(PO_4)_2(s)$$

21. Write the balanced complete and net ionic equations for the reaction, if any, that occurs when solutions of sodium sulfate and barium chloride are mixed.

Complete Ionic Equation:

$$2\ Na^+(aq) + SO_4^{2-}(aq) + Ba^{2+}(aq) + 2\ Cl^-(aq) \rightarrow BaSO_4(s) + 2\ Na^+(aq) + 2\ Cl^-(aq)$$

Net Ionic Equation:

$$SO_4^{2-}(aq) + Ba^{2+}(aq) \rightarrow BaSO_4(s)$$

22. Write the balanced complete and net ionic equations for the reaction, if any, that occurs when solutions of sodium chloride and silver nitrate are mixed.

Complete Ionic Equation:

$$Na^+(aq) + Cl^-(aq) + Ag^+(aq) + NO_3^-(aq) \rightarrow AgCl(s) + Na^+(aq) + NO_3^-(aq)$$

Net Ionic Equation:

$$Cl^-(aq) + Ag^+(aq) \rightarrow AgCl(s)$$

23. Write the balanced complete and net ionic equations for the reaction, if any, that occurs when solutions of potassium phosphate and lithium-chloride are mixed.

    No Reaction.

24. Write the balanced complete and net ionic equations for the reaction, if any, that occurs when solutions of nickel(II) bromide and ammonium sulfide are mixed.

    Complete Ionic Equation:

$$Ni^{2+}(aq) + 2\,Br^-(aq) + 2\,NH_4^+(aq) + S^{2-}(aq) \rightarrow NiS(s) + 2\,NH_4^+(aq) + 2\,Br^-(aq)$$

    Net Ionic Equation:

$$Ni^{2+}(aq) + S^{2-}(aq) \rightarrow NiS(s)$$

WRITING CHEMICAL EQUATIONS OF REACTIONS IN AQUEOUS SOLUTION – ACID/BASE NEUTRALIZATIONS AND GAS EVOLVING REACTIONS

25. Explain the difference between a strong acid and a strong base.

    A strong acid is a compound that when dissolved in water will completely dissociate to form H^+ ions. Strong bases will dissociate completely to produce OH^- ions.

26. Explain the difference between strong and weak acids.

    Weak acids are molecular compounds which dissociate only partially in water to produce H^+ ions. However, because they only partially dissociate, they generate fewer H^+ ions and therefore exhibit weaker acidity than strong acids. Strong acids completely dissociate when dissolved in water.

27. Write the molecular, complete ionic and net ionic equations for the following combinations of acids and bases:

    a. $HCl(aq) + NaOH(aq)$

        Molecular:

$$HCl(aq) + NaOH(aq) \rightarrow NaCl(aq) + H_2O(l)$$

Complete Ionic:

$$H^+(aq) + Cl^-(aq) + Na^+(aq) + OH^-(aq) \rightarrow Na^+(aq) + Cl^-(aq) + H_2O(l)$$

Net Ionic:

$$H^+(aq) + OH^-(aq) \rightarrow H_2O(l)$$

b. $H_2SO_4(aq) + Ba(OH)_2(aq)$

Molecular:

$$H_2SO_4(aq) + Ba(OH)_2(aq) \rightarrow BaSO_4(s) + 2\ H_2O(l)$$

Complete Ionic:

$$2\ H^+(aq) + SO_4^{2-}(aq) + Ba^{2+}(aq) + 2\ OH^-(aq) \rightarrow BaSO_4(s) + 2\ H_2O(l)$$

Net Ionic:

$$2\ H^+(aq) + SO_4^{2-}(aq) + Ba^{2+}(aq) + 2\ OH^-(aq) \rightarrow BaSO_4(s) + 2\ H_2O(l)$$

c. $HCl(aq) + Ca(OH)_2(aq)$

Molecular:

$$2HCl(aq) + Ca(OH)_2(aq) \rightarrow CaCl_2(aq) + 2\ H_2O(l)$$

Complete Ionic:

$$2\ H^+(aq) + 2\ Cl^-(aq) + Ca^{2+}(aq) + 2\ OH^-(aq) \rightarrow Ca^{2+}(aq) + 2\ Cl^-(aq) + 2\ H_2O(l)$$

Net Ionic:

$$2\ H^+(aq) + 2\ OH^-(aq) \rightarrow 2\ H_2O(l)$$

28. Write the molecular, complete ionic and net ionic equations for the following combinations of acids and bases:

a. $HNO_3(aq) + NaOH(aq)$

Molecular:

$$HNO_3(aq) + NaOH(aq) \rightarrow NaNO_3(aq) + H_2O(l)$$

Complete Ionic:

$$H^+(aq) + NO_3^-(aq) + Na^+(aq) + OH^-(aq) \rightarrow Na^+(aq) + NO_3^-(aq) + H_2O(l)$$

Net Ionic:

$$H^+(aq) + OH^-(aq) \rightarrow H_2O(l)$$

b. $H_2SO_4(aq) + KOH(aq)$

Molecular:

$$H_2SO_4(aq) + 2\ KOH(aq) \rightarrow K_2SO_4(aq) + 2\ H_2O(l)$$

Complete Ionic:

$$2\ H^+(aq) + SO_4^{2-}(aq) + 2\ K^+(aq) + 2\ OH^-(aq) \rightarrow 2\ K^+(aq) + SO_4^{2-}(aq) + 2\ H_2O(l)$$

Net Ionic:

$$2\ H^+(aq) + 2\ OH^-(aq) \rightarrow 2\ H_2O(l)$$

c. $HI(aq) + Sr(OH)_2(aq)$

Molecular:

$$2\ HI(aq) + Sr(OH)_2(aq) \rightarrow SrI_2(aq) + 2\ H_2O(l)$$

Complete Ionic:

$$2\ H^+(aq) + 2\ I^-(aq) + Sr^{2+}(aq) + 2\ OH^-(aq) \rightarrow Sr^{2+}(aq) + 2\ I^-(aq) + 2\ H_2O(l)$$

Net Ionic:

$$2\ H^+(aq) + 2\ OH^-(aq) \rightarrow 2\ H_2O(l)$$

29. Write balanced molecular, complete ionic and net ionic equations for the following gas evolving reactions:

a. $HCl(aq) + Na_2S(aq) \rightarrow$

Molecular:

$$2\ HCl(aq) + Na_2S(aq) \rightarrow 2\ NaCl(aq) + H_2S(g)$$

Complete Ionic:

$$2\ H^+(aq) + 2\ Cl^-(aq) + 2\ Na^+(aq) + S^{2-}(aq) \rightarrow 2\ Na^+(aq) + 2\ Cl^-(aq) + H_2S(g)$$

Net Ionic:

$$2\,H^{+}(aq) + S^{2-}(aq) \rightarrow H_2S(g)$$

b. $HClO_4(aq) + K_2CO_4(aq) \rightarrow$

Molecular:

$$2\,HClO_4(aq) + K_2CO_3(aq) \rightarrow 2\,KClO_4(aq) + \left[H_2CO_3\right]$$

Complete Ionic:

$$2\,H^{+}(aq) + 2\,ClO_4^{-}(aq) + 2\,K^{+}(aq) + CO_3^{2-}(aq) \rightarrow 2\,K^{+}(aq) + 2\,ClO_4^{-}(aq) + H_2O(l) + CO_2(g)$$

Net Ionic:

$$2\,H^{+}(aq) + CO_3^{2-}(aq) \rightarrow H_2O(l) + CO_2(g)$$

c. $H_2SO_4(aq) + K_2SO_3(aq) \rightarrow$

Molecular:

$$H_2SO_4(aq) + K_2SO_3(aq) \rightarrow K_2SO_4(aq) + \left[H_2SO_3\right]$$

$$H_2SO_4(aq) + K_2SO_3(aq) \rightarrow K_2SO_4(aq) + H_2O(l) + SO_2(g)$$

Complete Ionic:

$$2\,H^{+}(aq) + SO_4^{2-}(aq) + 2\,K^{+}(aq) + SO_3^{2-}(aq) \rightarrow 2\,K^{+}(aq) + SO_4^{2-}(aq) + H_2O(l) + SO_2(g)$$

Net Ionic:

$$2\,H^{+}(aq) + SO_3^{2-}(aq) \rightarrow H_2O(l) + SO_2(g)$$

30. Write balanced molecular, complete ionic and net ionic equations for the following gas evolving reactions:

a. $HBr(aq) + NaHCO_3(aq) \rightarrow$

Molecular:

$$HBr(aq) + NaHCO_3(aq) \rightarrow NaBr(aq) + \left[H_2CO_3\right]$$

$$HBr(aq) + NaHCO_3(aq) \rightarrow NaBr(aq) + H_2O(l) + CO_2(g)$$

Complete Ionic:

$$H^{+}(aq) + Br^{-}(aq) + Na^{+}(aq) + HCO_3^{-}(aq) \rightarrow Na^{+}(aq) + Br^{-}(aq) + H_2O(l) + CO_2(g)$$

Net Ionic:

$$H^+(aq) + HCO_3^-(aq) \rightarrow H_2O(l) + CO_2(g)$$

b. $HNO_3(aq) + K_2S(aq) \rightarrow$

Molecular:

$$2\ HNO_3(aq) + K_2S(aq) \rightarrow 2\ KNO_3(aq) + H_2S(g)$$

Complete Ionic:

$$2\ H^+(aq) + 2\ NO_3^-(aq) + 2\ K^+(aq) + S^{2-}(aq) \rightarrow 2\ K^+(aq) + 2\ NO_3^-(aq) + H_2S(g)$$

Net Ionic:

$$2\ H^+(aq) + S^{2-}(aq) \rightarrow H_2S(g)$$

c. $H_3PO_4(aq) + NiCO_3(aq) \rightarrow$

Molecular:

$$2\ H_3PO_4(aq) + 3\ NiCO_3(aq) \rightarrow Ni_3(PO_4)_2(aq) + 3\left[H_2CO_3\right]$$

$$2\ H_3PO_4(aq) + 3\ NiCO_3(aq) \rightarrow Ni_3(PO_4)_2(s) + 3\ H_2O(l) + 3\ CO_2(g)$$

Complete Ionic:

$$6\ H^+(aq) + 2\ PO_4^{3-}(aq) + 3\ Ni^{2+}(aq) + 3\ CO_3^{2-}(aq) \rightarrow Ni_3(PO_4)_2(s) + 3\ H_2O(l) + 3\ CO_2(g)$$

Net Ionic:

$$6\ H^+(aq) + 2\ PO_4^{3-}(aq) + 3\ Ni^{2+}(aq) + 3\ CO_3^{2-}(aq) \rightarrow Ni_3(PO_4)_2(s) + 3\ H_2O(l) + 3\ CO_2(g)$$

SOLUTION CONCENTRATION – MOLARITY AND DILUTION

31. Calculate the molarity of each of the following solutions:

   a. 16.31 g **NaCl** in 167.0 ml of solution.

   $$16.31\ g\ NaCl \times \frac{1\ mol\ NaCl}{58.44\ g\ NaCl} \times \frac{1}{167.0\ ml} \times \frac{1000\ ml}{1\ L} = 1.67\ M\ NaCl$$

   b. 12.31 g $C_{12}H_{22}O_{11}$ in 556.0 ml of solution.

$$12.31 g\ C_{12}H_{22}O_{11} \times \frac{1\ mol\ C_{12}H_{22}O_{11}}{342.31\ g\ C_{12}H_{22}O_{11}} \times \frac{1}{556.0\ ml} \times \frac{1000\ ml}{1\ L} = 0.0647\ M\ C_{12}H_{22}O_{11}$$

c.   3.65 g Na_2CO_3 in 150.00 ml of solution.

$$3.65 g\ Na_2CO_3 \times \frac{1\ mol\ Na_2CO_3}{105.99\ g\ Na_2CO_3} \times \frac{1}{150.00\ ml} \times \frac{1000\ ml}{1\ L} = 0.230\ M\ Na_2CO_3$$

32. Calculate the molarity of each of the following solutions:

   a.   2.33 g $Al_2(SO_4)_3$ in 75.00 ml of solution.

$$2.33 g\ Al_2(SO_4)_3 \times \frac{1\ mol\ Al_2(SO_4)_3}{342.17\ g\ Al_2(SO_4)_3} \times \frac{1}{75.00\ ml} \times \frac{1000\ ml}{1\ L} = 0.0908\ M\ Al_2(SO_4)_3$$

   b.   6.12 g KCl in 45.00 ml of solution.

$$6.12 g\ KCl \times \frac{1\ mol\ KCl}{74.55\ g\ KCl} \times \frac{1}{45.00\ ml} \times \frac{1000\ ml}{1\ L} = 1.82\ M\ KCl$$

   c.   23.11 g $CaCl_2$ in 500.0 ml solution.

$$23.11 g\ CaCl_2 \times \frac{1\ mol\ CaCl_2}{110.98\ g\ CaCl_2} \times \frac{1}{500.0\ ml} \times \frac{1000\ ml}{1\ L} = 0.416\ M\ CaCl_2$$

33. What mass of Na_2SO_4 will be required to prepare 500 ml of a 1.50 M Na_2SO_4 solution?

$$500\ ml \times \frac{1\ L}{1000\ ml} \times \frac{1.50\ mol\ Na_2SO_4}{1\ L} \times \frac{142.05\ g\ Na_2SO_4}{1\ mol\ Na_2SO_4} = 106.5\ g\ Na_2SO_4$$

34. What mass of $NaOH$ is required to prepare 250 ml of a 0.500 M $NaOH$ solution?

$$250\ ml \times \frac{1\ L}{1000\ ml} \times \frac{0.500\ mol\ NaOH}{1\ L} \times \frac{40.00\ g\ NaOH}{1\ mol\ NaOH} = 5.0\ g\ NaOH$$

35. What volume of a 1.00 M KOH solution contains 5.61 g KOH ?

$$5.61 g\ KOH \times \frac{1\ mol\ KOH}{56.11\ g\ KOH} \times \frac{1\ L}{1.00\ mol\ KOH} = 0.100\ L = 100.\ ml$$

36. What volume of a 0.453 M $MgSO_4$ solution contains 2.311 g $MgSO_4$?

$$2.311 g\ MgSO_4 \times \frac{1\ mol\ MgSO_4}{120.38\ g\ MgSO_4} \times \frac{1\ L}{0.453\ mol\ MgSO_4} = 0.0424\ L = 42.4\ ml$$

37. What mass of K_2CO_3 is required to produce 500 ml of a solution that has a K^+ concentration of 0.150 M?

$$K_2CO_3(s) \xrightarrow{H_2O} 2\ K^+(aq) + CO_3^{2-}(aq)$$

$$500 \ ml \times \frac{1 \ L}{1000 \ ml} \times \frac{0.150 \ mol \ K^+}{1 \ L} \times \frac{1 \ mol \ K_2CO_3}{2 \ mol \ K^+} \times \frac{138.21 \ g \ K_2CO_3}{1 \ mol \ K_2CO_3} = 5.18 \ g \ K_2CO_3$$

38. If a 1.75 M $MgCl_2$ is prepared, what is the concentration (molarity) of Cl^- ions?

$$MgCl_2(s) \xrightarrow{H_2O} Mg^{2+}(aq) + 2 \ Cl^-(aq)$$

$$\frac{1.75 \ mol \ MgCl_2}{1 \ L} \times \frac{2 \ mol \ Cl^-}{1 \ mol \ MgCl} = \frac{3.50 \ mol \ Cl^-}{1 \ L} = 3.50 \ M \ Cl^-$$

39. What is the concentration (molarity) of acetate ions in the following solutions?
    a. 0.125 M $NaC_2H_3O_2$ – 0.125 M
    b. 0.125 M $Mg(C_2H_3O_2)_2$ – 0.250 M
    c. 0.125 M $Al(C_2H_3O_2)_3$ – 0.375 M

40. What is the concentration (molarity) of ammonium ions in the following solutions?
    a. 0.300 M $NH_4C_2H_3O_2$ – 0.300 M
    b. 0.300 M $(NH_4)_2SO_4$ – 0.600 M
    c. 0.300 M $(NH_4)_3PO_4$ – 0.900 M

41. How many moles of sulfate ions are present in the following solutions?
    a. 42.6 ml of 0.125 M $ZnSO_4$ – 0.00533 mols
    b. 77.22 ml 0.255 M $Al_2(SO_4)_3$ – 0.0591 mols
    c. 3.89 ml of 0.413 M $(NH_4)_2SO_4$ – 0.00161 mols

42. How many moles of nitrate ions are present in the following solutions?
    a. 1.33 ml of 0.478 M NH_4NO_3 – 0.000636 mols
    b. 0.550 ml of 1.67 M $Al(NO_3)_3$ – 0.00276 mols
    c. 26.75 ml of 0.250 M $Mg(NO_3)_2$ – 0.0134 mols

43. What volume of a 5.00 M $BaCl_2$ solution is required to prepare 500.0 ml of a 0.200 M $BaCl_2$ solution?

$$M_i V_i = M_f V_f$$

$$M_i = 5.00 \ M$$

$$V_i = ?$$

$$M_f = 0.200 \ M$$

$$V_f = 500.0 \ ml$$

$$V_i = \frac{M_f V_f}{M_i} = \frac{(0.200\ M)(500.0\ ml)}{5.00\ M} = \textbf{20.0 ml}$$

44. What volume of a 12.00 M *HCl* solution is required to prepare 225.0 ml of a 1.25 M *HCl* solution?

$$M_i V_i = M_f V_f$$

$$M_i = 12.00\ M$$

$$V_i = ?$$

$$M_f = 1.25\ M$$

$$V_f = 225.0\ ml$$

$$V_i = \frac{M_f V_f}{M_i} = \frac{(1.25\ M)(225.0\ ml)}{12.00\ M} = \textbf{23.44 ml}$$

45. If 10.00 ml of a 0.156 M *SrCl$_2$* solution is diluted to 75.00 ml, what is the concentration (molarity) of the diluted solution?

$$M_i V_i = M_f V_f$$

$$M_i = 0.156\ M$$

$$V_i = 10.00$$

$$M_f = ?$$

$$V_f = 75.00\ ml$$

$$M_f = \frac{M_i V_i}{V_f} = \frac{(0.156\ M)(10.00\ ml)}{75.00\ ml} = \textbf{0.0208 M}$$

46. If 150.00 ml of a 1.13 M *NaOH* solution is diluted to 765.0 ml, what is the concentration (molarity) of the diluted solution?

$$M_i V_i = M_f V_f$$

$$M_i = 1.13\ M$$

$$V_i = 150.00\ ml$$

$$M_f = ?$$

$$V_f = 765.0\ ml$$

$$M_f = \frac{M_iV_i}{V_f} = \frac{(1.13 \; M)(150.00 \; ml)}{765.0 \; ml} = \textbf{0.222 M}$$

47. A sucrose solution is diluted from 100.0 ml to 565.0 ml and a new (diluted) concentration of 1.56 M. What is the initial concentration of the sucrose solution?

$$M_iV_i = M_fV_f$$

$$M_i = ?$$

$$V_i = 100.0 \; ml$$

$$M_f = 1.56 \; M$$

$$V_f = 565.0 \; ml$$

$$M_i = \frac{M_fV_f}{V_i} = \frac{(1.56 \; M)(565.0 \; ml)}{100.0 \; ml} = \textbf{8.81 M}$$

48. An NH_4NO_3 solution is diluted from 50.00 ml to 325.0 ml and a new (diluted) concentration of 0.0750 M. What was the initial concentration of the NH_4NO_3 solution?

$$M_iV_i = M_fV_f$$

$$M_i = ?$$

$$V_i = 50.00 \; ml$$

$$M_f = 0.0750 \; M$$

$$V_f = 325.0 \; ml$$

$$M_i = \frac{M_fV_f}{V_i} = \frac{(0.0750)(325.0 \; ml)}{50.00 \; ml} = \textbf{0.488 M}$$

49. To what volume must you dilute 10.00 ml of a 15.0 M HNO_3 solution to achieve a concentration of 1.45 M?

$$M_iV_i = M_fV_f$$

$$M_i = 15.0 \; M$$

$$V_i = 10.00 \; ml$$

$$M_f = 1.45 \; M$$

$$V_f = ?$$

$$V_f = \frac{M_i V_i}{M_f} = \frac{(15.0\ M)(10.00\ ml)}{1.45\ M} = \textbf{103 ml}$$

50. To what volume must you dilute 75.00 ml of a 3.50 M *NaOH* solution to achieve a concentration of 0.850 M?

$$M_i V_i = M_f V_f$$

$$M_i = 3.50\ M$$

$$V_i = 75.0\ ml$$

$$M_f = 0.850M$$

$$V_f = ?$$

$$V_f = \frac{M_i V_i}{M_f} = \frac{(3.50\ M)(75.0\ ml)}{0.850\ M} = \textbf{309 ml}$$

SOLUTION CONCENTRATION – MOLALITY, MOLE FRACTION, AND MASS PERCENT

51. Calculate the molality of the following solutions:

   a. 36.19 g of ethanol (C_2H_5OH) in 1.15 kg of water.

$$m = \frac{(36.19\ g\ C_2H_5OH) \times \left(\frac{1\ mol\ C_2H_5OH}{46.08\ g\ C_2H_5OH}\right)}{1.15\ kg\ water} = \frac{0.78554\ mol\ C_2H_5OH}{1.15\ kg\ water} = \textbf{0.683 m } C_2H_5OH$$

   b. 23.67 g $HClO_4$ in 450.0 g of water.

$$m = \frac{(23.67\ g\ HClO_4) \times \left(\frac{1\ mol\ HClO_4}{100.46\ g\ HClO_4}\right)}{0.4500\ kg\ water} = \frac{0.2356\ mol\ HClO_4}{0.4500\ kg\ water} = \textbf{0.524 m } HClO_4$$

   c. 86.45 g K_3PO_4 in 546 g of water.

$$m = \frac{(86.45\ g\ K_3PO_4) \times \left(\frac{1\ mol\ K_3PO_4}{212.27\ g\ K_3PO_4}\right)}{0.546\ kg\ water} = \frac{0.4073\ mol\ K_3PO_4}{0.546\ kg\ water} = \textbf{0.746 m } K_3PO_4$$

52. Calculate the molality of the following solutions:

   a. 42.49 g of isopropyl alcohol (C_3H_7OH) in 965 g of water. – 0.733 *m*

    b. 25.72 g ethylene glycol ($C_2H_6O_2$) in 333.0 g of water. – 1.24 m

    c. 86.45 g $Ba(NO_3)_2$ in 678 g of water. – 0.488 m

53. Calculate the mole fraction of the solute in the following solutions:

    a. 36.19 g of ethanol (C_2H_5OH) in 1.15 kg of water.

$$\chi_{C_2H_5OH} = \frac{n_{C_2H_5OH}}{n_{H_2O} + n_{C_2H_5OH}} = \frac{0.7855 \; mol \; C_2H_5OH}{0.7855 \; mol + 63.818 \; mol} = \mathbf{0.0122}$$

    b. 23.67 g $HClO_4$ in 450.0 g of water.

$$\chi_{HClO_4} = \frac{n_{HClO_4}}{n_{H_2O} + n_{HClO_4}} = \frac{0.2356 \; mol \; HClO_4}{24.972 \; mol + 0.2356 \; mol} = \mathbf{0.00935}$$

    c. 86.45 g K_3PO_4 in 546 g of water.

$$\chi_{K_3PO_4} = \frac{n_{K_3PO_4}}{n_{H_2O} + n_{K_3PO_4}} = \frac{0.4073 \; mol \; K_3PO_4}{30.300 \; mol + 0.4073 \; mol} = \mathbf{0.0133}$$

54. Calculate the mole fraction of the solute in the following solutions:

    a. 42.49 g of isopropyl alcohol (C_3H_7OH) in 965 g of water. – 0.0130

    b. 25.72 g ethylene glycol ($C_2H_6O_2$) in 333.0 g of water. – 0.0219

    c. 86.45 g $Ba(NO_3)_2$ in 678 g of water. – 0.00871

55. Calculate the mass percent of the following solutions:

    a. 36.19 g of ethanol (C_2H_5OH) in 1.15 kg of water.

$$Mass \; \% = \frac{36.19 \; g \; C_2H_5OH}{(36.19 \; g + 1150 \; g)} \times 100\% = \mathbf{3.05\%}$$

    b. 23.67 g $HClO_4$ in 450.0 g of water.

$$Mass \; \% = \frac{23.67 \; g \; HClO_4}{(23.67 \; g + 450.0 \; g)} \times 100\% = \mathbf{5.00\%}$$

    c. 86.45 g K_3PO_4 in 546 g of water.

$$Mass \; \% = \frac{86.45 \; g \; K_3PO_4}{(86.45 \; g + 546 \; g)} \times 100\% = \mathbf{13.7\%}$$

56. Calculate the mass percent of the following solutions:

    a. 42.49 g of isopropyl alcohol (C_3H_7OH) in 965 g of water. – 4.22 %

    b. 25.72 g ethylene glycol ($C_2H_6O_2$) in 333.0 g of water. – 7.17 %

c.   86.45 g $Ba(NO_3)_2$ in 678 g of water. – 11.3 %

57. An aqueous solution is 31.00 % H_2SO_4 by mass. Express this concentration in molality and mole fraction.

$$100 \ g \ Solution \rightarrow n_{H_2SO_4} = 31.00 \ g \ H_2SO_4 \times \frac{1 \ mol \ H_2SO_4}{98.09 \ g \ H_2SO_4} = 0.31604 \ mol \ H_2SO_4$$

$$100 \ g \ Solution \rightarrow n_{H_2O} = 69.00 \ g \ H_2O \times \frac{1 \ mol \ H_2O}{18.02 \ g \ H_2O} = 3.8291 \ mol \ H_2O$$

$$molality = m = \frac{n_{H_2SO_4}}{mass \ H_2O} = \frac{0.31604 \ mol \ H_2SO_4}{0.069 \ kg \ H_2O} = \textbf{4.58 m } \boldsymbol{H_2SO_4}$$

$$mole \ fraction = \chi_{H_2SO_4} = \frac{n_{H_2SO_4}}{n_{H_2SO_4} + n_{H_2O}} = \frac{0.31604 \ mol}{0.31604 \ mol + 3.8291 \ mol} = \textbf{0.0762}$$

58. An aqueous solution is 17.00 % $NaHCO_3$ by mass. Express this concentration in molality and mole fraction.

$$100 \ g \ Solution \rightarrow n_{NaHCO_3} = 17.00 \ g \ NaHCO_3 \times \frac{1 \ mol \ H_2SO_4}{84.01 \ g \ H_2SO_4} = 0.20236 \ mol \ H_2SO_4$$

$$100 \ g \ Solution \rightarrow n_{H_2O} = 83.00 \ g \ H_2O \times \frac{1 \ mol \ H_2O}{18.02 \ g \ H_2O} = 4.6060 \ mol \ H_2O$$

$$molality = m = \frac{n_{NaHCO_3}}{mass \ H_2O} = \frac{0.20236 \ mol \ NaHCO_3}{0.083 \ kg \ H_2O} = \textbf{2.44 m } \boldsymbol{NaHCO_3}$$

$$mole \ fraction = \chi_{NaHCO_3} = \frac{n_{NaHCO_3}}{n_{NaHCO_3} + n_{H_2O}} = \frac{0.20236 \ mol}{0.20236 \ mol + 4.6060 \ mol} = \textbf{0.0421}$$

59. Give the concentration of a 0.567 m $SrCl_2$ solution in units of mass percent and mole fraction.

$$Mass \ \% = \frac{0.567 \ mol \ SrCl_2}{1 \ kg \ water} \times \frac{158.52 \ g \ SrCl_2}{1 \ mol \ SrCl_2} \times \frac{1 \ kg}{1000 \ g} \times 100\% = \textbf{8.99\%}$$

$$\chi_{SrCl_2} = \frac{0.567 \ mol \ SrCl_2}{\left(1 \ kg \ H_2O \times \dfrac{1000 \ g \ H_2O}{1 \ kg \ H_2O} \times \dfrac{1 \ mol \ H_2O}{18.02 \ g \ H_2O}\right) + 0.567 \ mol \ SrCl_2} = \textbf{0.0101}$$

60. Give the concentration of a 1.41 m K_2SO_4 solution in units of mass percent and mole fraction.

$$Mass\ \% = \frac{1.41\ mol\ K_2SO_4}{1\ kg\ water} \times \frac{174.27\ g\ K_2SO_4}{1\ mol\ K_2SO_4} \times \frac{1\ kg}{1000\ g} \times 100\% = \mathbf{24.6\%}$$

$$\chi_{K_2SO_4} = \frac{1.41\ mol\ K_2SO_4}{\left(1\ kg\ H_2O \times \dfrac{1000\ g\ H_2O}{1\ kg\ H_2O} \times \dfrac{1\ mol\ H_2O}{18.02\ g\ H_2O}\right) + 1.41\ mol\ K_2SO_4} = \mathbf{0.0248}$$

STOICHIOMETRY OF REACTIONS IN SOLUTION

61. What volume (in milliliters) of 0.133 M H_2SO_4 is required to completely react with 5.00 ml of a 0.100 M $NaOH$ solution according to the following reaction equation?

$$H_2SO_4(aq) + 2\ NaOH(aq) \rightarrow Na_2SO_4(aq) + 2\ H_2O(l)$$

$$5.00\ ml \times \frac{1\ L}{1000\ ml} \times \frac{0.100\ mol\ NaOH}{1\ L\ NaOH} \times \frac{1\ mol\ H_2SO_4}{2\ mol\ NaOH} \times \frac{1\ L\ H_2SO_4}{0.133\ mol\ H_2SO_4} \times \frac{1000\ ml}{1\ L} = \mathbf{1.88\ ml}$$

62. What volume (in milliliters) of 0.245 M $Pb(NO_3)_2$ is required to completely react with 12.00 ml of a 0.250 M KI solution according to the following reaction equation?

$$Pb(NO_3)_2(aq) + 2\ KI(aq) \rightarrow PbI_2(s) + 2\ KNO_3(aq)$$

$$12.00\ ml \times \frac{1\ L}{1000\ ml} \times \frac{0.250\ mol\ KI}{1\ L\ KI} \times \frac{1\ mol\ Pb(NO_3)_2}{2\ mol\ KI} \times \frac{1\ L\ Pb(NO_3)_2}{0.245\ mol\ Pb(NO_3)_2} \times \frac{1000\ ml}{1\ L} = \mathbf{6.12\ ml}$$

63. When 15.67 ml of 0.250 M $NaCl$ is mixed with 23.11 ml of 0.187 M $Ba(NO_3)_2$ a precipitation reaction occurs according to the reaction equation below. This reaction was carried out and 0.351 g of $BaCl_2$ was recovered.

$$2\ NaCl(aq) + Ba(NO_3)_2(aq) \rightarrow BaCl_2(s) + 2\ NaNO_3(aq)$$

Determine the following:
a. Limiting Reagent - $NaCl$
b. Theoretical Yield ($BaCl_2$) – 0.408 g
c. % Yield – 86.0%

$$15.67\ ml\ NaCl \times \frac{1\ L}{1000\ ml} \times \frac{0.250\ mol\ NaCl}{1\ L\ NaCl} \times \frac{1\ mol\ BaCl_2}{2\ mol\ NaCl} \times \frac{208.23\ g\ BaCl_2}{1\ mol\ BaCl_2} = \mathbf{0.408\ g\ BaCl_2}$$

$$23.11\ ml\ Ba(NO_3)_2 \times \frac{1\ L}{1000\ ml} \times \frac{0.187\ mol\ Ba(NO_3)_2}{1\ L\ Ba(NO_3)_2} \times \frac{1\ mol\ BaCl_2}{1\ mol\ Ba(NO_3)_2} \times \frac{208.23\ g\ BaCl_2}{1\ mol\ BaCl_2} = 0.900\ g\ BaCl_2$$

$$\% \, Yield = \frac{Actual \, Yield}{Theoretical \, Yield} \times 100\% = \frac{0.351 \, g \, Bacl_2}{0.408 \, g \, Bacl_2} \times 100\% = \textbf{86.0\%}$$

64. When 308.3 ml of 4.78 M HNO_3 is allowed to react with 15.75 g Al a reaction occurs according to the reaction equation below. This reaction was carried out and 1.12 g of H_2 gas was recovered.

$$2 \, Al(s) + 6 \, HNO_3(aq) \rightarrow 2 \, Al(NO_3)_3(aq) + 3 \, H_2(g)$$

Determine the following:
a. Limiting Reagent - HNO_3
b. Theoretical Yield $(g \, H_2) - 1.49$ g
c. % Yield – 75.2%
d. The mass of excess reagent remaining after the reaction – 2.50 g

COLLIGATIVE PROPERTIES – RAOULT'S LAW

65. What is the vapor pressure of a solution containing 35.6 g glycerin $(C_3H_8O_3)$ in 150 g water at 35°C? The vapor pressure of pure water at the same temperature is 42.2 torr.

$$\chi_{solv} = \frac{n_{solv}}{n_{tot}} = \frac{n_{solv}}{n_{solv} + n_{solute}} = \frac{n_{water}}{n_{water} + n_{glycerin}}$$

$$n_{glycerin} = 35.6 \, g \, C_3H_8O_3 \times \frac{1 \, mol \, C_3H_8O_3}{92.11 \, g \, C_3H_8O_3} = 0.3865 \, mol \, C_3H_8O_3$$

$$n_{water} = 150 \, g \, H_2O \times \frac{1 \, mol \, H_2O}{18.02 \, g \, H_2O} = 8.324 \, mol \, H_2O$$

$$\chi_{solv} = \frac{n_{water}}{n_{water} + n_{glycerin}} = \frac{8.324 \, mol \, H_2O}{8.324 \, mol \, H_2O + 0.3865 \, mol \, C_3H_8O_3} = 0.9556$$

$$P_{solution} = \chi_{water} P^o_{water} = (0.9556)(42.2 \, torr) = \textbf{40.33 torr}$$

66. What is the vapor pressure of a solution of containing 25.34 g $NaCl$ in 132 g water at 25°C? The vapor pressure of pure water at the same temperature is 23.76 torr.

$$n_{glycerin} = 25.34 \, g \, NaCl \times \frac{1 \, mol \, NaCl}{58.44 \, g \, NaCl} \times \frac{2 \, mol \, ions}{1 \, mol \, NaCl} = 0.8672 \, mol \, ions$$

$$n_{water} = 132 \, g \, H_2O \times \frac{1 \, mol \, H_2O}{18.02 \, g \, H_2O} = 7.325 \, mol \, H_2O$$

$$\chi_{solv} = \frac{n_{water}}{n_{water} + n_{glycerin}} = \frac{7.325 \ mol \ H_2O}{7.325 \ mol \ H_2O + 0.8672 \ mol \ ions} = 0.8941$$

$$P_{solution} = \chi_{water} P^o_{water} = (0.8941)(23.76 \ torr) = \textbf{21.2 torr}$$

67. If the vapor pressure of a solution containing an unknown mass of glycerin ($C_3H_8O_3$) and 123 g water is 22.86 torr at 25°C, what is the mole fraction of water? What is the mole fraction of glycerin?

$$P_{solution} = \chi_{water} P^o_{water}$$

$$\chi_{water} = \frac{P_{solution}}{P^o_{water}} = \frac{22.86 \ torr}{23.76 \ torr} = \textbf{0.9621}$$

$$\chi_{glycerin} = 1 - \chi_{water} = 1 - 0.9621 = \textbf{0.0379}$$

68. If the vapor pressure of a solution containing sucrose ($C_{12}H_{22}O_{11}$) and 100.0 g water is 23.453 torr at 25°C, what is the mole fraction of sucrose? What is the mass (g) of sucrose in the solution?

$$P_{solution} = \chi_{water} P^o_{water}$$

$$\chi_{water} = \frac{P_{solution}}{P^o_{water}} = \frac{23.453 \ torr}{23.76 \ torr} = 0.9871$$

$$\chi_{glycerin} = 1 - \chi_{water} = 1 - 0.9871 = \textbf{0.0129}$$

$$n_{glycerin} = \frac{n_{water}}{\chi_{water}} - n_{water} = 0.08935 \ mol \ C_{12}H_{22}O_{11}$$

$$0.08935 \ mol \ C_{12}H_{22}O_{11} \times \frac{342.31 \ g \ C_{12}H_{22}O_{11}}{1 \ mol \ C_{12}H_{22}O_{11}} = 30.58 \ g \ C_{12}H_{22}O_{11}$$

69. If the vapor pressure of a solution containing 23.88 g of an unknown carbohydrate and 250 g water is 26.204 torr at 27°C, what is the mole fraction of water in the solution? What is the molar mass of the unknown? (The vapor pressure of pure water at 27°C is 26.74 torr.)

$$P_{solution} = \chi_{water} P^o_{water}$$

$$\chi_{water} = \frac{P_{solution}}{P^o_{water}} = \frac{26.204 \ torr}{26.74 \ torr} = \textbf{0.9800}$$

$$\chi_{solute} = 1 - \chi_{water} = 1 - 0.9800 = 0.0200$$

$$n_{solute} = \frac{n_{water}}{\chi_{water}} - n_{water} = 0.2838 \ mol \ solute$$

$$\frac{23.88 \ g \ solute}{0.2838 \ mol \ solute} = \textbf{84.15 g/mol}$$

COLLIGATIVE PROPERTIES – BOILING POINT ELEVATION AND FREEZING POINT DEPRESSION

70. Which of the following solutions has a higher boiling point?
    a. **27.00 g of ethanol (C_2H_5OH) in 350 g water.**
    b. 27.00 g of isopropanol (C_3H_7OH) in 350 g water.

    Since the ethanol solution will have the higher concentration, it will exhibit the higher boiling point.

71. Which of the following solutions has a higher boiling point?
    a. **17.00 g of glucose ($C_6H_{12}O_6$) in 200 g water.**
    b. 17.00 g of sucrose ($C_{12}H_{22}O_{11}$) in 200 g water.

    Since the glucose solution will have the higher concentration, it will exhibit the higher boiling point.

72. What is the boiling point of a solution comprised of 20.00 g of ethanol (C_2H_5OH) in 200.0 g water?

$$20.00 \ g \ C_2H_5OH \times \frac{1 \ mol \ C_2H_5OH}{46.08 \ g \ C_2H_5OH} \times \frac{1}{200.0 \ g \ solvent} \times \frac{1000 \ g}{1 \ kg} = 2.17014 \ m \ C_2H_5OH$$

$$\Delta T_b = iK_b m = (1)(0.512 \ °C/m)(2.17014 \ m) = 1.11°C$$

$$T_b(solution) = T_b(water) + \Delta T_b = 100.00°C + 1.11°C = \textbf{101.11°C}$$

73. What is the boiling point of a solution comprised of 15.00 g of potassium chloride (KCl) in 200.0 g water? (Assume ideal behavior respecting the van't Hoff factor.)

$$15.00 \ g \ KCl \times \frac{1 \ mol \ KCl}{74.55 \ g \ KCl} \times \frac{1}{200.0 \ g \ solvent} \times \frac{1000 \ g}{1 \ kg} = 1.006036 \ m \ KCl$$

$$\Delta T_b = iK_b m = (2)(0.512 \ °C/m)(1.006036 \ m) = 1.03°C$$

$$T_b(solution) = T_b(water) + \Delta T_b = 100.00°C + 1.03°C = \textbf{101.03°C}$$

74. What is the boiling point of a solution comprised of 15.00 g of isopropanol (C_3H_7OH) in 200 g water?

    100.639°C

75. What is the boiling point of 0.198 m glucose in water?

    $$\Delta T_b = iK_b m = (1)(0.512 \ °C/m)(0.198 \ m) = 0.101°C$$

    $$T_b(solution) = T_b(water) + \Delta T_b = 100.00°C + 0.101 \ °C = \textbf{100.101°C}$$

76. What is the boiling point of 0.267 m ethylene glycol in water?

    $$\Delta T_b = iK_b m = (1)(0.512 \ °C/m)(0.267m) = 0.137°C$$

    $$T_b(solution) = T_b(water) + \Delta T_b = 100.00°C + 0.137 \ °C = \textbf{100.137°C}$$

77. What is the boiling point of a solution prepared by dissolving 23.4 g spartiene ($C_{15}H_{26}N_2$) in 523 g of chloroform. The boiling point of pure chloroform is 61.7°C.

    $$23.4 \ g \ C_{15}H_{26}N_2 \times \frac{1 \ mol \ C_{15}H_{26}N_2}{234.43 \ g \ C_{15}H_{26}N_2} \times \frac{1}{523 \ g \ solvent} \times \frac{1000 \ g}{1 \ kg} = 0.190854 \ m \ C_{15}H_{26}N_2$$

    $$\Delta T_b = iK_b m = (1)(3.63 \ °C/m)(0.190854 \ m) = 0.693°C$$

    $$T_b(solution) = T_b(Chloroform) + \Delta T_b = 61.7°C + 0.693 \ °C = \textbf{62.4°C}$$

78. Which of the following solutions has a lower freezing point?
    a. **27.00 g of ethanol (C_2H_5OH) in 350 g water.**
    b. 27.00 g of isopropanol (C_3H_7OH) in 350 g water.

    Since the ethanol solution will have the higher concentration, it will exhibit the lower freezing point.

79. Which of the following solutions has a lower freezing point?
    a. 15.00 g of t-butylphenol ($C_{10}H_{14}O$) in 200 g ethanol.
    b. **15.00 g of butyrolactone ($C_4H_6O_2$) in 200 g ethanol.**

    Since the butyrolactone solution will have the higher concentration, it will exhibit the lower freezing point.

80. What is the Freezing point of an aqueous 0.224 m sucrose solution?

    $$\Delta T_f = iK_f m = (1)(1.86 \ °C/m)(0.224m) = 0.417°C$$

    $$T_f(solution) = T_f(water) - \Delta T_f = 0.00°C - 0.417 \ °C = \textbf{--0.417°C}$$

81. What is the Freezing point of an aqueous 0.885 m glycerin solution?

    −1.65°

82. What is the freezing point of a solution consisting of 19.34 g of t-butylpehnol ($C_{10}H_{14}O$) and 340 g ethanol?

$$19.34 \ g \ C_{10}H_{14}O \times \frac{1 \ mol \ C_{10}H_{14}O}{150.24 \ g \ C_{10}H_{14}O} \times \frac{1}{340.0 \ g \ solvent} \times \frac{1000 \ g}{1 \ kg} = 0.37861 \ m \ C_{10}H_{14}O$$

$$\Delta T_f = iK_f m = (1)(1.99 \ °C/m)(0.37861 \ m) = 0.753°C$$

$$T_f(solution) = T_f(water) - \Delta T_f = -114.1°C - 0.753 \ °C = \textbf{-114.9°C}$$

83. What is the freezing point of a solution consisting of 12.37 g of butyrolactone ($C_4H_6O_2$) in 200.0 g of benzene?

1.8°C

84. The boiling point of a solution which contains 32.65 g of an unknown organic compound dissolved in 334 g of diethyl ether is 35.517°C. If the boiling point of pure ethyl ether is 34.5°C, what is the molar mass of the unknown compound?

$$\Delta T_b = T_b(solution) - T_b(ether) = 35.517°C - 34.5°C = 1.017°C$$

$$m = \frac{\Delta T_b}{iK_b} = \frac{1.017°C}{(1)(2.02°C/m)} = 0.503465 \ m \ Unk.$$

$$334 \ g \ ether \times \frac{1 \ kg \ ether}{1000 \ g \ ether} \times \frac{0.503465 \ mol \ Unk.}{1 \ kg \ ether} = 0.168157 \ mol \ Unk.$$

$$\frac{32.65 \ g \ Unk.}{0.168157 \ mol \ Unk.} = \textbf{194.2 \ g/mol}$$

194.2 g/mol – n-butyl p-hydroxybenzoate

85. The boiling point is found to be 78.745°C for a solution that consists of 45.32 g of an unknown organic compound dissolved in 298 g of ethanol. If the empirical formula of the compound was determined to be $C_{11}H_{22}O$ by combustion analysis, what is its molecular formula?

$C_{22}H_{44}O_2$ – Butyl Stearate

86. The freezing point is found to be –64.221°C for a solution consisting of 10.50 g of an unknown organic compound and 342 g or chloroform. If the boiling point of pure chloroform is -63.5°C and the empirical formula of the unknown compound is found to be $C_5H_8O_2$ by combustion analysis, what is the molecular formula of the unknown?

$C_{10}H_{16}O_2$ – Camphoric Acid

COLLIGATIVE PROPERTIES – OSMOSIS

87. Explain what is meant by isotonic.

Solutions with identical osmotic pressures are referred to as isotonic.

88. Explain what is meant by hypertonic and hypotonic.

Hypotonic solutions are those with solute concentrations less than that of blood cells. Hypertonic solutions are those with solute concentrations greater than that of blood cells.

89. What is the osmotic pressure of a 500.0-ml solution containing 5.50 g of glycerin ($C_3H_8O_3$) at 25°C?

$$5.50 \ g \ C_3H_8O_3 \times \frac{1 \ mol \ C_3H_8O_3}{92.11 \ g \ C_3H_8O_3} \times \frac{1}{500.0 \ ml} \times \frac{1000 \ ml}{1 \ L} = 0.119422 \ M \ C_3H_8O_3$$

$$\Pi = cRT = \left(0.119422 \ \frac{mol}{L}\right)\left(0.08206 \ \frac{atm \cdot L}{mol \cdot K}\right)(298 \ K) = \textbf{2.92 atm}$$

90. What mass of sucrose ($C_{12}H_{22}O_{11}$) is required to achieve an osmotic pressure of 4.34 atm when combined with enough water to generate 345 ml of solution at 25°C?

$$c = \frac{\Pi}{RT} = \frac{4.34 \ atm}{\left(0.08206 \ \frac{atm \cdot L}{mol \cdot K}\right)(298 \ K)} = 0.177477 \ M \ C_{12}H_{22}O_{11}$$

$$345 \ ml \times \frac{1 \ L}{1000 \ ml} \times \frac{0.177477 \ mol \ C_{12}H_{22}O_{11}}{1 \ L} \times \frac{342.34 \ g \ C_{12}H_{22}O_{11}}{1 \ mol \ C_{12}H_{22}O_{11}} = \textbf{20.96 g } \boldsymbol{C_{12}H_{22}O_{11}}$$

KEY TERMS

Acids   Acids are unique in that they are covalent compounds; however, when they dissolve in water, they dissociate into ions. To be more precise, acids dissociate in such a fashion that they produce H^+(aq) ions when dissolved in water.

Acid/base neutralization reaction   When acids and bases are mixed, OH^- anions from the base combine with the H^+ cations from the acid to form water, H_2O. Hence, the reaction of an acid with a base produces a salt (ionic compound) and water. This is referred to as an *acid/base neutralization reaction.*

Aqueous solution   A homogeneous mixture in which water acts as the *solvent.*

Bases   Bases are compounds that, when dissolved in water, produce hydroxide ions, OH^-.

Boiling point elevation   The boiling point of a solution is always higher than that of the pure solvent under the same conditions. The degree of deviation is dependent on the concentration of dissolved particles in the solution. For this reason, we say that the boiling point is a colligative property.

Colligative properties   Properties of solutions which depend on the relative ratio of the number of solute particles (ions or molecules) to the number of solvent molecules in a given solution.

Complete ionic equation   A chemical equation describing a reaction between two reactants both in aqueous solution wherein all dissolved, strong electrolytes are represented as freely solvated ions rather than constituents in the molecular formulae of ionic compounds or acids.

Concentration   The amount of solute dissolved in a given amount of solvent or solution.

Dissociation   The process wherein the constituent ions which compose an ionic solid break away from the solid compound and move into the aqueous phase as "freely *solvated* ions" (see Figure 5.2).

Double displacement reaction   Reactions which are described as an exchange of ions. These are also referred to as metathesis reactions.

Electric dipole   A term describing the circumstance within a molecule wherein two opposite (but equal) electric charges are separated by a distance.

Electrolytes   Compounds which, when dissolved in water, form solutions that will conduct electricity.

Freezing point depression   The freezing point of a solution is always lower than that of the pure solvent under the same conditions. The degree of deviation is dependent on the concentration of dissolved particles in the solution. For this reason, we say that the freezing point is a colligative property.

Gas evolving reactions   Reactions that occur when an insoluble gas is produced by the reaction of two ionic compounds in aqueous solution.

Hypernatremia   An illness characterized as a severe disruption of *osmoregulation* of the tissues of the body due to ingestion of fluids with very high concentrations of sodium (hypertonic fluids).

Hypertonic   Hypertonic solutions are those with solute concentrations higher than the physiological concentrations in the tissues and blood cells of the body.

Hypotonic   Hypotonic solutions are those with solute concentrations lower than the physiological concentrations in the tissues and blood cells of the body.

Insoluble   Compounds which do not dissolve in water (or other solvents of interest) under specified conditions.

Isotonic   Isotonic solutions are those with solute concentrations identical to the physiological concentrations in the tissues and blood cells of the body.

Mass percent   Perhaps the simplest of the units of concentration to calculate, mass percent is defined as the mass of solute divided by the mass of the solution (times 100%).

Metathesis reaction   See double displacement reactions above.

Molality A unit of concentration that is defined as the amount of solute (moles) per kg of solvent.

Molarity A unit of concentration that is defined as the amount of solute (moles) divided by the volume of solution in liters.

Mole fraction A unit of concentration that is defined as the amount (moles) of one component of a mixture divided by the total amount (moles) of all the components of a mixture.

Molecular equation Molecular equations represent all reactants and products in a reaction as if they are *not* dissociated, freely-solvated ions in solution. Rather, in a molecular equation each reactant and product is represented as a compound rather than ions.

Net ionic equation Net ionic equations are written such that all species which undergo no change during the reaction are omitted from the equation. Such species are referred to as *spectator ions* and are identified in the complete ionic equation as ions which are the same on the left and right side of the reaction arrow. These are understood to be undergoing no chemical change and as a consequence, are incidental to the reaction in question and need not always be represented in the reaction equation.

Nonelectrolyte Compounds which, when dissolved in water, produce solutions which do not conduct electricity.

Osmosis The net flow of solvent molecules from a solution of lower concentration to a solution of higher concentration. Osmosis will typically occur in circumstances where two solutions are separated only by a *semipermeable barrier or membrane.*

Polar The term *polar* arises from two opposite charges separated by a distance, a circumstance which is referred to as an *electric dipole.* The term is applied to bonds as well as molecules wherein there is a net charge separation due to an uneven distribution of bonding electrons.

Polar bond A chemical bond between two atoms wherein there is a net charge separation resulting in an electric dipole.

Polar molecule A molecule wherein there is a net charge separation resulting in an electric dipole over the whole molecule. This is the result of one or more polar bonds within the molecule.

Precipitate The solid, insoluble product that forms in a precipitation reaction.

Precipitation reaction A reaction that occurs when two aqueous solutions of ionic compounds are brought together and react to form an insoluble, solid product, a *precipitate.*

Raoult's law The mathematical statement which says that the vapor pressure of a solution is equal to the product of the mole fraction of the solvent and the vapor pressure of the pure solvent at the same temperature in question.

Solubility The relative propensity of a compound to dissolve in a given solvent.

Soluble Compounds that dissolve in a given solvent under specified conditions are said to be soluble in that solvent.

Solvated A circumstance wherein solute molecules or ions are in a state of aggregation with multiple solvent molecules and as such are effectively, physically isolated from other ions or molecules of the solute.

Solvation sphere   The solvent molecules which aggregate with and surround a molecule or ion of a solute in solution.

Solvent   The major component of a solution (homogeneous mixture).

Spectator ion   See net ionic equations above.

Strong acid   These acids completely dissociate into ions when dissolved in water and therefore, they behave as strong electrolytes in the same fashion as soluble ionic compounds.

van't Hoff factor   For soluble compounds, the ratio of dissolved particles to dissolved formula units (when dealing with strong electrolytes) is referred to as the van't Hoff factor (i).

Vapor pressure   The contribution to the overall pressure in a closed container which is due to the evaporation of a liquid contained therein.

Weak acid   Some acids, referred to as *weak acids*, are only partially ionized when dissolved in water.

CHAPTER 6

Gases

KEY CONCEPTS

- Pressure, Units of Pressure, and Converting between Units of Pressure
- The Simple Gas Laws
- The Ideal Gas Law
- The Density of Gases and the Ideal Gas Law
- Gas Stoichiometry
- Dalton's Law of Partial Pressures
- Real Gases and the Van der Waals Equation
- The Kinetic Molecular Theory

PHYSICAL PROPERTIES RELATED TO GAS LAWS

1. How do we define pressure?

    Pressure is defined as the force applied to the surface of an object (such as the container within which the gas is contained) per unit area over which that force is distributed.

2. Fill in the missing information in the following chart:

Unit of Pressure	Numerical Values at Sea Level
atmosphere (*atm*)	1
millimeters of mercury (*mm Hg*)	760
torr (*torr*)	760
pounds per square inch (*psi*)	14.7
pascal (*Pa*)	101,325

3. Convert 1.42 *atm* to the following units:
    a. *torr*

    $$1.42 \ atm \times \frac{760 \ torr}{1 \ atm} = 1.08 \times 10^3 \ torr$$

    b. *Pa*

    $$1.42 \ atm \times \frac{101{,}325 \ Pa}{1 \ atm} = 1.44 \times 10^5 \ Pa$$

    c. *mmHg*

    $$1.42 \ atm \times \frac{760 \ mmHg}{1 \ atm} = 1.08 \times 10^3 \ mmHg$$

    d. *Psi*

    $$1.42 \ atm \times \frac{14.7 \ psi}{1 \ atm} = 20.9 \ psi$$

4. Convert 546 *torr* to the following units:
    a. *atm*

    $$546 \ torr \times \frac{1 \ atm}{760 \ torr} = 0.718 \ atm$$

    b. *in Hg*

    $$546 \ torr \times \frac{29.92 \ in \ Hg}{760 \ torr} = 21.5 \ in \ Hg$$

c.   *psi*

$$546 \ torr \times \frac{14.7 \ psi}{760 \ torr} = 10.6 \ psi$$

d.   *bar*

$$546 \ torr \times \frac{1.01325 \ bar}{760 \ torr} = 0.728 \ bar$$

5.   How do we define volume?

Volume is defined as the space occupied by a particular substance.

6.   How do we define temperature?

Temperature is defined as being a measurement of the average kinetic energy of the molecules or particles that make up a particular sample.

7.   Covert the following temperatures to Kelvin:

a.   32.0 °C

$32.0°C + 273.15 = 305.2 \ K$

b.   112.0 °F

$$K = \frac{5}{9}(112.0° \ F - 32) + 273.15 = 318 \ K$$

c.   213.0 °F

$$K = \frac{5}{9}(213.0°F - 32) + 273.15 = 374 \ K$$

d.   58.0 °C

$58.0°C + 273.15 = 331.2 \ K$

8.   Covert the following temperatures to Kelvin:

a.   25.0 °C

$25.0°C + 273.15 = 298.2 \ K$

b.   202.0 °F

$$K = \frac{5}{9}(202.0°F - 32) + 273.15 = 368 \ K$$

c.   98.6 °F

$$K = \frac{5}{9}(98.6°F - 32) + 273.15 = 310 \ K$$

d.   37.0 °C

$37.0°C + 273.15 = 310.2 \ K$

SIMPLE GAS LAWS (BOYLE'S, CHARLES'S, AND AVOGADRO'S LAWS)

9. What is Boyle's law?

    Boyle's law states that the pressure and volume of a gas are inversely related given a constant temperature in a closed system. Thus,

    $$P_1V_1 = P_2V_2$$

10. A particular sample of gas has an initial volume of 4.1 L and a pressure of 1.3 *atm*. If the volume is increased to 5.8 L, what is the new pressure (*atm*)?

    $$P_1V_1 = P_2V_2$$

    $$P_2 = \frac{P_1V_1}{V_2}$$

    $$P_2 = \frac{(1.3\ atm) \times (4.1\ L)}{(5.8\ L)} = 0.92\ atm$$

11. A sample of hydrogen gas has an initial volume of 2.82 L and a pressure of 16.2 *psi*. What is the pressure (*atm*) if the volume is decreased to 1.68 L?

    First, we convert *psi* to *atm*:

    $$16.2\ psi \times \frac{1\ atm}{14.7\ psi} = 1.10\ atm$$

    Now, we solve for P_2:

    $$P_2 = \frac{P_1V_1}{V_2} = \frac{(1.10\ atm) \times (2.82\ L)}{(1.68\ L)} = 1.85\ atm$$

12. If a sample of oxygen gas in a cylinder originally occupies a volume of 6.72 L and has a pressure of 775 *mmHg*, and is then decompressed such that the gas has a new pressure of 0.832 *atm*, what is the new volume?

    First, we convert *mmHg* to *atm*:

    $$775\ mmHg \times \frac{1\ atm}{760\ mmHg} = 1.02\ atm$$

    Now, we solve for V_2:

    $$V_2 = \frac{P_1V_1}{P_2} = \frac{(1.02\ atm) \times (6.72\ L)}{(0.832\ atm)} = 8.24\ L$$

13. What is Charles's law?

Charles's law states that if a given quantity of gas is maintained at constant pressure, then the volume of the gas is directly proportional to the Kelvin temperature. Thus,

$$\frac{V_1}{T_1} = \frac{V_2}{T_2}$$

14. If a 5.2 L sample of gas in a container is cooled from 36.0 °C to 20.0 °C, what is the final volume (L) of the gas?

First, we need to convert Celsius to Kelvin:

$$T_1 = 36.0°C + 273.15 = 309.2 \ K$$

$$T_2 = 20.0°C + 273.15 = 293.2 \ K$$

Now we solve for V_2:

$$V_2 = \frac{V_1 T_2}{T_1} = \frac{(5.2 \ L) \times (293.2 \ K)}{(309.2 \ K)} = 4.9 \ L$$

15. If a 32.5 ml sample of gas in a container is heated from 78.8 °F to 93.2 °F, what is the final volume (L) of the gas?

First, we need to convert milliliters to liters and Fahrenheit to Kelvin:

$$32.5 \ ml \times \frac{1 \ L}{1,000 \ ml} = 3.25 \times 10^{-2} \ L$$

$$T_1 = \frac{5}{9} \times (78.8°F - 32) + 273.15 = 299 \ K$$

$$T_2 = \frac{5}{9} \times (93.2°F - 32) + 273.15 = 307 \ K$$

Now we solve for V_2:

$$V_2 = \frac{V_1 T_2}{T_1} = \frac{(3.25 \times 10^{-2} \ L) \times (307 \ K)}{(299 \ K)} = 3.34 \times 10^{-2} \ L \ (33.4 \ ml)$$

16. A particular sample of carbon dioxide gas has a volume of 4.60 L at 25.0 °C. This sample is then heated up and now has a volume of 6.10 L. What is the new temperature (°C) of the gas?

First, we need to convert Celsius to Kelvin:

$$T_1 = 25.0°C + 273.15 = 298.2 \ K$$

Now we solve for T_2:

$$T_2 = \frac{V_2 T_1}{V_1} = \frac{(6.10\ L) \times (298.2\ K)}{(4.60\ L)} = 395\ K$$

Now, convert Kelvin to Celsius:

$$°C = K - 273.15 = 395\ K - 273.15 = 122°C$$

17. What is the mathematical equation involving pressure, volume, and temperature that we get by combining Boyle's and Charles's laws?

If we combine Boyle's and Charles's laws:

$$P_1 V_1 = P_2 V_2 \text{ and } \frac{V_1}{T_1} = \frac{V_2}{T_2}$$

We get:

$$\frac{P_1 V_1}{T_1} = \frac{P_2 V_2}{T_2}$$

18. Hydrogen gas is placed in a 3.20 L container and has a pressure of 0.78 *atm* and temperature of 24.0 °C. If the container is then heated up to 36.0 °C, what is the new pressure (*atm*) assuming the volume is maintained?

First, we convert our temperatures from Celsius to Kelvin:

$$T_1 = 24.0°C + 273.15 = 297.2\ K$$

$$T_2 = 36.0°C + 273.15 = 309.2\ K$$

We can use the combination of Boyle's and Charles's law:

$$\frac{P_1 V_1}{T_1} = \frac{P_2 V_2}{T_2}$$

This can then be simplified, as volume is maintained and not changing:

$$\frac{P_1}{T_1} = \frac{P_2}{T_2}$$

Now rearrange to solve for P_2:

$$P_2 = \frac{P_1 T_2}{T_1}$$

Now plug in our numbers:

$$P_2 = \frac{(0.78\ atm) \times (309.2\ K)}{(297.2\ K)} = 0.81\ atm$$

19. A balloon is inflated such that it has a volume 9.80 L and is maintained at 1.10 *atm* of pressure and a temperature of 28.0 °C. If the temperature and pressure is then increased to 44.0 °C and 1.98 *atm*, what is the new volume (L) assuming the balloon can readily shrink and expand?

First, we convert our temperatures from Celsius to Kelvin:

$$T_1 = 28.0°C + 273.15 = 301.2 \ K$$

$$T_2 = 44.0°C + 273.15 = 317.2 \ K$$

We can use the combination of Boyle's and Charles's laws:

$$\frac{P_1 V_1}{T_1} = \frac{P_2 V_2}{T_2}$$

Now rearrange to solve for V_2:

$$V_2 = \frac{P_1 V_1 T_2}{P_2 T_1}$$

Now plug in our numbers:

$$V_2 = \frac{(1.10 \ atm \ ) \times (9.80 \ L) \times (317.2 \ K)}{(1.98 \ atm) \times (301.2 \ K)} = 5.73 \ L$$

20. If a gas-filled balloon that originally had a volume of 7.20 L and pressure of 465 *mmHg* now has a volume of 3.50 L, temperature of 11.9 °C, and pressure of 828 *mmHg*, what was the original temperature (°C)?

First, we convert our temperature (T_2) from Celsius to Kelvin:

$$T_2 = 11.9°C + 273.15 = 285.1 \ K$$

We can use the combination of Boyle's and Charles's laws:

$$\frac{P_1 V_1}{T_1} = \frac{P_2 V_2}{T_2}$$

Now rearrange to solve for T_1:

$$T_1 = \frac{P_1 V_1 T_2}{P_2 V_2}$$

Now plug in our numbers:

$$T_1 = \frac{(465 \ mmHg) \times (7.20 \ L) \times (285.1 \ K)}{(828 \ mmHg) \times (3.50 \ L)} = 329 \ K$$

Now we convert to Celsius:

$$T_1 = 329 \ K - 273.15 = 56°C$$

**Note, the units for pressure in this question does not have to be in *atm*, as is necessary with other equations used in this chapter (i.e. ideal gas law). However, as mentioned in the text, if you wanted to convert the pressure to *atm* for this problem in order to be safe (and not have to memorize when you can and cannot use units other than *atm*), you can do so in this problem and you will get the correct answer.

Thus,

$$T_1 = \left(\frac{(0.612\ atm) \times (7.20\ L) \times (285.1\ K)}{(1.09\ atm) \times (3.50\ L)} \right) - 273.15 = 56°C$$

21. What is Avogadro's law?

Avogadro's law states that the volume of a gas is directly related to the amount of mols (n) of the gas at a given temperature and pressure. Thus,

$$\frac{V_1}{n_1} = \frac{V_2}{n_2}$$

22. A balloon originally contains 4.33 mols of helium gas and has a volume of 3.21 L. If 2.11 mols of gas are then released from the balloon, what is the new volume (L)? Assume constant pressure and temperature.

Since we are dealing with volume and mols at constant pressure and temperature, we can use Avogadro's law:

$$\frac{V_1}{n_1} = \frac{V_2}{n_2}$$

We can then rearrange to solve for V_2:

$$V_2 = \frac{V_1 n_2}{n_1}$$

Now plug in our numbers:

$$V_2 = \frac{(3.21\ L) \times (4.33\ mols\ He - 2.11\ mols\ He)}{(4.33\ mols\ He)} = 1.65\ L$$

23. If a particular gas is added to a balloon that already contains 0.712 mols of that gas with a volume of 2.85 L, how many additional mols were added knowing that the new volume is now 4.12 L? Assume constant pressure and temperature.

First, we need to find the total mols (n_2) of gas that are now in the balloon. So, we will use Avogadro's law since we are dealing with volume and mols at constant pressure and temperature.

$$\frac{V_1}{n_1} = \frac{V_2}{n_2}$$

We can then rearrange to solve for n_2:

$$n_2 = \frac{V_2 n_1}{V_1}$$

Now plug in our numbers:

$$n_2 = \frac{(4.12 \ L) \times (0.712 \ mols)}{(2.85 \ L)} = 1.03 \ mols$$

Since 1.03 mols is the total mols that the balloon now contains, that must mean that 0.32 additional mols of the gas must have been added to the original 0.712 mols of gas. That is:

$$1.03 \ mols - 0.712 \ mols = 0.32 \ mols \ of \ additional \ gas \ added$$

24. A balloon contains 1.43 mols of a particular gas and has a volume of 5.08 L. If 0.812 mols are then added to the balloon, what is the new volume (L)? Assume constant pressure and temperature.

    First, we calculate the total final mols (n_2):

    $$n_2 = 1.43 \ mols + 0.812 \ mols = 2.24 \ mols$$

    Since we are dealing with volume and mols at constant pressure and temperature, we can use Avogadro's law:

    $$\frac{V_1}{n_1} = \frac{V_2}{n_2}$$

    We can then rearrange to solve for V_2:

    $$V_2 = \frac{V_1 n_2}{n_1}$$

    Now plug in our numbers:

    $$V_2 = \frac{(5.08 \ L) \times (2.24 \ mols)}{(1.43 \ mols)} = 7.96 \ L$$

THE IDEAL GAS LAW

25. What is the Ideal Gas Law?

    The ideal gas law is an equation that can be obtained by combining Boyle's, Charles's, and Avogadro's laws. It essentially describes a hypothetical ideal gas, and as such has limitations when it comes to describing the behavior of "real" gases. However, it is a good approximation of the behavior of "real" gases, which tend to behave close enough to what we call an ideal gas such that $PV = nRT$ can be used to describe their behavior, where R is the gas constant and is $0.082057 \ \frac{atm \cdot L}{mol \cdot K}$.

26. When using the ideal gas law, is the identity of the gas an important factor that is accounted for in the equation?

    No, the identity of the gas is not a factor that is accounted for in the equation.

27. What volume would 0.286 mols of argon gas occupy at a pressure of 1.35 *atm* and a temperature of 265 K?

We can use the ideal gas law to solve this problem:

$$PV = nRT$$

Rearrange to solve for V:

$$V = \frac{nRT}{P}$$

Now plug in our numbers:

$$V = \frac{(0.286 \; mols) \times \left(0.082057 \; \frac{atm \cdot L}{mol \cdot K} \right) \times (265 \; K)}{(1.35 \; atm)} = 4.61 \; L$$

28. How many mols of an ideal gas are there in a 2.10 L container maintained at 36.0 °C and 1.87 *atm* of pressure?

We can use the ideal gas law to solve this problem:

$$PV = nRT$$

Rearrange to solve for n:

$$n = \frac{PV}{RT}$$

We then convert Celsius to Kelvin:

$$36.0°C + 273.15 = 309.2 \; K$$

Now plug in our numbers:

$$n = \frac{(1.87 \; atm) \times (2.10L)}{\left(0.082057 \; \frac{atm \cdot L}{mol \cdot K} \right) \times (309.2 \; K)} = 0.155 \; mols$$

29. What volume would 0.311 mols of hydrogen gas occupy at a pressure of 17.3 *psi* and a temperature of 252 K?

We can use the ideal gas law to solve this problem:

$$PV = nRT$$

Rearrange to solve for V:

$$V = \frac{nRT}{P}$$

We then convert *psi* to *atm*:

$$17.3 \; psi \times \frac{1 \; atm}{14.7 \; psi} = 1.18 \; atm$$

Now plug in our numbers:

$$V = \frac{(0.311 \; mols) \times \left(0.082057 \; \frac{atm \cdot L}{mol \cdot K} \right) \times (252 \; K)}{(1.18 \; atm)} = 5.45 \; L$$

30. What is the temperature (°C) if 1.48 mols of an ideal gas are maintained at 921 *mmHg* of pressure in a 31.4 L container?

We can use the ideal gas law to solve this problem:

$$PV = nRT$$

Rearrange to solve for T :

$$T = \frac{PV}{nR}$$

We then convert *mmHg* to *atm* :

$$921 \; mmHg \times \frac{1 \; atm}{760 \; mmHg} = 1.21 \; atm$$

Now plug in our numbers:

$$T = \frac{(1.21 \; atm) \times (31.4 \; L \;)}{(1.48 \; mols) \times \left(0.082057 \; \frac{atm \cdot L}{mol \cdot K} \right)} = 313 \; K$$

Now convert to °C:

$$313 \; K - 273.15 = 40°C$$

31. How many mols of an ideal gas are there in a 13.5 L container maintained at 32.9 °C and 1.79 *atm* of pressure?

We can use the ideal gas law to solve this problem:

$$PV = nRT$$

Rearrange to solve for n :

$$n = \frac{PV}{RT}$$

We then convert Celsius to Kelvin:

$$32.9°C + 273.15 = 306.1 \; K$$

Now plug in our numbers:

$$n = \frac{(1.79 \; atm) \times (13.5L)}{\left(0.082057 \; \frac{atm \cdot L}{mol \cdot K}\right) \times (306.1 \; K)} = 0.962 \; mols$$

32. What volume would 0.431 mols of an ideal gas occupy at a pressure of 28.0 *in Hg* and a temperature of 278 K?

We can use the ideal gas law to solve this problem:

$$PV = nRT$$

Rearrange to solve for V :

$$V = \frac{nRT}{P}$$

We then convert *in Hg* to *atm* :

$$28.0 \; in \; Hg \times \frac{1 \; atm}{29.92 \; in \; Hg} = 0.936 \; atm$$

Now plug in our numbers:

$$V = \frac{(0.431 \; mols) \times \left(0.082057 \; \frac{atm \cdot L}{mol \cdot K}\right) \times (278 \; K)}{(0.936 \; atm)} = 10.5 \; L$$

33. What is the temperature (K) if 1.21 mols of an ideal gas are maintained at 23.7 *psi* of pressure in an 18.3 L container?

We can use the ideal gas law to solve this problem:

$$PV = nRT$$

Rearrange to solve for T :

$$T = \frac{PV}{nR}$$

We then convert *psi* to *atm*:

$$23.7 \; psi \times \frac{1 \; atm}{14.7 \; psi} = 1.61 \; atm$$

Now plug in our numbers:

$$T = \frac{(1.61 \; atm) \times (18.3 \; L)}{(1.21 \; mols) \times \left(0.082057 \; \frac{atm \cdot L}{mol \cdot K}\right)} = 297 \; K$$

34. What is the pressure (*atm*) if 0.473 mols of oxygen gas are maintained at a temperature of 18 °C in an 11.2 L container?

    We can use the ideal gas law to solve this problem:

    $$PV = nRT$$

    Rearrange to solve for P:

    $$P = \frac{nRT}{V}$$

    We then convert Celsius to Kelvin:

    $$18°C + 273.12\ K = 291\ K$$

    Now plug in our numbers:

    $$P = \frac{(0.473\ mols) \times \left(0.082057\ \frac{atm \cdot L}{mol \cdot K}\right) \times (291\ K)}{(11.2\ L)} = 1.01\ atm$$

35. How many mols of hydrogen gas are there in a 26.3 L container maintained at 42.9 °C and 22.6 *psi* of pressure?

    We can use the ideal gas law to solve this problem:

    $$PV = nRT$$

    Rearrange to solve for n:

    $$n = \frac{PV}{RT}$$

    We then convert Celsius to Kelvin and *psi* to *atm*:

    $$42.9°C + 273.15 = 316.1\ K$$

    $$22.6\ psi \times \frac{1\ atm}{14.7\ psi} = 1.54\ atm$$

    Now plug in our numbers:

    $$n = \frac{(1.54\ atm) \times (26.3\ L)}{\left(0.082057\ \frac{atm \cdot L}{mol \cdot K}\right) \times (316.1\ K)} = 1.56\ mols$$

36. What volume would 2.01 mols of carbon dioxide gas occupy at a pressure of 711 *torr* and a temperature of 65 °F?

We can use the ideal gas law to solve this problem:

$$PV = nRT$$

Rearrange to solve for V:

$$V = \frac{nRT}{P}$$

We then convert *in torr* to *atm* and Fahrenheit to Kelvin:

$$711 \; torr \times \frac{1 \; atm}{760 \; torr} = 0.936 \; atm$$

$$K = \frac{5}{9}\left(65°F - 32\right) + 273.15 = 291 \; K$$

Now plug in our numbers:

$$V = \frac{(2.01 \; mols) \times \left(0.082057 \; \frac{atm \cdot L}{mol \cdot K}\right) \times (291 \; K)}{(0.936 \; atm)} = 51.3 \; L$$

37. What is the temperature (°C) if 1.26 mols of helium gas are maintained at 659 *mmHg* of pressure in a 33.7 L cylinder?

We can use the ideal gas law to solve this problem:

$$PV = nRT$$

Rearrange to solve for T:

$$T = \frac{PV}{nR}$$

We then convert *mmHg* to *atm* :

$$659 \; mmHg \times \frac{1 \; atm}{760 \; mmHg} = 0.867 \; atm$$

Now plug in our numbers:

$$T = \frac{(0.867 \; atm) \times (33.7 \; L)}{(1.26 \; mols) \times \left(0.082057 \; \frac{atm \cdot L}{mol \cdot K}\right)} = 283 \; K$$

Now convert to °C:

$$283 \; K - 273.15 = 10°C$$

38. What is the pressure (*psi*) if 1.07 mols of an ideal gas are maintained at a temperature of 39 °C in a 20.3 L container?

    We can use the ideal gas law to solve this problem:

    $$PV = nRT$$

    Rearrange to solve for P :

    $$P = \frac{nRT}{V}$$

    We then convert Celsius to Kelvin:

    $$39°C + 273.12\ K = 312\ K$$

    Now plug in our numbers:

    $$P = \frac{(1.07\ mols) \times \left(0.082057\ \frac{atm \cdot L}{mol \cdot K}\right) \times (312\ K)}{(20.3\ L)} = 1.35\ atm$$

    Now convert to psi:

    $$1.35\ atm \times \frac{14.7\ psi}{1\ atm} = 19.8\ psi$$

39. A balloon is inflated to a volume of 32.4 L at a pressure of 736 *torr* and a temperature of 29 °C. How many mols of gas must the balloon contain?

    We can use the ideal gas law to solve this problem:

    $$PV = nRT$$

    Rearrange to solve for n :

    $$n = \frac{PV}{RT}$$

    We then convert Celsius to Kelvin and *torr* to *atm* :

    $$29°C + 273.12\ K = 302\ K$$

    $$736\ torr \times \frac{1\ atm}{760\ torr} = 0.968\ atm$$

    Now plug in our numbers:

    $$n = \frac{(0.968\ atm) \times (32.4\ L)}{\left(0.082057\ \frac{atm \cdot L}{mol \cdot K}\right) \times (302\ K)} = 1.27\ mols$$

40. If a 19.2 g block of dry ice (carbon dioxide) undergoes complete sublimation (conversion from solid to gas) in a 3.21 L container that is maintained at 24 °C, what is the pressure of the container?

We can use the ideal gas law to solve this problem:

$$PV = nRT$$

Rearrange to solve for P:

$$P = \frac{nRT}{V}$$

We then convert Celsius to Kelvin and calculate mols from grams of CO_2:

$$24°C + 273.12 \; K = 297 \; K$$

$$19.2 \; g \; CO_2 \times \frac{1 \; mol \; CO_2}{44.01 \; g \; CO_2} = 0.436 \; mols \; CO_2$$

Now plug in our numbers:

$$P = \frac{\left(0.436 \; mols \; CO_2\right) \times \left(0.082057 \; \frac{atm \cdot L}{mol \cdot K}\right) \times (297 \; K)}{(3.21 \; L)} = 3.31 \; atm$$

APPLICATIONS OF THE IDEAL GAS LAW

41. What is the equation that we get when we rearrange the ideal gas law to solve for density of a gas?

First, we note that mols (n) is simply mass (m) divided by molar mass (MM), thus we can substitute this in for mols:

$$PV = \frac{m}{MM} RT$$

Now, we know that density is mass (m) divided by volume (V). Thus, we can rearrange the above equation such that we have m/V (density) on one side of the equation:

$$Density = \frac{m}{V} = \frac{P \cdot MM}{R \cdot T}$$

42. What is STP?

STP stands for the standard temperature and pressure. For gases, it is 1 atm of pressure and 273.15 K (0 °C) for temperature.

43. What is the standard molar volume?

The standard molar volume is the volume of 1 mol of an ideal gas at STP. We can calculate this number as follows:

$$PV = nRT$$

$$V = \frac{nRT}{P}$$

$$V = \frac{(1\ mol) \times \left(0.082057\ \frac{atm \cdot L}{mol \cdot K}\right) \times (273.15\ K)}{1\ atm} = 22.414\ L$$

44. What is the density of hydrogen gas at STP?

$$Density = \frac{P \cdot MM}{R \cdot T}$$

$$Density = \frac{P \cdot MM}{R \cdot T} = \frac{(1\ atm) \times \left(2.02\ \frac{g}{mol}\right)}{\left(0.082057\ \frac{atm \cdot L}{mol \cdot K}\right) \times (273.15\ K)} = 9.01 \times 10^{-2}\ \frac{g}{L}$$

45. What is the density of nitrogen gas at STP?

$$Density = \frac{P \cdot MM}{R \cdot T}$$

$$Density = \frac{P \cdot MM}{R \cdot T} = \frac{(1\ atm) \times \left(28.02\ \frac{g}{mol}\right)}{\left(0.082057\ \frac{atm \cdot L}{mol \cdot K}\right) \times (273.15\ K)} = 1.250\ \frac{g}{L}$$

46. What is the density of argon gas at STP?

$$Density = \frac{P \cdot MM}{R \cdot T}$$

$$Density = \frac{P \cdot MM}{R \cdot T} = \frac{(1\ atm) \times \left(39.95\ \frac{g}{mol}\right)}{\left(0.082057\ \frac{atm \cdot L}{mol \cdot K}\right) \times (273.15\ K)} = 1.782\ \frac{g}{L}$$

47. What is the density of carbon dioxide gas at STP?

$$Density = \frac{P \cdot MM}{R \cdot T}$$

$$Density = \frac{P \cdot MM}{R \cdot T} = \frac{(1\ atm) \times \left(44.01\ \frac{g}{mol}\right)}{\left(0.082057\ \frac{atm \cdot L}{mol \cdot K}\right) \times (273.15\ K)} = 1.964\ \frac{g}{L}$$

48. Rank the gases in questions #44–47 from the least dense gas to the gas with the highest density.

From the least dense to the most:

$$H_2 < N_2 < Ar < CO_2$$

Notice that the gas density increases with increasing molar mass.

49. A particular sample of gas has a density of 1.78 g/L at a temperature and pressure of 39 °C and 1.03 *atm*. What is the molar mass of the gas?

First, we convert Celsius to Kelvin:

$$39°C + 273.15 = 312 \ K$$

Next, we can use our density equation and rearrange to solve for molar mass (MM):

$$Density \ (D) = \frac{P \cdot MM}{R \cdot T}$$

$$MM = \frac{D \cdot R \cdot T}{P}$$

Now plug in our numbers:

$$MM = \frac{\left(1.78 \ \frac{g}{L}\right) \times \left(0.082057 \ \frac{atm \cdot L}{mol \cdot K}\right) \times (312 \ K)}{(1.03 \ atm)} = 44.2 \ \frac{g}{mol}$$

50. What is the density of a gas (molar mass = 44.2 g/mol) that is stored at a temperature and pressure of 39 °C and 1.03 *atm*?

First, we convert Celsius to Kelvin:

$$39°C + 273.15 = 312 \ K$$

Next, we can use our density equation:

$$Density \ (D) = \frac{P \cdot MM}{R \cdot T}$$

Now plug in our numbers:

$$Density \ (D) = \frac{P \cdot MM}{R \cdot T} = \frac{(1.03 \ atm) \times \left(44.2 \ \frac{g}{mol}\right)}{\left(0.082057 \ \frac{atm \cdot L}{mol \cdot K}\right) \times (312 \ K)} = 1.78 \ \frac{g}{L}$$

51. A particular sample of gas has a mass of 0.496 g and volume of 279 ml at a temperature and pressure of 22 °C and 741 *torr*. What is the molar mass of the gas?

First, we convert Celsius to Kelvin and *torr* to *atm*:

$$22°C + 273.15 = 295 \ K$$

$$741 \ torr \times \frac{1 \ atm}{760 \ torr} = 0.975 \ atm$$

Next, since we have the mass (0.496 g) and volume (279 ml), we can calculate the density of the gas (g/L) after we convert ml to L:

$$279 \ ml \times \frac{1 \ L}{1,000 \ ml} = 0.279 \ L$$

$$Density = \frac{mass \ (g)}{volume \ (L)} = \frac{0.496 \ g}{0.279 \ L} = 1.78 \ \frac{g}{L}$$

Now, we can use our density equation and rearrange to solve for molar mass (MM):

$$Density \ (D) = \frac{P \cdot MM}{R \cdot T}$$

$$MM = \frac{D \cdot R \cdot T}{P}$$

Now plug in our numbers:

$$MM = \frac{\left(1.78 \ \frac{g}{L}\right) \times \left(0.082057 \ \frac{atm \cdot L}{mol \cdot K}\right) \times (295 \ K)}{(0.975 \ atm)} = 44.2 \ \frac{g}{mol}$$

52. If a given sample of gas has a density of 2.64 g/L at a temperature and pressure of 34 °C and 16.8 *psi*, what is the molar mass of the gas?

First, we convert Celsius to Kelvin and *psi* to *atm*:

$$34°C + 273.15 = 307 \ K$$

$$16.8 \ psi \times \frac{1 \ atm}{14.7 \ psi} = 1.14 \ atm$$

Next, we can use our density equation and rearrange to solve for molar mass (MM):

$$Density \ (D) = \frac{P \cdot MM}{R \cdot T}$$

$$MM = \frac{D \cdot R \cdot T}{P}$$

Now plug in our numbers:

$$MM = \frac{\left(2.64 \frac{g}{L}\right) \times \left(0.082057 \frac{atm \cdot L}{mol \cdot K}\right) \times (307\ K)}{(1.14\ atm)} = 58.3 \frac{g}{mol}$$

53. Aluminum powder reacts with oxygen gas to form aluminum oxide according to the following unbalanced equation:

$$Al\ (s) + O_2\ (g) \rightarrow Al_2O_3\ (unbalanced)$$

What is the balanced equation for this reaction?

$$4\ Al\ (s) + 3\ O_2\ (g) \rightarrow 2\ Al_2O_3$$

54. According to the balanced chemical equation from question #53, what volume (L) of oxygen gas is required to completely react with 38.6 g of aluminum powder at a temperature and pressure of 24 °C and 927 $mmHg$?

$$4\ Al\ (s) + 3\ O_2\ (g) \rightarrow 2\ Al_2O_3$$

From this balanced chemical equation, we know that the stoichiometric ratio between aluminum and oxygen is 4:3 respectively. Therefore, we can convert 38.6 g Al to mols Al, and then get mols oxygen using this ratio:

$$38.6\ g\ Al \times \frac{1\ mol\ Al}{26.98\ g\ Al} \times \frac{3\ mols\ O_2}{4\ mols\ Al} = 1.07\ mols\ O_2$$

Next, we convert Celsius to Kelvin and $mmHg$ to atm :

$$24°C + 273.15 = 297\ K$$

$$927\ mmHg \times \frac{1\ atm}{760\ mmHg} = 1.22\ atm$$

We can now rearrange the ideal gas law to solve for the volume of oxygen at the given temperature and pressure:

$$PV = nRT$$

$$V = \frac{nRT}{P}$$

$$V = \frac{nRT}{P} = \frac{\left(1.07\ mols\ O_2\right) \times \left(0.082057 \frac{atm \cdot L}{mol \cdot K}\right) \times (297\ K)}{(1.22\ atm)} = 21.4\ L\ of\ oxygen$$

55. Methanol gas can be formed by reacting carbon monoxide gas with hydrogen gas according to the following balanced chemical equation:

$$CO\ (g) + 2\ H_2\ (g) \rightarrow CH_3OH\ (g)$$

What volume (L) of hydrogen gas is needed to completely react with 2.73 mols of carbon monoxide at a temperature and pressure of 77 °F and 1.28 *atm*?

From the balanced chemical equation, we know that the stoichiometric ratio between carbon monoxide and hydrogen is 1:2 respectively. Therefore, we can calculate the mols of hydrogen from mols carbon monoxide using this ratio:

$$2.73 \; mols \; CO \times \frac{2 \; mols \; H_2}{1 \; mol \; CO} = 5.46 \; mols \; H_2$$

Next, we convert Fahrenheit to Kelvin:

$$K = \frac{5}{9}\left(77°F - 32\right) + 273.15 = 298 \; K$$

Now that we have mols hydrogen, we can rearrange the ideal gas law to solve for the volume of hydrogen at the given temperature and pressure:

$$PV = nRT$$

$$V = \frac{nRT}{P}$$

$$V = \frac{nRT}{P} = \frac{\left(5.46 \; mols \; H_2\right) \times \left(0.082057 \; \frac{atm \cdot L}{mol \cdot K}\right) \times \left(298 \; K\right)}{\left(1.28 \; atm\right)} = 104 \; L \; of \; hydrogen$$

56. Consider the following balanced chemical equation involving the burning of ethane (C_2H_6) in air:

$$2 \; C_2H_6 \; (g) + 7 \; O_2 \; (g) \rightarrow 4 \; CO_2 \; (g) + 6H_2O \; (g)$$

What volume (L) of carbon dioxide is produced if 1.86 mols of ethane are completely consumed at a temperature and pressure of 25 °C and 17.5 *psi*?

From the balanced chemical equation, we know that the stoichiometric ratio between ethane and carbon dioxide is 2:4 respectively. Therefore, we can calculate the mols of carbon dioxide from mols ethane using this ratio:

$$1.86 \; mols \; C_2H_6 \times \frac{4 \; mols \; CO_2}{2 \; mols \; C_2H_6} = 3.72 \; mols \; CO_2$$

Next, we convert Celsius to Kelvin and *psi* to *atm* :

$$25°C + 273.15 = 298 \; K$$

$$17.5 \; psi \times \frac{1 \; atm}{14.7 \; psi} = 1.19 \; atm$$

Now that we have mols of carbon dioxide, we can rearrange the ideal gas law to solve for the volume of carbon dioxide at the given temperature and pressure:

$$PV = nRT$$

$$V = \frac{nRT}{P}$$

$$V = \frac{nRT}{P} = \frac{(3.72 \; mols \; CO_2) \times \left(0.082057 \; \frac{atm \cdot L}{mol \cdot K}\right) \times (298 \; K)}{(1.19 \; atm)} = 76.4 \; L \; of \; carbon \; dioxide$$

MIXTURES OF GASES AND PARTIAL PRESSURES

57. What is Dalton's law of partial pressures?

Dalton's law of partial pressures states that the total pressure exerted in a mixture of gases is equal to the sum of the individual partial pressures of the gases involved in the mixture.

58. What is the total pressure (*atm*) of a gas mixture containing 0.894 g hydrogen gas and 3.95 g neon gas in a 12 liter container at 28 °C?

First, we have to convert the grams of each to mols in order to eventually get total mols:

$$0.894 \; g \; H_2 \times \frac{1 \; mol \; H_2}{2.02 \; g \; H_2} \; 0.443 \; mols \; H_2$$

$$3.95 \; g \; Ne \times \frac{1 \; mol \; Ne}{20.18 \; g \; Ne} \; 0.196 \; mols \; Ne$$

Total mols = mols H_2 *+ mols Ne =* 0.443 *mols* H_2 *+* 0.196 *mols Ne =* 0.639 *total mols*

Next, we convert Celsius to Kelvin:

$$28°C + 273.15 = 301 \; K$$

Now we can rearrange the ideal gas law to solve for total pressure using total mols:

$$PV = nRT$$

$$P_{total} = \frac{n_{total}RT}{V}$$

$$P_{total} = \frac{n_{total}RT}{V} = \frac{(0.639 \; mols) \times \left(0.082057 \; \frac{atm \cdot L}{mol \cdot K}\right) \times (301 \; K)}{(12 \; L)} = 1.3 \; atm$$

59. What are the partial pressures of the hydrogen and neon gases from question #58?

We can use the ideal gas law for each gas as long as we plug in the mols of each gas (NOT total mols) in order to get the partial pressures:

$$P_{H_2} = \frac{n_{H_2}RT}{V} = \frac{\left(0.443 \; mols \; H_2\right) \times \left(0.082057 \; \frac{atm \cdot L}{mol \cdot K}\right) \times \left(301 \; K\right)}{\left(12 \; L\right)} = 0.91 \; atm$$

$$P_{Ne} = \frac{n_{Ne}RT}{V} = \frac{\left(0.196 \; mols \; Ne\right) \times \left(0.082057 \; \frac{atm \cdot L}{mol \cdot K}\right) \times \left(301 \; K\right)}{\left(12 \; L\right)} = 0.40 \; atm$$

60. What are the mol fractions of the hydrogen and neon gases from question #58?

To find the mol fractions (X) of each gas in the mixture, we can use the following:

$$X_{H_2} = \frac{n_{H_2}}{n_{total}}$$

$$X_{Ne} = \frac{n_{Ne}}{n_{total}}$$

Therefore:

$$X_{H_2} = \frac{n_{H_2}}{n_{total}} = \frac{0.443 \; mols \; H_2}{0.639 \; mols \; total} = 0.693$$

$$X_{Ne} = \frac{n_{Ne}}{n_{total}} = \frac{0.196 \; mols \; Ne}{0.639 \; mols \; total} = 0.307$$

61. What is the total pressure (atm) of a mixture of the following gases given their individual partial pressures: Ne (255 $mmHg$), N_2 (112 $mmHg$), and CO_2 (156 $mmHg$)?

First, we add everything up to get the total pressure in $mmHg$, and then convert our answer to atm:

$$255 \; mmHg \; Ne + 112 \; mmHg \; N_2 + 156 \; mmHg \; CO_2 = 523 \; mmHg \; total \; pressure$$

$$523 \; mmHg \; total \; pressure \times \frac{1 \; atm}{760 \; mmHg} = 0.688 \; atm$$

62. How many total mols are there in the mixture of gases from question #61 in a 24.2 L container at 30 °C? How many mols of each component (Ne, N_2, and CO_2) are there?

First, we convert Celsius to Kelvin:

$$30°C + 273.15 = 303 \; K$$

For total mols, we can plug in our answer from question #61 for total pressure (0.688 *atm*) into the ideal gas law to get total mols of all three gases:

$$PV = nRT$$

$$n_{total} = \frac{P_{total}V}{RT}$$

$$n_{total} = \frac{P_{total}V}{RT} = \frac{(0.688 \; atm) \times (24.2 \; L)}{\left(0.082057 \; \frac{atm \cdot L}{mol \cdot K}\right) \times (303 \; K)} = 0.670 \; total \; mols$$

For the number of mols of each component, we can convert each of their partial pressures given in question #61 to *atm*, and then use the ideal gas law to solve for mols of each gas in the mixture:

$$255 \; mmHg \; Ne \times \frac{1 \; atm}{760 \; mmHg} = 0.336 \; atm \; Ne$$

$$112 \; mmHg \; N_2 \times \frac{1 \; atm}{760 \; mmHg} = 0.147 \; atm \; N_2$$

$$156 \; mmHg \; CO_2 \times \frac{1 \; atm}{760 \; mmHg} = 0.205 \; atm \; CO_2$$

Notice that if we add up all three partial pressures, we get the total pressure of the mixture of gases:

$$0.336 \; atm \; Ne + 0.147 \; atm \; N_2 + 0.205 \; atm \; CO_2 = 0.688 \; atm.$$

Now we use the rearranged equation for the ideal gas law to solve for mols of each component using their individual respective partial pressures:

$$n_{Ne} = \frac{P_{Ne}V}{RT} = \frac{(0.336 \; atm) \times (24.2 \; L)}{\left(0.082057 \; \frac{atm \cdot L}{mol \cdot K}\right) \times (303 \; K)} = 0.327 \; mols \; Ne$$

$$n_{N_2} = \frac{P_{N_2}V}{RT} = \frac{(0.147 \; atm) \times (24.2 \; L)}{\left(0.082057 \; \frac{atm \cdot L}{mol \cdot K}\right) \times (303 \; K)} = 0.143 \; mols \; N_2$$

$$n_{CO_2} = \frac{P_{CO_2}V}{RT} = \frac{(0.205 \; atm) \times (24.2 \; L)}{\left(0.082057 \; \frac{atm \cdot L}{mol \cdot K}\right) \times (303 \; K)} = 0.200 \; mols \; CO_2$$

Notice that if we add the mols of all three components, we get the total mols of the mixture of gases:

$$0.327 \; mols \; Ne + 0.143 \; mols \; N_2 + 0.200 \; mols \; CO_2 = 0.670 \; mols \; total.$$

63. If a mixture of 3.5 g of oxygen gas and 7.2 g of helium gas are maintained in a container at 1.9 *atm*, what is the mol fraction and the partial pressure (*atm*) of oxygen?

First, we convert grams to mols and then find the mol fraction (X_{O_2}) of oxygen:

$$3.5 \ g \ O_2 \times \frac{1 \ mol \ O_2}{32.00 \ g \ O_2} = 0.11 \ mols \ O_2$$

$$7.2 \ g \ He \times \frac{1 \ mol \ He}{4.00 \ g \ He} = 1.8 \ mols \ He$$

$$X_{O_2} = \frac{mols \ O_2}{total \ mols} = \frac{0.11 \ mols \ O_2}{(0.11 \ mols \ O_2 + 1.8 \ mols \ He)} = 5.8 \times 10^{-2}$$

Now to find the partial pressure of oxygen (P_{O_2}), we simply multiply the mol fraction of oxygen (X_{O_2}) by the total pressure (1.9 *atm*):

$$P_{O_2} = 5.8 \times 10^{-2} \times 1.9 \ atm = 0.11 \ atm$$

64. From the information given in question #63, what is the mol fraction and the partial pressure (*atm*) of helium?

First we convert grams to mols and then find the mol fraction (X_{He}) of helium:

$$3.5 \ g \ O_2 \times \frac{1 \ mol \ O_2}{32.00 \ g \ O_2} = 0.11 \ mols \ O_2$$

$$7.2 \ g \ He \times \frac{1 \ mol \ He}{4.00 \ g \ He} = 1.8 \ mols \ He$$

$$X_{He} = \frac{mols \ He}{total \ mols} = \frac{1.8 \ mols \ He}{(0.11 \ mols \ O_2 + 1.8 \ mols \ He)} = 0.94$$

Now to find the partial pressure of helium (P_{He}), we simply multiply the mol fraction of helium (X_{He}) by the total pressure (1.9 *atm*):

$$P_{He} = 0.94 \times 1.9 \ atm = 1.8 \ atm$$

Notice that if we add the partial pressure of oxygen from question #63 (0.11 *atm*) to the partial pressure of helium found here (1.8 *atm*), we get the total pressure (1.9 *atm*): $0.11 \ atm + 1.8 \ atm = 1.9 \ atm$.

65. What are the mol fractions and partial pressures of a mixture of 0.687 mols of helium gas and 0.219 mols of carbon dioxide gas maintained in a container with a total pressure of 2.11 *atm*?

First, we find the mol fractions of each component:

$$X_{He} = \frac{mols \ He}{total \ mols} = \frac{0.687 \ mols \ He}{(0.687 \ mols \ He + 0.219 \ mols \ CO_2)} = 0.758$$

$$X_{CO_2} = \frac{mols\ CO_2}{total\ mols} = \frac{0.219\ mols\ CO_2}{(0.687\ mols\ He + 0.219\ mols\ CO_2)} = 0.242$$

Now we multiply the mol fractions by the total pressure to get partial pressures of each gas in the mixture:

$$P_{He} = 0.758 \times 2.11\ atm = 1.60\ atm$$

$$P_{CO_2} = 0.242 \times 2.11\ atm = 0.511\ atm$$

Notice that if we add the two partial pressures together, we get the total pressure (2.11 atm):

$$1.60\ atm + 0.511\ atm = 2.11\ atm$$

66. What are the mol fractions and partial pressures of a mixture of 2.22 mols of argon gas and 1.09 mols of oxygen gas maintained in a 38.4 L container at a temperature of 28 °C?

First, we convert Celsius to Kelvin:

$$28°C + 273.15 = 301\ K$$

In order to find the total pressure of the mixture of gases, we need to first find the total mols:

$$2.22\ mols\ Ar + 1.09\ mols\ O_2 = 3.31\ mols\ total$$

Now we use the ideal gas law to solve for total pressure:

$$PV = nRT$$

$$P_{total} = \frac{n_{total}RT}{V}$$

$$P_{total} = \frac{n_{total}RT}{V} = \frac{(3.31\ mols) \times \left(0.082057\ \frac{atm \cdot L}{mol \cdot K}\right) \times (301\ K)}{(38.4\ L)} = 2.13\ atm$$

Now we can find the mol fractions for both argon and oxygen gases in the mixture, then use these numbers to determine partial pressures from the total pressure.

$$X_{Ar} = \frac{mols\ Ar}{total\ mols} = \frac{2.22\ mols\ Ar}{(2.22\ mols\ Ar + 1.09\ mols\ O_2)} = 0.671$$

$$X_{O_2} = \frac{mols\ O_2}{total\ mols} = \frac{1.09\ mols\ O_2}{(2.22\ mols\ Ar + 1.09\ mols\ O_2)} = 0.329$$

$$P_{Ar} = 0.671 \times 2.13\ atm = 1.43\ atm$$

$$P_{O_2} = 0.329 \times 2.13\ atm = 0.701\ atm$$

Notice that if we add the two partial pressures together, we get the total pressure (2.13 atm):

$$1.43\ atm + 0.701\ atm = 2.13\ atm$$

REAL GASES AND DEVIATIONS FROM IDEAL BEHAVIOR

67. Describe why the kinetic molecular theory breaks down at high pressures.

    The theory relies on the fact that most of the space in a gas is "empty space," and therefore the individual size of the gas molecules is somewhat insignificant. However, at high pressures, we squeeze out all that empty space and now the size of the individual gas molecules becomes significant and can in fact affect the overall volume.

68. Describe why the kinetic molecular theory breaks down at low temperatures.

    The theory relies on the fact that gas molecules are moving very fast past one another (especially at higher temperatures), and therefore do not have the opportunity for much interaction with one another. However, at lower temperatures, the molecules are moving much slower and can interact with each other. Thus, gas molecules are not colliding with the sides of the container as hard as the theory may predict which ultimately affects the overall pressure of the gas.

69. What is van der Waals equation?

    Van der Waals equation is written as follows:

    $$\left(P + a\left[\frac{n}{V}\right]^2\right) \times (V - bn) = nRT$$

    Where a and b are experimentally determined constants specific to the identity of the gas.

70. Using the ideal gas law, calculate the pressure of 1.00 mol of carbon dioxide gas at 273 K in a 5.00 L container. What is the pressure if we were to use van der Waals equation (where $a = 3.59 \dfrac{L^2 \cdot atm}{mol^2}$ and $b = 0.0427 \dfrac{L}{mol}$)?

    First, we use the ideal gas law and rearrange to solve for pressure:

    $$PV = nRT$$

    $$P = \frac{nRT}{V}$$

    $$P = \frac{nRT}{V} = \frac{\left(1.00 \ mol \ CO_2\right) \times \left(0.082057 \ \frac{atm \cdot L}{mol \cdot K}\right) \times \left(273 \ K\right)}{(5.00 \ L)} = 4.48 \ atm$$

    Now we rearrange van der Waals equation to solve for pressure:

    $$\left(P + a\left[\frac{n}{V}\right]^2\right) \times (V - bn) = nRT$$

    $$P = \frac{nRT}{(V - nb)} - \frac{an^2}{V^2}$$

$$P = \frac{nRT}{(V - nb)} - \frac{an^2}{V^2}$$

$$= \frac{\left(1.00 \ mol \ CO_2\right) \times \left(0.082057 \ \frac{atm \cdot L}{mol \cdot K}\right) \times (273 \ K)}{5.00 \ L - \left(1.00 \ mol \ CO_2 \times 0.0427 \ \frac{L}{mol}\right)} - \frac{3.59 \ \frac{L^2 \cdot atm}{mol^2} \times \left(1.00 \ mol \ CO_2\right)^2}{(5.00 \ L)^2}$$

$$= 4.38 \ atm$$

Notice that the "real" pressure is less than what the ideal gas law would predict. This answer makes sense because of the low temperature.

KEY TERMS

Avogadro's law   One of the simple gas laws, Avogadro's law states that the volume of a gas is directly related to the amount of moles (n) of the gas at a given temperature and pressure.

Bar   A metric unit of pressure equivalent to slightly less than 1 atmosphere.

Barometer   A scientific instrument used to measure the atmospheric pressure. It consists of a glass tube, closed at the top, containing a column of mercury over a mercury filled pool or basin. Changes in atmosphereic pressure result in changes in the height of the mercury column.

Boyle's law   One of the simple gas laws, Boyle's law states that the volume of a gas is inversely related to the pressure of the gas (holding the sample size and temperature constant).

Dalton's law of partial pressures   Dalton's law states that the total pressure exerted in a mixture of gases is equal to the sum of the individual partial pressures of the gases involved in the mixture.

Diastolic pressure   The pressure placed on the arterial walls while the heart is at rest.

Diffusion   The process by which gas molecules spread out in response to a concentration gradient.

Effusion   The process by which a gas escapes a container through a small hole.

Inches of mercury   A unit of pressure. 29.92 inches of mercury is equivalent to 1 atmosphere.

Kilopascal   A unit of pressure in the SI system equal to 1 newton per square meter.

Millibar   A unit of pressure equal to 1/1000 bar. See the definition of *bar* above.

Millimeters of mercury   A unit of pressure. 760 millimeters of mercury is equivalent to 1 atmosphere.

Mole fraction   A unit of concentration that is defined as the amount (moles) of one component of a mixture divided by the total amount (moles) of all the components of a mixture.

Pascal   A unit of pressure equal to 1/1000 of a kilopascal. See *kilopascal* above.

Pounds per square inch (psi)   A unit of pressure equal to 1 pound per square inch. 14.7 psi is equivalent to 1 atmosphere.

Pressure   Pressure is defined as the force applied to the surface of an object (such as the inner surfaces of a container within which the gas is contained) per unit area over which that force is distributed.

Sphygmomanometer   An instrument commonly used by doctors and nurses to measure blood pressure.

Standard atmosphere   A unit of pressure defined as the atmospheric pressure at sea level.

Standard molar volume   The volume of an ideal gas at STP.

Standard temperature and pressure (STP)   Conditions of temperature and pressure defined as 1 atm and 273.15 K.

Systolic pressure   The arterial pressure when the heart is in contraction.

Temperature   The average kinetic energy of the molecules or particles that make up a particular sample.

Torr   A unit of pressure equal to 1/760 of 1 standard atmosphere.

Vapor pressure   See *vapor pressure* in Chapter 5 of this manual.

Volume   The space occupied by a particular sample or substance.

The Quantum Atom: Atomic Structure and Periodicity

CHAPTER 7

KEY CONCEPTS

- The Wave Mechanics of EM Radiation
- The Particle Nature of EM Radiation and the Energy of a Photon
- The Photoelectric Effect
- The Bohr Model of the Atom
- de Broglie and the Wave Nature of Electrons
- Heisenberg's Uncertainty Principle
- Schrödinger's Equation and the Quantum Model of the Atom
- Ground State Electron Configurations
- Periodic Trends

THE WAVE NATURE OF LIGHT – ELECTROMAGNETIC RADIATION

1. What is light?

   Light is the common word for electromagnetic radiation, a form of radiant energy which consists of oscillating, mutually perpendicular electric and magnetic fields.

2. What is the speed of light?

   The speed of EM radiation in a vacuum is 2.9979×10^8 m/s.

3. Define wavelength.

   The *wavelength* (λ) is defined as the distance along the x-coordinate between adjacent peaks (maxima – highest points) or adjacent troughs (minima – lowest points) on a wave.

4. Define amplitude.

   We can define *amplitude* as simply the "height" of the wave. In other words, if we describe a wave as a mathematical function, the amplitude is the "value" of that function at any point along the x-coordinate.

5. Define frequency.

   Frequency (ν) is defined as the number of cycles (wavelengths) which pass an arbitrary point in space in one second.

   As such, the *frequency* is a function of both the velocity of the wave and its *wavelength* and is typically expressed in units of *cycles per second*, or simply, "*per second*" ($\frac{1}{s}$ or s^{-1}), also known as *Hertz* (*Hz*).

6. Write the equation which describes the relationship between wavelength, frequency, and velocity of light wave waves.

$$\nu = \frac{c}{\lambda}$$

   Where ν is frequency, λ is the wavelength and c is the speed of light.

7. For the following pairs, which has less energy:
   a. Microwaves or radio waves

      Radio waves

   b. Gamma rays or infrared radiation

      Infrared radiation

8. For the following pairs, which has less energy:
   a. Green light or red light

      Red light

   b. Ultraviolet or infrared

      Ultraviolet

9. Which of the following wavelengths of light is associated with the highest frequency?
   a. **10 nm**
   b. 100 nm
   c. 100 µm
   d. 100 mm

   The lowest wavelength corresponds to the highest frequency.

10. Which of the following wavelengths of light is associated with the lowest frequency?
    a. 10 nm
    b. 100 nm
    c. 100 µm
    d. **100 mm**

    The lowest wavelength corresponds to the highest frequency.

11. What is the frequency of EM radiation with a wavelength of 300 *nm*?

$$v = \frac{c}{\lambda} = \frac{2.9979 \times 10^8 \ m \cdot s^{-1}}{\left(300 \ nm \times \frac{1 \ m}{10^9 \ nm}\right)} = 9.99 \times 10^{14} \ s^{-1}$$

12. What is the frequency of EM radiation with a wavelength of $4.55 \times 10^{-5} \ m$?

$$v = \frac{c}{\lambda} = \frac{2.9979 \times 10^8 \ m \cdot s^{-1}}{\left(4.55 \times 10^{-5} \ m\right)} = 6.59 \times 10^{12} \ s^{-1}$$

13. What is the frequency of EM radiation with a wavelength of $7.34 \times 10^{-14} \ m$?

$$v = \frac{c}{\lambda} = \frac{2.9979 \times 10^8 \ m \cdot s^{-1}}{\left(7.34 \times 10^{-14} \ m\right)} = 4.08 \times 10^{21} \ s^{-1}$$

14. What is the frequency of EM radiation with a wavelength of $5.97 \times 10^{-6} \ m$?

$$v = \frac{c}{\lambda} = \frac{2.9979 \times 10^8 \ m \cdot s^{-1}}{\left(5.97 \times 10^{-6} \ m\right)} = 5.02 \times 10^{13} \ s^{-1}$$

15. What is the wavelength of EM radiation with a frequency of $3.21 \times 10^{20} \ s^{-1}$?

$$\lambda = \frac{c}{v} = \frac{2.9979 \times 10^8 \ m \cdot s^{-1}}{\left(3.21 \times 10^{20} \ s^{-1}\right)} = 9.34 \times 10^{-13} \ m$$

16. What is the wavelength of EM radiation with a frequency of $4.94 \times 10^{14} \ s^{-1}$?

$$\lambda = \frac{c}{v} = \frac{2.9979 \times 10^8 \ m \cdot s^{-1}}{\left(4.94 \times 10^{14} \ s^{-1}\right)} = 6.07 \times 10^{-7} \ m = 607 \ nm$$

17. What is the wavelength of EM radiation with a frequency of $6.33 \times 10^6 \ s^{-1}$?

$$\lambda = \frac{c}{v} = \frac{2.9979 \times 10^8 \ m \cdot s^{-1}}{\left(6.33 \times 10^6 \ s^{-1}\right)} = 47.4 \ m$$

18. What is the wavelength of EM radiation with a frequency of $8.22 \times 10^{10} s^{-1}$?

$$\lambda = \frac{c}{v} = \frac{2.9979 \times 10^8 \ m \cdot s^{-1}}{\left(8.22 \times 10^{10} \ s^{-1}\right)} = 3.65 \times 10^{-3} \ m$$

THE PARTICLE NATURE OF LIGHT

19. Which of following forms of EM radiation has the highest energy photons?
    a. **Gamma rays**
    b. Ultraviolet radiation
    c. Visible light
    d. Microwaves
    e. Radio waves

    Gamma Rays are the highest energy EM radiation.

20. Which of following forms of EM radiation has the lowest energy photons?
    a. Gamma rays
    b. Ultraviolet radiation
    c. Visible light
    d. Microwaves
    e. **Radio waves**

    Radio waves are the lowest energy form of EM radiation listed.

21. If monochromatic visible light has a wavelength of 495 nm, what is the energy of one photon of this light? What is the energy of 1 mol of such photons?

    Energy of a Photon:

$$E = hv = \frac{hc}{\lambda} = \frac{\left(6.626 \times 10^{-34} \ J \cdot s\right)\left(2.9979 \times 10^8 \ m \cdot s^{-1}\right)}{\left(495 \ nm \times \frac{1 \ m}{10^9 \ nm}\right)} = \mathbf{4.01 \times 10^{-19} \ J}$$

    Energy of 1 mole of Photons:

$$E = \left(4.01 \times 10^{-19} \ J\right) \times \left(6.022 \times 10^{23} \ mol^{-1}\right)\left(\frac{1 \ kJ}{1000 \ J}\right) = \mathbf{242 \ kJ \cdot mol^{-1}}$$

22. If EM radiation has a frequency of $\mathbf{7.43 \times 10^{14}\, s^{-1}}$, what is its wavelength and energy? What is the energy of 1 mol of such photons?

    Wavelength:

$$\lambda = \frac{c}{v} = \frac{2.9979 \times 10^8\ m \cdot s^{-1}}{\left(7.43 \times 10^{14}\ s^{-1}\right)} = \mathbf{4.03 \times 10^{-7}\ m = 403\ nm}$$

    Energy of a Photon:

$$E = hv = \left(6.626 \times 10^{-34}\ J \cdot s\right)\left(7.43 \times 10^{14}\ s^{-1}\right) = \mathbf{4.92 \times 10^{-19}\ J}$$

    Energy of 1 mole of Photons:

$$E = \left(4.92 \times 10^{-19}\ J\right) \times \left(6.022 \times 10^{23}\ mol^{-1}\right)\left(\frac{1\ kJ}{1000\ J}\right) = \mathbf{296\ kJ \cdot mol^{-1}}$$

23. If a photon has an energy of $\mathbf{4.78 \times 10^{-19}\, J}$, what is its wavelength? What is its frequency?

$$E = \frac{hc}{\lambda} \rightarrow \lambda = \frac{hc}{E} = \frac{\left(6.626 \times 10^{-34}\ J \cdot s\right)\left(2.9979 \times 10^8\ m \cdot s^{-1}\right)}{\left(4.78 \times 10^{-19}\ J\right)} = \mathbf{4.16 \times 10^{-7}\ m = 416\ nm}$$

$$E = hv \rightarrow v = \frac{E}{h} = \frac{\left(4.78 \times 10^{-19}\ J\right)}{\left(6.626 \times 10^{-34}\ J \cdot s\right)} = \mathbf{7.21 \times 10^{14}\ s^{-1}}$$

24. If violet light has a wavelength of 390 nm, what is the energy of one photon of this light? What is the energy of 1 mol of such photons?

    Energy of a Photon:

$$E = hv = \frac{hc}{\lambda} = \frac{\left(6.626 \times 10^{-34}\ J \cdot s\right)\left(2.9979 \times 10^8\ m \cdot s^{-1}\right)}{\left(390\ nm \times \dfrac{1\ m}{10^9\ nm}\right)} = \mathbf{5.09 \times 10^{-19}\ J}$$

    Energy of 1 mole of Photons:

$$E = \left(5.09 \times 10^{-19}\ J\right) \times \left(6.022 \times 10^{23}\ mol^{-1}\right)\left(\frac{1\ kJ}{1000\ J}\right) = \mathbf{307\ kJ \cdot mol^{-1}}$$

25. If EM radiation has a frequency of $4.33 \times 10^{10}\,s^{-1}$, what is its wavelength and energy? What is the energy of 1 mol of such photons?

    Wavelength:

    $$\lambda = \frac{c}{v} = \frac{2.9979 \times 10^{8}\ m \cdot s^{-1}}{\left(4.33 \times 10^{10}\ s^{-1}\right)} = 6.92 \times 10^{-3}\,m$$

    Energy of a Photon:

    $$E = hv = \left(6.626 \times 10^{-34}\ J \cdot s\right)\left(4.33 \times 10^{10}\ s^{-1}\right) = 2.87 \times 10^{-23}\,J$$

    Energy of 1 mole of Photons:

    $$E = \left(2.87 \times 10^{-23}\ J\right) \times \left(6.022 \times 10^{23}\ mol^{-1}\right) = 17.3\,J \cdot mol^{-1}$$

26. If a photon has an energy of $6.08 \times 10^{-19}\,J$, what is its wavelength? What is its frequency?

    $$E = \frac{hc}{\lambda} \rightarrow \lambda = \frac{hc}{E} = \frac{\left(6.626 \times 10^{-34}\ J \cdot s\right)\left(2.9979 \times 10^{8}\ m \cdot s^{-1}\right)}{\left(6.08 \times 10^{-19}\ J\right)} = 3.27 \times 10^{-7}\,m = 327\,nm$$

    $$E = hv \rightarrow v = \frac{E}{h} = \frac{\left(6.08 \times 10^{-19}\ J\right)}{\left(6.626 \times 10^{-34}\ J \cdot s\right)} = 9.18 \times 10^{14}\,s^{-1}$$

27. One of the "lines" in the emission spectrum of mercury is green light with a wavelength of 546 nm. What is the frequency of this line? What is the energy of a photon of this radiation? What is the energy of 1 mol of such photons?

    Frequency:

    $$v = \frac{c}{\lambda} = \frac{2.9979 \times 10^{8}\ m \cdot s^{-1}}{\left(546\ nm \times \dfrac{1\ m}{10^{9}\ nm}\right)} = 5.49 \times 10^{14}\,s^{-1}$$

    Energy of a Photon:

    $$E = hv = \frac{hc}{\lambda} = \frac{\left(6.626 \times 10^{-34}\ J \cdot s\right)\left(2.9979 \times 10^{8}\ m \cdot s^{-1}\right)}{\left(546\ nm \times \dfrac{1\ m}{10^{9}\ nm}\right)} = 3.64 \times 10^{-19}\,J$$

Energy of 1 mole of Photons:

$$E = \left(3.64 \times 10^{-19}\, J\right) \times \left(6.022 \times 10^{23}\ mol^{-1}\right)\left(\frac{1\, kJ}{1000\, J}\right) = \textbf{219}\ \textbf{\textit{kJ} · \textit{mol}}^{-1}$$

28. The emission spectrum of mercury has lines at 436, 546, 577, and 579 nm. Which of these has the highest energy? What is the energy of a mole of photons of this radiation?

The highest energy radiation will have the highest frequency or the lowest wavelength; therefore the highest energy line is the one at 436 nm.

Energy of a Photon:

$$E = h\nu = \frac{hc}{\lambda} = \frac{\left(6.626 \times 10^{-34}\, J \cdot s\right)\left(2.9979 \times 10^{8}\ m \cdot s^{-1}\right)}{\left(436\ nm \times \dfrac{1\, m}{10^{9}\, nm}\right)} = \textbf{4.56} \times \textbf{10}^{-19}\ \textbf{\textit{J}}$$

Energy of 1 mole of Photons:

$$E = \left(4.56 \times 10^{-19}\, J\right) \times \left(6.022 \times 10^{23}\ mol^{-1}\right)\left(\frac{1\, kJ}{1000\, J}\right) = \textbf{274}\ \textbf{\textit{kJ} · \textit{mol}}^{-1}$$

29. One of the lines in the emission spectrum of lithium is at 671 nm. What is the frequency and energy of a photon of this radiation? What is the energy of 1 mole of such photons?

Frequency:

$$\nu = \frac{c}{\lambda} = \frac{2.9979 \times 10^{8}\ m \cdot s^{-1}}{\left(671\ nm \times \dfrac{1\, m}{10^{9}\, nm}\right)} = \textbf{4.47} \times \textbf{10}^{14}\ \textbf{\textit{s}}^{-1}$$

Energy of a Photon:

$$E = h\nu = \frac{hc}{\lambda} = \frac{\left(6.626 \times 10^{-34}\, J \cdot s\right)\left(2.9979 \times 10^{8}\ m \cdot s^{-1}\right)}{\left(671\ nm \times \dfrac{1\, m}{10^{9}\, nm}\right)} = \textbf{2.96} \times \textbf{10}^{-19}\ \textbf{\textit{J}}$$

Energy of 1 mole of Photons:

$$E = \left(2.96 \times 10^{-19}\, J\right) \times \left(6.022 \times 10^{23}\ mol^{-1}\right)\left(\frac{1\, kJ}{1000\, J}\right) = \textbf{178}\ \textbf{\textit{kJ} · \textit{mol}}^{-1}$$

30. If the energy required to eject photoelectrons from copper (the binding energy, ϕ) is 437.1 kJ/mol, what is the threshold frequency of this metal?

$$\phi = h v_t$$

$$\frac{\phi}{h} = \frac{h v_t}{h} \rightarrow v_t = \frac{\phi}{h}$$

$$v_t = \frac{\phi}{h} = \frac{\left(437.1 \frac{kJ}{mol}\right)\left(\frac{1000\ J}{kJ}\right)\left(\frac{1\ mol}{6.022 \times 10^{23}}\right)}{\left(6.626 \times 10^{-34}\ J \cdot s\right)} = \mathbf{1.10 \times 10^{15}\ s^{-1}}$$

31. If the threshold frequency of magnesium is $\mathbf{8.85 \times 10^{14}\ s^{-1}}$, what is its binding energy, ϕ?

$$\phi = h v_t$$

$$\phi = \left(6.626 \times 10^{-34}\ J \cdot s\right)\left(8.85 \times 10^{14}\ s^{-1}\right)\left(\frac{1\ kJ}{1000\ J}\right)\left(6.022 \times 10^{23}\ mol^{-1}\right) = \mathbf{353\ kJ \cdot mol^{-1}}$$

32. If vanadium has a threshold frequency of $\mathbf{1.04 \times 10^{15}\ s^{-1}}$ and is irradiated with light of wavelength $\lambda = \mathbf{334\ nm}$, should we expect to observe photoelectrons ejected from the metal? Why or Why not?

Frequency of light:

$$v = \frac{c}{\lambda} = \frac{2.9979 \times 10^{8}\ m \cdot s^{-1}}{\left(334\ nm \times \frac{1\ m}{10^{9}\ nm}\right)} = 8.98 \times 10^{14}\ s^{-1}$$

Because $8.98 \times 10^{14}\ s^{-1} < 1.04 \times 10^{15}\ s^{-1}$, $(v < v_t)$ we would not expect to see any ejected photoelectrons.

33. Will visible light with a wavelength of 654 nm eject photoelectrons from gold if its binding energy is 527.8 kJ/mol?

Energy of 1 mol of photons of light:

$$E = h v = \frac{hc}{\lambda} = \frac{\left(6.626 \times 10^{-34}\ J \cdot s\right)\left(2.9979 \times 10^{8}\ m \cdot s^{-1}\right)}{\left(654\ nm \times \frac{1\ m}{10^{9}\ nm}\right)} \times \left(\frac{1\ kJ}{1000\ J}\right) \times \left(6.022 \times 10^{23}\ mol^{-1}\right) = \mathbf{183\ kJ \cdot mol^{-1}}$$

Since $183\ kJ \cdot mol^{-1} < 527.8\ kJ \cdot mol^{-1}$, it will not eject photoelectrons from gold.

ATOMIC SPECTRA AND THE BOHR MODEL OF THE HYDROGEN ATOM

34. What are two main postulates of the Bohr theory of the atom?
    a. The first is that electrons "orbit" the nucleus in circular paths with fixed distances from the nucleus. This constraint quantizes the energy of the electron such that it can only exist in these allowed, stationary states.
    b. The second is that the atom will remain in its ground state (the electron remains in its lowest energy state, $n = 1$) unless perturbed by absortion of a photon of EM radiation.

35. What is the equation for the energy of an electron in the nth orbit, or energy state, of a hydrogen atom (according to Bohr)?

$$E_n = -R_H Z^2 \left(\frac{1}{n^2} \right)$$

36. Describe what is meant when the hydrogen atom is said to be in the ground state. How is this different than the hydrogen atom in an excited state?

    The hydrogen atom is in its ground state when its electron resides in the lowest energy orbit. This is the most stable state and as such, the atom remains in this state unless perturbed by absorption of energy. If energy is absorbed the electron can be excited into a higher energy orbit ($n > 1$) referred to as an excited state.

37. What is the rationale for the emission of a photon from the hydrogen atom according to Bohr?

    When an electron in an excited state of the hydrogen atom relaxes to a lower energy state, the excess energy lost due to this transition is released as a photon of light the frequency of which must correspond precisely to the difference in energy between the two energy states involved in the transition.

38. According to Bohr's model of the hydrogen atom, what is the energy of an electron in the 4th orbit or stationary state?

$$E_4 = -R_H Z^2 \left(\frac{1}{4^2} \right) = -\left(2.18 \times 10^{-18}\,J \right)\left(1^2 \right)\left(\frac{1}{16} \right) = -1.36 \times 10^{-19}\,J$$

39. According to Bohr's model of the hydrogen atom, what is the energy of an electron in the 7th orbit or stationary state?

$$E_7 = -R_H Z^2 \left(\frac{1}{7^2} \right) = -\left(2.18 \times 10^{-18}\,J \right)\left(1^2 \right)\left(\frac{1}{49} \right) = -4.45 \times 10^{-20}\,J$$

40. Assuming the Bohr model of the hydrogen atom can be applied to any "hydrogen-like" system (a single electron atom), what is the energy of an electron in the ground state of a He^+ cation?

    For He, $Z = 2$:

$$E_1^{Z=2} = -R_H Z^2 \left(\frac{1}{1^2} \right) = -\left(2.18 \times 10^{-18}\,J \right)\left(2^2 \right)\left(\frac{1}{1} \right) = -8.72 \times 10^{-18}\,J.$$

41. Assuming the Bohr model of the hydrogen atom can be applied to any "hydrogen-like" system (a single electron atom), what is the energy of an electron in the ground state of a Li^{2+} cation?

    For Li, $Z = 3$:

    $$E_1^{Z=3} = -R_H Z^2 \left(\frac{1}{1^2}\right) = -\left(2.18 \times 10^{-18}\,J\right)\left(3^2\right)\left(\frac{1}{1}\right) = -1.96 \times 10^{-17}\,J.$$

42. Which of the following transitions results in emission of a photon of highest energy?
    a. $n = 4 \rightarrow n = 3$
    b. $n = 5 \rightarrow n = 4$
    c. $n = 2 \rightarrow n = 1$

43. Which of the following transitions results in emission of a photon of lowest energy?
    a. $n = 4 \rightarrow n = 3$
    b. $n = 5 \rightarrow n = 4$
    c. $n = 7 \rightarrow n = 6$

44. The following transitions are associated with the "Paschen Series" of lines in the emission spectrum of hydrogen. Calculate the wavelength and frequency of photons emitted due to these transitions:
    a. $n = 7 \rightarrow n = 3$
    b. $n = 6 \rightarrow n = 3$
    c. $n = 5 \rightarrow n = 3$
    d. $n = 4 \rightarrow n = 3$

    a. $n = 7 \rightarrow n = 3$:

    $$E_{photon} = \left|\Delta E_{atom}\right|$$

    $$\frac{hc}{\lambda} = \left|-R_H \left(\frac{1}{3^2} - \frac{1}{7^2}\right)\right|$$

    $$\frac{hc}{\lambda} = \left|-1.977 \times 10^{-19}\,J\right|$$

    $$\lambda = \frac{hc}{1.977 \times 10^{-19}\,J} = \frac{\left(6.626 \times 10^{-34}\,J \cdot s\right)\left(2.9979 \times 10^8\,m \cdot s^{-1}\right)}{1.977 \times 10^{-19}\,J} = 1.00 \times 10^{-6}\,m$$

    $$v = \frac{c}{\lambda} = \frac{2.9979 \times 10^8\,m \cdot s^{-1}}{\left(1.00 \times 10^{-6}\,m\right)} = 3.00 \times 10^{14}\,s^{-1}$$

b. $n = 6 \rightarrow n = 3$:

$E_{photon} = \left| \Delta E_{atom} \right|$

$\dfrac{hc}{\lambda} = \left| -R_H \left(\dfrac{1}{3^2} - \dfrac{1}{6^2} \right) \right|$

$\dfrac{hc}{\lambda} = \left| -1.817 \times 10^{-19} \, J \right|$

$\lambda = \dfrac{hc}{1.817 \times 10^{-19} \, J} = \dfrac{\left(6.626 \times 10^{-34} \, J \cdot s \right)\left(2.9979 \times 10^8 \, m \cdot s^{-1} \right)}{1.817 \times 10^{-19} \, J} = \mathbf{1.09 \times 10^{-6} \, m}$

$v = \dfrac{c}{\lambda} = \dfrac{2.9979 \times 10^8 \, m \cdot s^{-1}}{\left(1.09 \times 10^{-6} \, m \right)} = \mathbf{2.75 \times 10^{14} \, s^{-1}}$

c. $n = 5 \rightarrow n = 3$:

$E_{photon} = \left| \Delta E_{atom} \right|$

$\dfrac{hc}{\lambda} = \left| -R_H \left(\dfrac{1}{3^2} - \dfrac{1}{5^2} \right) \right|$

$\dfrac{hc}{\lambda} = \left| -1.550 \times 10^{-19} \, J \right|$

$\lambda = \dfrac{hc}{1.550 \times 10^{-19} \, J} = \dfrac{\left(6.626 \times 10^{-34} \, J \cdot s \right)\left(2.9979 \times 10^8 \, m \cdot s^{-1} \right)}{1.550 \times 10^{-19} \, J} = \mathbf{1.28 \times 10^{-6} \, m}$

$v = \dfrac{c}{\lambda} = \dfrac{2.9979 \times 10^8 \, m \cdot s^{-1}}{\left(1.28 \times 10^{-6} \, m \right)} = \mathbf{2.34 \times 10^{14} \, s^{-1}}$

d. $n = 4 \rightarrow n = 3$:

$E_{photon} = \left| \Delta E_{atom} \right|$

$\dfrac{hc}{\lambda} = \left| -R_H \left(\dfrac{1}{3^2} - \dfrac{1}{4^2} \right) \right|$

$\dfrac{hc}{\lambda} = \left| -1.060 \times 10^{-19} \, J \right|$

$$\lambda = \frac{hc}{1.060 \times 10^{-19}\,J} = \frac{\left(6.626 \times 10^{-34}\,J \cdot s\right)\left(2.9979 \times 10^{8}\,m \cdot s^{-1}\right)}{1.060 \times 10^{-19}\,J} = \mathbf{1.87 \times 10^{-6}\,m}$$

$$v = \frac{c}{\lambda} = \frac{2.9979 \times 10^{8}\,m \cdot s^{-1}}{\left(1.87 \times 10^{-6}\,m\right)} = \mathbf{1.60 \times 10^{14}\,s^{-1}}$$

45. The following transitions are associated with the "Lyman Series" of lines in the emission spectrum of hydrogen. Calculate the wavelength and frequency of photons emitted due to these transitions:

   a. $n = 5 \rightarrow n = 1$

   b. $n = 4 \rightarrow n = 1$

   c. $n = 3 \rightarrow n = 1$

   d. $n = 2 \rightarrow n = 1$

   a. $n = 5 \rightarrow n = 1$:

$$E_{photon} = \left| \Delta E_{atom} \right|$$

$$\frac{hc}{\lambda} = \left| -R_H \left(\frac{1}{1^2} - \frac{1}{5^2} \right) \right|$$

$$\frac{hc}{\lambda} = \left| -2.093 \times 10^{-18}\,J \right|$$

$$\lambda = \frac{hc}{2.093 \times 10^{-18}\,J} = \frac{\left(6.626 \times 10^{-34}\,J \cdot s\right)\left(2.9979 \times 10^{8}\,m \cdot s^{-1}\right)}{2.093 \times 10^{-18}\,J} = \mathbf{9.49 \times 10^{-8}\,m}$$

$$v = \frac{c}{\lambda} = \frac{2.9979 \times 10^{8}\,m \cdot s^{-1}}{\left(9.49 \times 10^{-8}\,m\right)} = \mathbf{3.16 \times 10^{15}\,s^{-1}}$$

   b. $n = 4 \rightarrow n = 1$:

$$E_{photon} = \left| \Delta E_{atom} \right|$$

$$\frac{hc}{\lambda} = \left| -R_H \left(\frac{1}{1^2} - \frac{1}{4^2} \right) \right|$$

$$\frac{hc}{\lambda} = \left| -2.044 \times 10^{-18}\,J \right|$$

$$\lambda = \frac{hc}{2.044 \times 10^{-18} \, J} = \frac{\left(6.626 \times 10^{-34} \, J \cdot s\right)\left(2.9979 \times 10^{8} \, m \cdot s^{-1}\right)}{2.044 \times 10^{-18} \, J} = \mathbf{9.72 \times 10^{-8} \, m}$$

$$v = \frac{c}{\lambda} = \frac{2.9979 \times 10^{8} \, m \cdot s^{-1}}{\left(9.72 \times 10^{-8} \, m\right)} = \mathbf{3.08 \times 10^{15} \, s^{-1}}$$

c. $n = 3 \rightarrow n = 1$:

$$E_{photon} = \left| \Delta E_{atom} \right|$$

$$\frac{hc}{\lambda} = \left| -R_{H} \left(\frac{1}{1^{2}} - \frac{1}{3^{2}} \right) \right|$$

$$\frac{hc}{\lambda} = \left| -1.938 \times 10^{-18} \, J \right|$$

$$\lambda = \frac{hc}{1.938 \times 10^{-18} \, J} = \frac{\left(6.626 \times 10^{-34} \, J \cdot s\right)\left(2.9979 \times 10^{8} \, m \cdot s^{-1}\right)}{1.938 \times 10^{-18} \, J} = \mathbf{1.03 \times 10^{-7} \, m}$$

$$v = \frac{c}{\lambda} = \frac{2.9979 \times 10^{8} \, m \cdot s^{-1}}{\left(1.03 \times 10^{-7} \, m\right)} = \mathbf{2.91 \times 10^{15} \, s^{-1}}$$

d. $n = 2 \rightarrow n = 1$:

$$E_{photon} = \left| \Delta E_{atom} \right|$$

$$\frac{hc}{\lambda} = \left| -R_{H} \left(\frac{1}{1^{2}} - \frac{1}{2^{2}} \right) \right|$$

$$\frac{hc}{\lambda} = \left| -1.635 \times 10^{-18} \, J \right|$$

$$\lambda = \frac{hc}{1.635 \times 10^{-18} \, J} = \frac{\left(6.626 \times 10^{-34} \, J \cdot s\right)\left(2.9979 \times 10^{8} \, m \cdot s^{-1}\right)}{1.635 \times 10^{-18} \, J} = \mathbf{1.21 \times 10^{-7} \, m}$$

$$v = \frac{c}{\lambda} = \frac{2.9979 \times 10^{8} \, m \cdot s^{-1}}{\left(1.21 \times 10^{-7} \, m\right)} = \mathbf{2.48 \times 10^{15} \, s^{-1}}$$

46. A photon with a wavelength of 12.36 μm is emitted from a hydrogen atom in an excited state. Determine the value of n_i and n_f for this transition.

Energy of the photon:

$$E_{photon} = h\nu = \frac{hc}{\lambda} = \frac{\left(6.626 \times 10^{-34}\ J \cdot s\right)\left(2.9979 \times 10^{8}\ m \cdot s^{-1}\right)}{\left(12.36\ \mu m \times \dfrac{1\ m}{10^{6}\ nm}\right)} = \mathbf{1.61 \times 10^{-20}\ J}$$

$$E_{photon} = \left|\Delta E_{atom}\right|$$

$$E_{photon} = \left|-R_H\left(\frac{1}{n_f^2} - \frac{1}{n_i^2}\right)\right| = R_H\left(\frac{1}{n_f^2} - \frac{1}{n_i^2}\right)$$

$$1.61 \times 10^{-20}\ J = R_H\left(\frac{1}{n_f^2} - \frac{1}{n_i^2}\right)$$

$$\frac{1.61 \times 10^{-20}\ J}{2.18 \times 10^{-18}\ J} = 0.07370 = \left(\frac{1}{n_f^2} - \frac{1}{n_i^2}\right)$$

You can numerically solve this using a spreadsheet:

$$\left(\frac{1}{n_f^2} - \frac{1}{n_i^2}\right) = \left(\frac{1}{6^2} - \frac{1}{7^2}\right) = \frac{13}{1764} = 0.0737$$

$$\mathbf{n_f = 6} \qquad \mathbf{n_i = 7}$$

47. A photon with a wavelength of 2624 nm is emitted from a hydrogen atom in an excited state. Determine the value of n_i and n_f for this transition.

Energy of the photon:

$$E_{photon} = h\nu = \frac{hc}{\lambda} = \frac{\left(6.626 \times 10^{-34}\ J \cdot s\right)\left(2.9979 \times 10^{8}\ m \cdot s^{-1}\right)}{\left(2624\ nm \times \dfrac{1\ m}{10^{9}\ nm}\right)} = \mathbf{7.57 \times 10^{-20}\ J}$$

$$E_{photon} = \left|\Delta E_{atom}\right|$$

$$E_{photon} = \left| -R_H \left(\frac{1}{n_f^2} - \frac{1}{n_i^2} \right) \right| = R_H \left(\frac{1}{n_f^2} - \frac{1}{n_i^2} \right)$$

$$7.57 \times 10^{-20} \ J = R_H \left(\frac{1}{n_f^2} - \frac{1}{n_i^2} \right)$$

$$\frac{7.57 \times 10^{-20} \ J}{2.18 \times 10^{-18} \ J} = 0.03472 = \left(\frac{1}{n_f^2} - \frac{1}{n_i^2} \right)$$

You can numerically solve this using a spreadsheet:

$$\left(\frac{1}{n_f^2} - \frac{1}{n_i^2} \right) = \left(\frac{1}{4^2} - \frac{1}{6^2} \right) = \frac{20}{576} = 0.03472$$

$$\mathbf{\textit{n}_f = 4} \qquad \mathbf{\textit{n}_i = 6}$$

48. One of the lines of the emission spectrum of hydrogen is at 410.2 nm. What states are involved in the transition which results in this emission (what are the values of n_i and n_f)?

Energy of the photon:

$$E_{photon} = h\nu = \frac{hc}{\lambda} = \frac{\left(6.626 \times 10^{-34} \ J \cdot s \right) \left(2.9979 \times 10^8 \ m \cdot s^{-1} \right)}{\left(410.2 \ nm \times \frac{1 \ m}{10^9 \ nm} \right)} = \mathbf{4.84 \times 10^{-19} \ J}$$

$$E_{photon} = \left| \Delta E_{atom} \right|$$

$$E_{photon} = \left| -R_H \left(\frac{1}{n_f^2} - \frac{1}{n_i^2} \right) \right| = R_H \left(\frac{1}{n_f^2} - \frac{1}{n_i^2} \right)$$

$$4.84 \times 10^{-19} \ J = R_H \left(\frac{1}{n_f^2} - \frac{1}{n_i^2} \right)$$

$$\frac{4.84 \times 10^{-19} \ J}{2.18 \times 10^{-18} \ J} = 0.22222 = \left(\frac{1}{n_f^2} - \frac{1}{n_i^2} \right)$$

You can numerically solve this using a spreadsheet:

$$\left(\frac{1}{n_f^2} - \frac{1}{n_i^2}\right) = \left(\frac{1}{2^2} - \frac{1}{6^2}\right) = \frac{32}{144} = 0.22222$$

$$n_f = 2 \qquad n_i = 6$$

49. One of the lines of the emission spectrum of hydrogen is at 486 nm and is due to the transition $n = 4 \rightarrow n = 2$. What is the wavelength of a photon emitted from a He^+ cation due to this same transition? Explain why these are different.

$$E_{photon} = \left|\Delta E_{atom}\right|$$

$$\frac{hc}{\lambda} = \left|-R_H Z^2 \left(\frac{1}{n_f^2} - \frac{1}{n_i^2}\right)\right|$$

$$\lambda = \frac{hc}{\left|-R_H Z^2 \left(\frac{1}{n_f^2} - \frac{1}{n_i^2}\right)\right|} = \frac{\left(6.626 \times 10^{-34}\, J \cdot s\right)\left(2.9979 \times 10^8\, m \cdot s^{-1}\right)}{\left(2.18 \times 10^{-18}\, J\right)\left(2^2\right)\left(\frac{1}{2^2} - \frac{1}{4^2}\right)} = 1.21 \times 10^{-7}\, m = 121\ nm$$

The nuclear charge (Z) for the He^+ cation is 2, as opposed to 1 for H, which results in lower energies for the electron in its allowed orbits.

50. One of the lines of the emission spectrum of hydrogen is at 434 nm and is due to the transition $n = 5 \rightarrow n = 2$. What is the wavelength of a photon emitted from a Li^{2+} cation due to this same transition? Explain why these are different.

$$E_{photon} = \left|\Delta E_{atom}\right|$$

$$\frac{hc}{\lambda} = \left|-R_H Z^2 \left(\frac{1}{n_f^2} - \frac{1}{n_i^2}\right)\right|$$

$$\lambda = \frac{hc}{\left|-R_H Z^2 \left(\frac{1}{n_f^2} - \frac{1}{n_i^2}\right)\right|} = \frac{\left(6.626 \times 10^{-34}\, J \cdot s\right)\left(2.9979 \times 10^8\, m \cdot s^{-1}\right)}{\left(2.18 \times 10^{-18}\, J\right)\left(3^2\right)\left(\frac{1}{2^2} - \frac{1}{5^2}\right)} = 4.82 \times 10^{-8}\, m = 48.2\ nm$$

The nuclear charge (Z) for the Li^{2+} cation is 3, as opposed to 1 for H, which results in lower energies for the electron in its allowed orbits.

DE BROGLIE AND THE WAVE PROPERTY OF THE ELECTRON

51. What determines the de Broglie wavelength of a given particle?

    The de Broglie wavelength of a particle is given by:

    $$\lambda = \frac{h}{mv},$$

    Where m is the mass of the particle in kg and v is its velocity. As such, the velocity of a particle determines its wavelength.

52. What is the equation for the de Broglie wavelength?

    $$\lambda = \frac{h}{mv}$$

53. If an electron has a wavelength of 6.13 nm, what is its velocity? (Recall the mass of an electron is $m_e = 9.11 \times 10^{-28}\,g$)

    $$\lambda = \frac{h}{mv} = \frac{6.626 \times 10^{-34}\,J \cdot s}{\left(9.11 \times 10^{-28}\,g \times \frac{1\,kg}{1000\,g}\right)(v)}$$

    $$6.13\,nm \times \frac{1\,m}{10^9\,nm} = \frac{6.626 \times 10^{-34}\,J \cdot s}{\left(9.11 \times 10^{-28}\,g \times \frac{1\,kg}{1000\,g}\right)(v)}$$

    $$v = \frac{6.626 \times 10^{-34}\,J \cdot s}{\left(9.11 \times 10^{-28}\,g \times \frac{1\,kg}{1000\,g}\right)\left(6.13 \times 10^{-9}\,m\right)} = \mathbf{1.19 \times 10^5\,m \cdot s^{-1}}$$

54. If an electron has a wavelength of 5.87 nm, what is its velocity?

    $$v = \frac{6.626 \times 10^{-34}\,J \cdot s}{\left(9.11 \times 10^{-28}\,g \times \frac{1\,kg}{1000\,g}\right)\left(5.87 \times 10^{-9}\,m\right)} = \mathbf{1.24 \times 10^5\,m \cdot s^{-1}}$$

55. What is the de Broglie wavelength of an electron travelling at a velocity of $\mathbf{2.13 \times 10^5}$ *m/s.*

    $$\lambda = \frac{h}{mv} = \frac{6.626 \times 10^{-34}\,J \cdot s}{\left(9.11 \times 10^{-28}\,g \times \frac{1\,kg}{1000\,g}\right)\left(2.13 \times 10^5\,m \cdot s^{-1}\right)} = \mathbf{3.41 \times 10^{-9}\,m}$$

56. If a bullet leaves the barrel of a gun at a velocity of 690 m/s, what is the wavelength of the bullet if it weighs 30.0 g?

$$\lambda = \frac{h}{mv} = \frac{6.626 \times 10^{-34}\, J \cdot s}{\left(30.0\, g \times \frac{1\, kg}{1000\, g} \right)\left(690\, m \cdot s^{-1} \right)} = \mathbf{3.20 \times 10^{-35}\, m}$$

HEISENBERG'S UNCERTAINTY PRINCIPLE AND SCHRÖDINGER'S EQUATION

57. What was meant by Max Born when he postulated that the electron wave-function is a probability wave?

Max Born was stating that the amplitude of the electron-wave at any point was not "how much" of the electron is located there, but rather the probability of finding the electron at that point.

58. What is the physical meaning of the square of the wave-function, ψ^2?

ψ^2 is the probability density of the electron, which is the probability per unit volume.

59. What is an orbital?

The orbital is simply the region of space around the nucleus of an atom where it is most likely the electron will be found.

60. What are the three quantum numbers which describe an orbital?

The three quantum numbers are:

n, the Principal Quantum Number,

l, the Angular Momentum Quantum Number (also referred to as the Azimuthal Qunatum Number), and

m_l, the Magnetic Quantum Number.

61. What properties do each quantum number define or specify?

n, the Principal Quantum Number specifies the relative size and energy of an orbital.

l, the Angular Momentum Quantum Number specifies the shape of the orbital.

m_l, the Magnetic Quantum Number specifies the spatial orientation of the orbital.

62. Explain the rules for allowed combinations of quantum numbers in a given wave-function.

The principal quantum number can have any nonzero, positive integer value:

$$n = 1, 2, 3, 4, 5 \ldots \ldots$$

For each value of n, there is a number of allowed values of the angular momentum quantum number. l can have any integer value from zero to $n-1$:

$$l = 0, 1, 2, \ldots, (n-1).$$

For a given value of l, the magnetic quantum number can have any integer value from $-l$ to $+l$:

$$m_l = -l, \ldots, 0, \ldots, +l.$$

63. If $n = 3$, what are the allowed values of l?

    $l = 0, 1, 2$

64. If $n = 5$, what are the allowed values of l?

    $l = 0, 1, 2, 3, 4$

65. If $l = 2$, what are the possible values of m_l?

    $m_l = -2, -1, 0, 1, 2$

66. If $l = 3$, what are the possible values of m_l?

    $m_l = -3, -2, -1, 0, 1, 2, 3$

67. For a 2p orbital, what are the possible combinations of n, l, and m_l?

    $n = 2$

    $l = 1$

    $m_l = -1, 0, 1$

68. For a 3d orbital, what are the possible combinations of n, l, and m_l?

    $n = 3$

    $l = 2$

    $m_l = -2, -1, 0, 1, 2$

69. For a 5f orbital, what are the possible combinations of n, l, and m_l?

    $n = 5$

    $l = 3$

    $m_l = -3, -2, -1, 0, 1, 2, 3$

70. For a 1s orbital, what are the possible combinations of n, l, and m_l?

    $n = 1$

    $l = 0$

    $m_l = 0$

71. What values of l are associated with the labels s, p, d, and f.

$l = 0 \rightarrow s$

$l = 1 \rightarrow p$

$l = 2 \rightarrow d$

$l = 3 \rightarrow f$

72. Determine whether each of the following combinations of quantum numbers are allowed or erroneous. If allowed, identify which orbital is defined by each set. If erroneous, explain why each set is not allowed.

a. $n = 3$, $l = 2$, $m_l = +3$

Erroneous, +3 is not an allowed value of m_l when $l = 2$.

b. $n = 4$, $l = 3$, $m_l = -3$

Allowed, this combination describes an electron in a $4f$ orbital.

c. $n = 2$, $l = 1$, $m_l = +1$

Allowed, this combination describes an electron in a $2p$ orbital.

d. $n = 3$, $l = 0$, $m_l = -1$

Erroneous, -1 is not an allowed value of m_l when $l = 0$.

73. Determine whether each of the following combinations of quantum numbers are allowed or erroneous. If allowed, identify which orbital is defined by each set. If erroneous, explain why each set is not allowed.

a. $n = 5$, $l = 0$, $m_l = 0$

Allowed, this combination describes an electron in a $5s$ orbital.

b. $n = 4$, $l = 1$, $m_l = 0$

Allowed, this combination describes an electron in a $4p$ orbital.

c. $n = 1$, $l = 1$, $m_l = 0$

Erroneous, 1 is not an allowed value of l when $n = 1$.

d. $n = 3$, $l = 2$, $m_l = -1$

Allowed, this combination describes an electron in a $3d$ orbital.

74. List all possible sets of quantum numbers which describe a $5f$ orbital.

$n = 5$, $l = 3$, $m_l = 3$

$n = 5$, $l = 3$, $m_l = 2$

$n = 5$, $l = 3$, $m_l = 1$

$n = 5$, $l = 3$, $m_l = 0$

$n = 5, l = 3, m_l = -1$

$n = 5, l = 3, m_l = -2$

$n = 5, l = 3, m_l = -3$

75. List all possible sets of quantum numbers which describe a 4d orbital.

$n = 4, l = 2, m_l = 2$

$n = 4, l = 2, m_l = 1$

$n = 4, l = 2, m_l = 0$

$n = 4, l = 2, m_l = -1$

$n = 4, l = 2, m_l = -2$

76. Which of the following orbitals do not exist? Explain.
    a. 1s
    b. 2d
    c. 3f
    d. 4f

    The quantum rules do not allow for 2d or 3f orbitals.

77. Which of the following orbitals do not exist? Explain.
    a. 1p
    b. 2d
    c. 3d
    d. 2f

    The quantum rules do not allow for 1p, 2d or 2f orbitals.

78. How many orbitals are in the 4th shell?

    $n^2 = 4^2 = 16$

79. How many orbitals are the 2nd shell?

    $n^2 = 2^2 = 4$

ELECTRON SPIN AND GROUND STATE ELECTRON CONFIGURATIONS

80. What is the Pauli exclusion principle?

    No two electrons in an atom can have the same set of four quantum numbers.

81. What is Hund's rule?

    When filling degenerate orbitals, the orbitals are filled singly first with parallel spins.

82. What is meant by the term valence shell? Valence electrons?

   The valence shell is the shell which is occupied by one or more electrons and has the highest value of n. It is the highest energy, outer most occupied shell in an atom. Valence electrons are those electrons which occupy orbitals with the highest value of n for an atom in the ground state.

83. What is meant by the term core electrons?

   Core electrons are those which occupy the inner shells of an atom. In other words, they are not in the valence shell.

84. Explain the concept of shielding and effective nuclear charge.

   Shielding is the effect whereby electrons in the outer shells of an atom are shielded or screened from the full effect of the coulombic attraction to the nucleus. They blunt or diminish the positive nuclear charge "felt" by the outer shell electrons. This diminished or apparent nuclear charge which is experienced by the outer electrons is referred to as the effective nuclear charge.

85. What is the effective nuclear charge "felt" by the valence electrons of a **Mg** atom?

$$Z^{*} = Z - S = 12 - 10 = +\mathbf{2}$$

   The atomic number of Mg is $Z = 12$. The screening constant is $S = 10$. The screening constant in this approximation is simply all electrons which occupy a lower shell. In this case, that is all 10 core electrons.

86. What is the effective nuclear charge "felt" by the valence electrons of a N atom?

$$Z^{*} = Z - S = 7 - 2 = +\mathbf{5}$$

87. What is the s-block on the periodic table? Why is it called the s-block?

   The s-block consists of the groups 1A and 2A elements. The valence electron configuration of group 1A elements is ns^1 and for group 2A it is ns^2. For this reason, it is referred to as the s-block.

88. What is the d-block on the periodic table? Why is it called the d-block?

   The d-block consists of groups 3B, 4B, 5B, 6B, 7B, 8B, 1B, and 2B. These are also referred to as the transition elements.

89. What is the electron configuration of S? Draw the orbital diagram of the valence shell of S.

   $1s^2 2s^2 2p^6 3s^2 3p^4 = [Ne]3s^2 3p^4$

$\uparrow\downarrow$		$\uparrow\downarrow$	$\uparrow$	$\uparrow$
$3s$			$3p$	

90. What is the electron configuration of Br? Draw the orbital diagram of the valence shell of *Br*.

$$1s^2 2s^2 2p^6 3s^2 3p^6 4s^2 3d^{10} 4p^5 = [Ar]4s^2 3d^{10} 4p^5$$

4s   4p

91. What is the electron configuration of Sr? Draw the orbital diagram of the valence shell of *Sr*.

$$1s^2 2s^2 2p^6 3s^2 3p^6 4s^2 3d^{10} 4p^6 5s^2 = [Kr]5s^2$$

5s

92. What is the electron configuration of Li? Draw the orbital diagram of the valence shell of *Li*.

$$1s^2 2s^1$$

2s

93. What is the electron configuration of C? Draw the orbital diagram of the valence shell of *C*.

$$1s^2 2s^2 2p^2$$

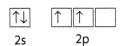

2s   2p

94. What is the electron configuration of F? Draw the orbital diagram of the valence shell of *F*.

$$1s^2 2s^2 2p^5$$

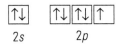

2s   2p

95. Using the condensed notation, write the electron configuration of the following elements:

a. Fe

$$[Ar]4s^2 3d^6$$

b. Sr

$$[Kr]5s^2$$

c. Pb

$$[Xe]6s^2 4f^{14} 5d^{10} 6p^2$$

d. Ti

$$[Ar]4s^2 3d^2$$

96. Using the condensed notation, write the electron configuration of the following elements:

a. Co

$$[Ar]4s^2 3d^7$$

b. Mn

$$[Ar]4s^2 3d^5$$

c. Se

$$[Ar]4s^2 3d^{10} 4p^4$$

d. I

$$[Kr]5s^2 4d^{10} 5p^5$$

IONIC ELECTRON CONFIGURATIONS

97. Write the electron configuration for each ion and indicate whether the ion is paramagnetic or diamagnetic.

a. Cu^{2+}

$$[Ar]3d^9$$

paramagnetic

b. Ag^+

$[Kr]4d^{10}$

diamagnetic

c. Br^-

$[Ar]4s^2 3d^{10} 4p^6$

diamagnetic

d. Se^{2-}

$[Ar]4s^2 3d^{10} 4p^6$

diamagnetic

98. Write the electron configuration for each ion and indicate whether the ion is paramagnetic or diamagnetic.

a. P^{3-}

$[Ne]3s^2 3p^6$

diamagnetic

b. Fe^{2+}

$[Ar]3d^6$

paramagnetic

c. Cd^{2+}

$[Kr]4d^{10}$

diamagnetic

d. Rb^+

$[Ar]4s^2 3d^{10} 4p^6$

diamagnetic

99. Write the electron configuration for each ion and indicate whether the ion is paramagnetic or diamagnetic.

a. V^{5+}

$[Ne]3s^2 3p^6$

diamagnetic

b. O^{2-}

$1s^2 2s^2 2p^6$

diamagnetic

c. K^+

$[Ne]3s^2 3p^6$

diamagnetic

d. Fe^{3+}

$[Ar]3d^5$

paramagnetic

100. Write the electron configuration for each ion and indicate whether the ion is paramagnetic or diamagnetic.

a. Al^{3+}

$1s^2 2s^2 2p^6$

diamagnetic

b. Ge^{2+}

$[Ar]4s^2 3d^{10}$

diamagnetic

c. Ti^{4+}

$[Ne]3s^2 3p^6$

diamagnetic

d. F^-

$1s^2 2s^2 2p^6$

diamagnetic

PERIODIC TRENDS

101. Arrange the following elements according to increasing size: Li, Ca, Sr, Ba.

Li, Ca, Sr, Ba Atomic radius increases down a column on the periodic table.

102. Arrange the following elements according to increasing size: Te, F, Br, I.

F, Br, Te, I Atomic radius increases down a column and decreases from left to right on the periodic table.

103. Arrange the following elements according to increasing size: Li, Fr, Cs, K.

Li, K, Cs, Fr Atomic radius increases down a column on the periodic table.

104. Arrange the following elements according to increasing size: C, Al, K, Na.

C, Al, Na, K Atomic radius increases down a column and decreases from left to right on the periodic table.

105. Indicate which element or ion in each of the following pairs has the larger radius:
   a. F and F^-
   b. Mg and Mg^{2+} Atomic radius increases down a column and decreases from left to right on the
   c. Al and Al^{3+} periodic table. Additionally, cations are always smaller than the parent element
   d. Al and O and anions are always larger than the parent element.

106. Indicate which element or ion in each of the following pairs has the larger radius:
   a. O and O^{2-} Cations are always smaller than the parent element and anions are always
   b. Ne and Mg^{2+} larger than the parent element. Additionally, for isoelectronic species, the more
   c. Ar and S^{2-} negatively charged species have larger radii and the more positively charged
   d. S and S^{2-} have smaller radii.

107. Arrange the following elements according to increasing first ionization energy: Li, Ca, Sr, Ba.

The first ionization energy decreases down a column and increases from left to
Ba, Sr, Ca, Li right on the periodic table.

108. Arrange the following elements according to increasing first ionization energy: F, Br, Te, I .

The first ionization energy decreases down a column and increases from left to
I, Te, Br, F right on the periodic table.

109. Arrange the following elements according to increasing first ionization energy: Li, Fr, Cs, K.

The first ionization energy decreases down a column and increases from left to
Fr, Cs, K, Li right on the periodic table.

110. Arrange the following elements according to increasing first ionization energy: C, Al, K, Na.

The first ionization energy decreases down a column and increases from left to
K, Na, Al, C right on the periodic table.

111. Identify the 3rd row element with the following successive ionization energies:

$IE_1 = 578 \ kJ/mol$

$IE_2 = 1820 \ kJ/mol$

$IE_3 = 2750 \ kJ/mol$

$IE_4 = 11,600 \ kJ/mol$

Since the fourth ionization energy is so much larger than the previous ionization energies, we know that this element has three valence electrons: aluminum

112. Identify the 3rd row element with the following successive ionization energies:

$IE_1 = 786 \ kJ/mol$

$IE_2 = 1580 \ kJ/mol$

$IE_3 = 3230 \ kJ/mol$

$IE_4 = 4360 \ kJ/mol$

$IE_5 = 16{,}100 \ kJ/mol$

Since the fifth ionization energy is so much larger than the previous ionization energies, we know that this element has 4 valence electrons: silicon

KEY TERMS

Actinides   The elements with atomic numbers 89 through 103 (actinium through lawrencium). These are located in a part of the periodic referred to as the "f-block".

Amplitude   The "height" of a wave at a given point. In other words, if we describe a wave as a mathematical function, the amplitude is the "value" of that function at any point along the x-coordinate.

Angular momentum quantum number (l)   One of three quantum numbers which are solutions to Schrödinger's equation. The angular momentum quantum number defines the shape of an atomic orbital.

Atomic emission spectra   When atoms in the gaseous state are excited or energized by an electric potential, light is emitted. Atomic emission spectra are not continuous, but rather, exhibit only a few specific frequencies. The frequencies observed are very different for different elements. These are referred to as *atomic line emission spectra* and are like fingerprints for specific elements.

Atomic radius   The size of a given atom type, expressed as the radius of a sphere.

Aufbau principle   The principle that for a given number of electrons, these will occupy atomic orbitals resulting in the lowest total energy for the system. In other words, the electrons will sequentially "occupy" the lowest energy atomic orbitals available.

Balmer series   A series of electronic transitionis in the hydrogen atom for which $n_f = 2$.

Binding energy   In the context of the photoelectric effect, the binding energy refers to the energy required to free a photoelectron from a metal sample.

The Bohr model   In 1913 and in response to the experimental observations surrounding atomic line spectra, a Danish physicist named Niels Bohr proposed a quantum model for the hydrogen atom. He postulated that the electron in the hydrogen atom could only move in certain "allowed" *orbits* at fixed distances from the nucleus. This constraint effectively "quantizes" the energy of the electron. In other words, Bohr postulated that electrons could only have certain, specific, or "allowed", angular momenta and therefore only allowed energies at certain increments. This has since been referred to as the *Bohr Model of the Hydrogen Atom.*

Bond length   The distance between nuclei in two atoms mutually engaged in a covalent bond.

Condensed electron configuration   The electron configuration wherein the core electron configuration is represented by the symbol of the appropriate nobel gas in brackets.

Core electrons   Electrons which occupy the orbitals located in the "inner" principle quantum levels (excluding the valence shell).

Coulomb's law   A mathematical expression which relates the potential energy of interaction between two charged particles to the product of their charges and the distance between the particles.

d-Block   A region of the periodic table characterized by elements which have a partially filled valence d-subshell. This includes groups 1B through 8B (or 3 through12).

de Broglie wavelength   The wavelength of a particle calculated from its mass and velocity according to the equation derived by Louis de Broglie.

Degenerate   A term which refers to atomic orbitals of the same energy. In other words, orbitals which have the same energy are said to be degenerate orbitals.

Diamagnetic   A term which refers to materials which are slightly repelled by a magnetic field. This property arises from electron configurations wherein all electrons are spin-paired.

Effective nuclear charge   The net positive charge experienced by an outer electron in a multielectron atom. The actual nuclear charge is diminished by the presence of additional, core electrons which serve to shield valence electrons from the full effect of the nuclear charge.

Electromagnetic radiation   James Clerk Maxwell showed that light could be understood as oscillating electric and magnetic fields. Therefore, we refer to all forms (frequencies) of "light" as *electromagnetic (EM) radiation*.

Electron affinity   The energy released when an atom in the gaseous state gains an electron.

Electron configuration   A notation which details the orbitals which electrons occupy in an atom. Here the numeric coefficients "1" and "2" give the principal quantum number of each orbital, "s" and "p" indicate the value of *l*, and the number of electrons in each subshell is given by a superscript.

Electron density   The square of the wave function, ψ^2, is the probability density of an electron for a given region of space, also referred to the *electron density*.

Electron spin quantum number (m_s)   The fourth quantum number which describes the spin angular momentum of the electron (not to be confused with the orbital angular momentum).

Excited state   A state wherein the electron configuration is not the ground state.

f-Block   A region of the periodic table which includes the actinides and lanthanides and is characterized by elements with valence configurations with incomplete or partially filled f-subshells.

First ionization energy   The energy required to remove an electron from a neutral atom of a given element in the gaseous state.

Frequency   Referring to waves, *frequency* is defined as the number of cycles (wavelengths) which pass an arbitrary point in space in 1 second.

Ground state The state wherein the electron configuration of an atom is in its lowest total energy configuration.

Hamiltonian A mathematical operator which represents the total energy of an electron-wave.

Heisenberg's uncertainty principle The quantum mechanical principle proffered by Werner Heisenberg which states that it is not possible to know with great certainty both the simultaneous position and momentum of a quantum particle.

Hertz A unit of frequency defined as cycles per second.

Hund's rule This rule states that electrons occupying degenerate orbitals must do so such that their total spin is maximized. In other words, when filling orbitals which have the same energy, we fill the orbitals singly first with parallel spins.

Interference When two waves come together and interact, they engage in what is referred to as *interference*.

Ionic radius The size of an ion, expressed in terms of the radius of a sphere.

Ionization energy The energy required to remove an electron from an atom of that element in the gaseous state.

Irregular electron configurations These configurations do not completely correspond with the expected order of filling according to the aufbau principle.

Joule A unit of energy defined as 1 newton-meter.

Lanthanides The elements with atomic numbers 57 through 71 (lanthanum through lutetium). These are located in a part of the periodic referred to as the "*f*-block".

Magnetic quantum number (m_l) One of three quantum numbers which are solutions to Schrödinger's equation. The magnetic quantum number defines the orientation of an atomic orbital.

Monochromatic radiation EM radiation of a single uniform frequency.

Node A point where the amplitude of an electron wavefunction, or probability of finding an electron, goes to zero.

Orbital The region of space wherein the electron is most likely to be found according to ψ^2.

Orbital box diagram This diagram uses boxes to depict each orbital. Within an orbital (box), electrons are depicted with arrows pointed up or down to indicate their relative spin states.

Paramagnetic Paramagnetic refers to materials which are attracted to a magnetic field. This property arises from electron configurations wherein one or more electrons are unpaired.

Pauli exclusion principle No two electrons in an atom can have the same set of four quantum numbers (no more than two electrons can occupy the same orbital at the same time and their spins must be opposed).

p-**Block** A region of the periodic table which includes groups 3A through 8A and is characterized by elements with valence configurations with incomplete or partially filled *p*-subshells.

Photoelectric effect The phenomenon of electric current induced by light striking a metal. When monochromatic light of sufficient energy strikes a metal, electrons are ejected.

Photons   To understand the photelectric effect, Einstein postulated that rather than acting like a wave, light was particulate in nature. The idea here being that light could only be absorbed in discrete particles or bundles of energy which he termed *photons*.

Planck's constant   The physical constant derived by Max Planck which defines the size of a quantum of energy.

Planck's equation   The equation derived by Max Planck which gives the energy of a photon as a function of its frequency or wavelength.

Principle quantum number   One of three quantum numbers which are solutions to Schrödinger's equation. The principle quantum number defines the size and energy of an atomic orbital.

Probability density   The probability per unit volume of finding an electron within a given region.

Quanta   The plural form of quantum.

Quantum   The discrete quantity of energy which is defined by the frequency of EM radiation to which it is associated.

Rydberg constant   A physical constant relating the frequency of lines in atomic emission spectra to a series of inverse square integers.

Rydberg equation   An equation which is used to predict the frequency of lines in atomic emission spectra as a function of a series of inverse square integers.

s-Block   A region of the periodic table which includes groups 1A and 2A.

Shielding   The phenomenon whereby electron-electron repulsions counteract the electron-nuclear attraction "felt" by an electron. Generally speaking, an electron farther from the nucleus will "feel" a reduced, "effective" nuclear charge due to repulsions with other electrons which are closer to the nucleus.

Stationary states   Bohr postulated that electrons in the hydrogen atom could only have certain, specific, or "allowed", angular momenta and therefore only allowed energies at certain increments. Bohr referred to these allowed energy states as *stationary states*.

Valence electrons   Electrons which reside in the outermost principle quantum level.

Van der Waals radius   Atomic radius defined by the distance of closest approach which can be made to an atom by another atom to which it is not chemically bonded.

Wave-function   A three-dimensional mathematical description of the electron-wave.

Wavelength   The distance along the x-coordinate between adjacent peaks (maxima–highest points) or adjacent troughs (minima–lowest points). The wave length defines one complete cycle or oscillation of the wave and is expressed in units of distance (meters, etc.).

CHAPTER 8

Bonding and Molecular Geometry

KEY CONCEPTS

- Ionic, Covalent, and Metallic Bonding
- Lewis Theory
- Electronegativity and Bond Polarity
- Valence Shell Electron Pair Repulsion Theory
- Symmetry and Molecular Polarity
- Valence Bond Theory and Orbital Hybridization
- Molecular Orbital Theory

CHEMICAL BONDS AND ELECTRONEGATIVITY

1. Why do elements form chemical bonds with other elements?

    Bonding occurs between elements because it has the effect of lowering the energy of the elements involved in chemical bonding.

2. What type of bond forms between metals?

    Metallic bonding occurs when metals bond to metals and is characterized by pooling of valence electrons over a large number of atoms.

3. What type of bond will form between a metal and a nonmetal?

    Ionic bonding is characterized by the complete transfer of one or more electrons from a metal to a nonmetal. As such, we understand ionic bonding to occur between nonmetals and metals.

4. What type of bond will form between two nonmetals?

    Covalent bonding occurs between nonmetals and other nonmetals. When two nonmetals come together to form a bond they will do so by "sharing" electrons.

5. Describe covalent bonding.

    Covalent bonding occurs between nonmetals and other nonmetals. When two nonmetals come together to form a bond they will do so by "sharing" electrons. Each nucleus in such a bond will exert an attractive force for the valence electrons of a neighboring atom. This has the effect of keeping the two atoms bound close together. Additionally, we say that the atoms in a covalent bond share a "pair" of valence electrons, each atom donating one electron to the bonding interaction (see Figure 8.1).

6. Describe ionic bonding.

    Ionic bonding is characterized by the complete transfer of one or more electrons from a metal to a nonmetal. As such, we understand ionic bonding to occur between nonmetals and metals. Further, the transfer of electron(s) from the metal to nonmetal results in the formation of a metal cation and a nonmetal anion. The electrostatic attraction between atoms of opposite charge is the basis for this bonding interaction and has the effect of directing these ions into large 3-dimensional, solid arrays of ions (see Figure 8.1). As such, the formulas written for ionic solids provide only the simplest ratio of ion types in a compound and are therefore referred to as *formula units*.

7. Describe metallic bonding.

    Metallic bonding occurs when metals bond to metals and is characterized by pooling of valence electrons over a large number of atoms. Metals are relatively large compared to nonmetals (recall trends in atomic radii from Chapter 7) and in addition their outer valence electrons are not held very strongly (metals tend to have lower ionization energies) and as such, they tend to share their valence electrons with other metal atoms. Unlike covalent bonding, this arrangement is not localized to a pair of atoms but rather delocalized over an entire sample of metal. Therefore, it is appropriate to consider atoms which make up a metal sample as "cationic cores" (the nuclei plus the core electrons) surrounded by a "sea" of valence electrons which are delocalized over the entire sample (see Figure 8.1).

8. What is meant by the term electronegativity?

    Electronegativity refers to the relative attraction that a bonded atom has for shared, "bonding" electrons.

9. Which element has a greater attraction for bonding electrons, oxygen or magnesium?

    Oxygen is a nonmetal and therefore will have a greater electronegativity than magnesium.

10. Which element has a greater attraction for bonding electrons, aluminum or chlorine?

    Chlorine is a nonmetal and therefore will have a greater electronegativity than aluminum.

LEWIS THEORY – LEWIS SYMBOLS AND STRUCTURES

11. Write the Lewis symbol for the following elements:
    a. Mg – $\cdot Mg \cdot$

    b. P – $\cdot \overset{\cdot\cdot}{\underset{\cdot}{P}} \cdot$

    c. AS – $\cdot \overset{\cdot\cdot}{\underset{\cdot}{As}} \cdot$

    d. B – $\cdot \underset{\cdot}{B} \cdot$

12. Write the Lewis symbol for the following elements:
    a. Li – $Li \cdot$

    b. He – $\cdot He \cdot$

    c. Ne – $\colon \overset{\cdot\cdot}{\underset{\cdot\cdot}{Ne}} \colon$

    d. Se – $\cdot \overset{\cdot\cdot}{\underset{\cdot}{Se}} \colon$

13. Write the Lewis symbol for the following elements:
    a. N – $\cdot \overset{\cdot\cdot}{\underset{\cdot}{N}} \cdot$

    b. F – $\colon \overset{\cdot\cdot}{\underset{\cdot}{F}} \colon$

    c. Br – $\colon \overset{\cdot\cdot}{\underset{\cdot}{Br}} \colon$

    d. Ba – $\cdot Ba \cdot$

14. Write the Lewis symbol for the following elements:

    a. $O - \quad \cdot \overset{\displaystyle ..}{\underset{\displaystyle .}{O}} :$

    b. $Si - \quad \cdot \overset{\displaystyle .}{\underset{\displaystyle .}{Si}} \cdot$

    c. $I - \quad : \overset{\displaystyle ..}{\underset{\displaystyle .}{I}} :$

    d. $Rb - \quad Rb \cdot$

15. Write the Lewis symbol for each of the following monatomic ions:

    a. $Ca^{2+} - \quad Ca^{2+}$

    b. $Rb^+ - \quad Rb^+$

    c. $S^{2-} - \quad \left[: \overset{\displaystyle ..}{\underset{\displaystyle ..}{S}} : \right]^{2-}$

    d. $N^{3-} - \quad \left[: \overset{\displaystyle .}{\underset{\displaystyle ..}{N}} : \right]^{3-}$

16. Write the Lewis symbol for each of the following monatomic ions:

    a. $Na^+ - \quad Na^+$

    b. $Al^{3+} - \quad Al^{3+}$

    c. $Cl^- - \quad \left[: \overset{\displaystyle ..}{\underset{\displaystyle ..}{Cl}} : \right]^-$

    d. $O^{2-} - \quad \left[: \overset{\displaystyle ..}{\underset{\displaystyle ..}{O}} : \right]^{2-}$

17. Write the correct Lewis structure for the binary ionic compounds formed from the following pairs of elements:

    a. Barium and bromine

    $$\left[: \overset{..}{\underset{..}{Br}} : \right]^- \quad Ba^{2+} \quad \left[: \overset{..}{\underset{..}{Br}} : \right]^-$$

    b. Potassium and chlorine

    $$K^+ \quad \left[: \overset{..}{\underset{..}{Cl}} : \right]^-$$

    c. Aluminum and oxygen

    $$\left[: \overset{..}{\underset{..}{O}} : \right]^{2-} \quad Al^{3+} \quad \left[: \overset{..}{\underset{..}{O}} : \right]^{2-} \quad Al^{3+} \quad \left[: \overset{..}{\underset{..}{O}} : \right]^{2-}$$

18. Write the correct Lewis structure for the binary ionic compounds formed from the following pairs of elements:

    a. Calcium and nitrogen

    $$Ca^{2+} \quad \left[:\ddot{N}: \right]^{3-} \quad Ca^{2+} \quad \left[:\ddot{N}: \right]^{3-} \quad Ca^{2+}$$

    b. Lithium and fluorine

    $$Li^{+} \quad \left[:\ddot{F}: \right]^{-}$$

    c. Rubidium and oxygen

    $$Rb^{+} \quad \left[:\ddot{O}: \right]^{2-} \quad Rb^{+}$$

19. Explain why it is possible to have diatomic molecules with fewer than 16 valence electrons (total).

    Because elements share electrons in covalent bonding, this allows the atoms in a covalent compound to realize an octet, even though they have fewer than eight valence electrons.

20. What is meant by the term resonance hybrid?

    When Lewis theory predicts Lewis multiple structures for the same compound these are said to be resonance structures. The actual structure of the molecule is thought of as a sort of average or blend of the resonance structures, often referred to as a *resonance hybrid.*

21. Which of the following elements can never be a central atom when writing Lewis structures? Explain.

    a. *P*
    b. *Se*
    c. *H*
    d. *F*

    H – Because hydrogen forms a duet, it will only ever form one bond and as such, cannot be the central atom in a covalent molecule.

    F – Because fluorine is the most electronegative element, it will never be the least electronegative element in a compound. Since this is the criterion for determining the central atom, fluorine will never be the central atom.

22. Draw the Lewis structure for the following:

    a. *SiF*$_4$

    $$
    \begin{array}{c}
    :\ddot{F}: \\
    | \\
    :\ddot{F} - Si - \ddot{F}: \\
    | \\
    :\ddot{F}:
    \end{array}
    $$

b. *CS$_2$*

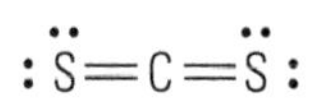

$$:\ddot{S}=C=\ddot{S}:$$

c. *COCl$_2$*

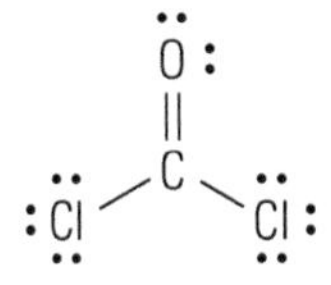

23. Draw the Lewis structure for the following:
    a. *NF$_3$*

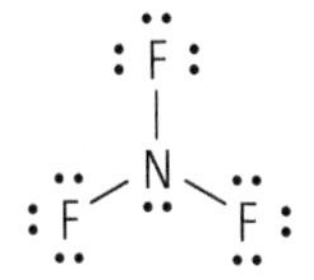

    b. *ClF$_4^-$*

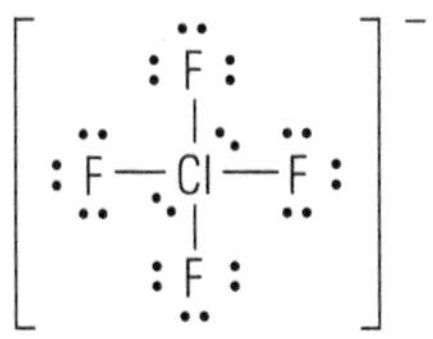

    c. *NH$_4^+$*

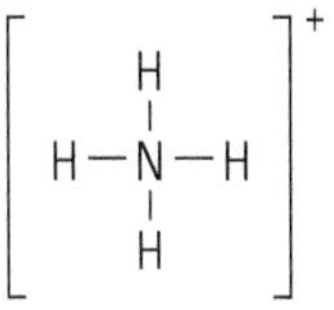

24. Draw the Lewis structure for the following:
    a. *SeCl$_4$*

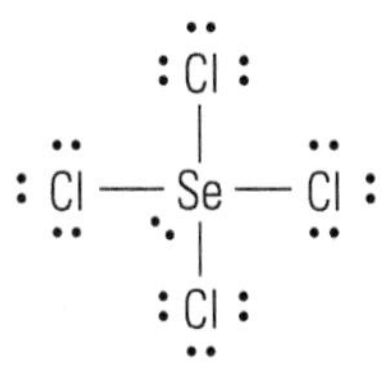

    b. *NO$_2^+$*

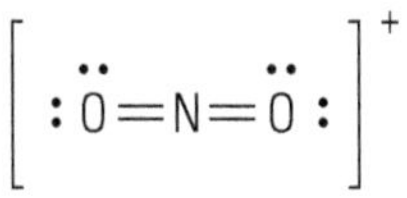

c. $SnCl_3^-$

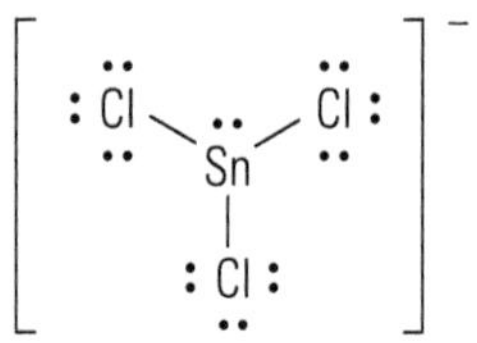

$$\left[\begin{array}{c} :\overset{..}{\underset{..}{Cl}} \diagdown \quad \overset{..}{\underset{..}{Cl}}: \\ \quad \underset{|}{\overset{..}{Sn}} \quad \\ :\overset{..}{\underset{..}{Cl}}: \end{array}\right]^-$$

25. Draw the Lewis structure for the following:
    a. GeH_4

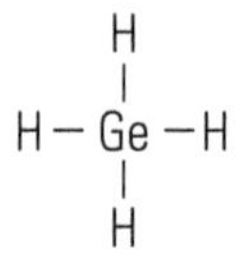

$$\begin{array}{c} H \\ | \\ H - Ge - H \\ | \\ H \end{array}$$

    b. NCl_3

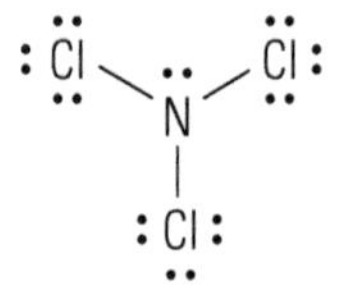

$$\begin{array}{c} :\overset{..}{\underset{..}{Cl}} \diagdown \quad \overset{..}{\underset{..}{Cl}}: \\ \quad \underset{|}{N} \quad \\ :\overset{..}{\underset{..}{Cl}}: \end{array}$$

    c. BF_4^-

$$\left[\begin{array}{c} :\overset{..}{\underset{..}{F}}: \\ | \\ :\overset{..}{\underset{..}{F}} - B - \overset{..}{\underset{..}{F}}: \\ | \\ :\overset{..}{\underset{..}{F}}: \end{array}\right]^-$$

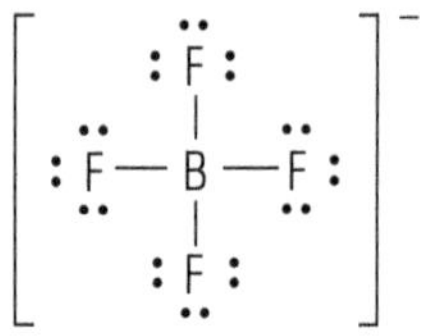

26. Draw the Lewis structure for the following:
    a. $CHClF_2$

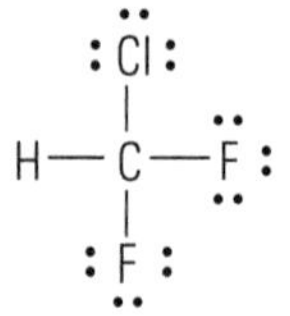

$$\begin{array}{c} :\overset{..}{\underset{..}{Cl}}: \\ | \\ H - C - \overset{..}{\underset{..}{F}}: \\ | \\ :\overset{..}{\underset{..}{F}}: \end{array}$$

    b. Cl_2SO

$$\begin{array}{c} :\overset{..}{O} \\ || \\ :\overset{..}{\underset{..}{Cl}} \diagup \overset{..}{S} \diagdown \overset{..}{\underset{..}{Cl}}: \end{array}$$

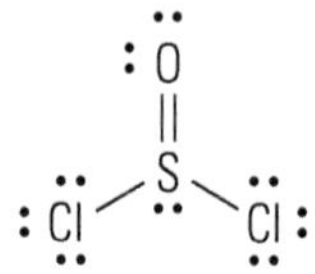

c. *XeO₂F₂*

27. Draw all possible resonance structures of sulfite, SO_3^{2-}.

28. Draw the resonance structures of phosphate, PO_4^{3-}.

29. Draw the resonance structures and the resonance hybrid of ozone, O_3.

Resonance hybrid:

30. Draw the Lewis structure of the following oxyacids:
    a. Sulfuric acid, *H₂SO₄*

b. Nitric acid, HNO_3

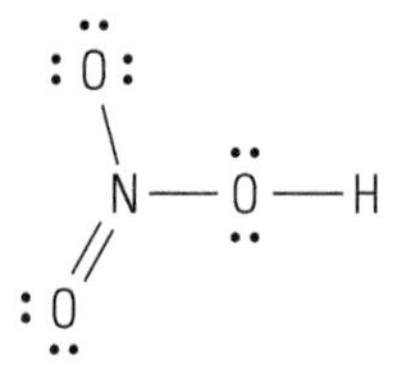

31. Draw the Lewis structure of the following oxyacids:

a. Boric acid, H_3BO_3

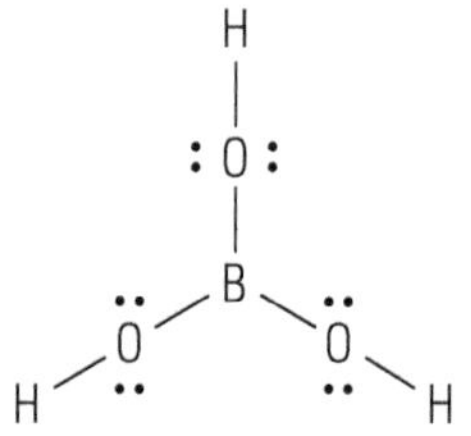

b. Carbonic acid, H_2CO_3

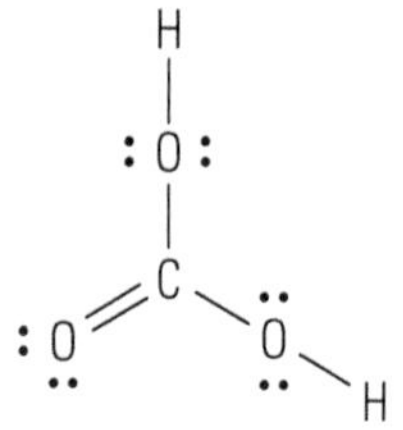

32. Draw the following compounds which exhibit exceptions to the octet rule:

a. BeH_2

H — Be — H

b. SiF_5^-

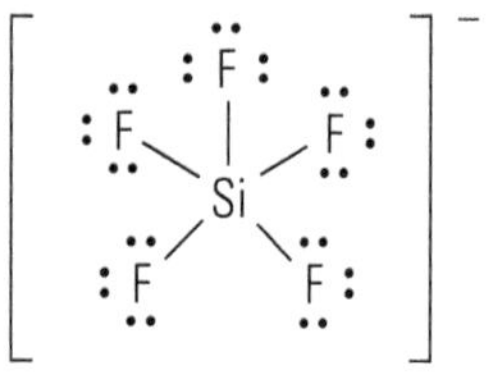

c. XeO_3

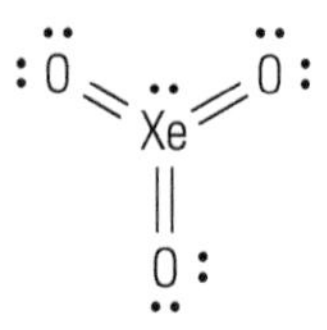

33. Draw the following compounds which exhibit exceptions to the octet rule:

    a. PF_5

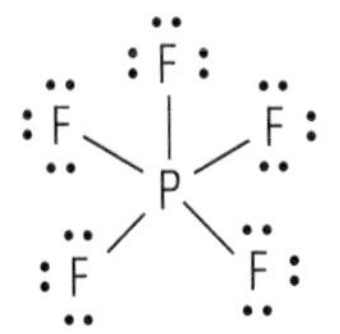

    b. SiF_6^{2-}

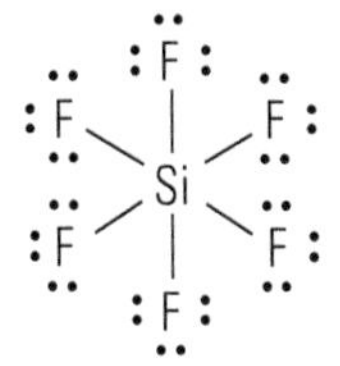

    c. BrF_5

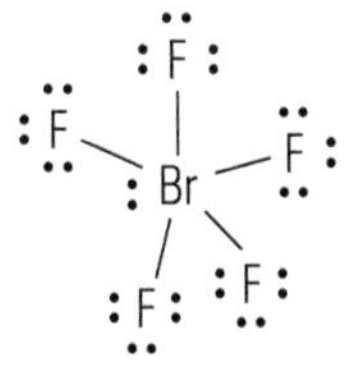

34. Draw the following compounds which exhibit exceptions to the octet rule:

    a. ClF_3

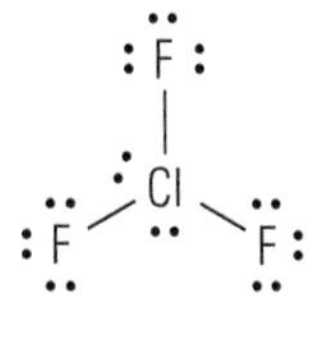

    b. SF_4

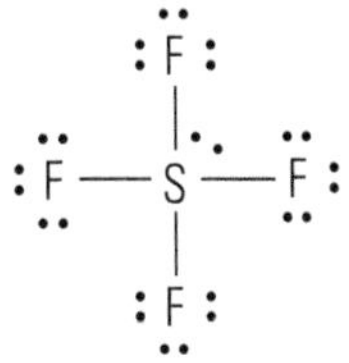

    c. BF_3

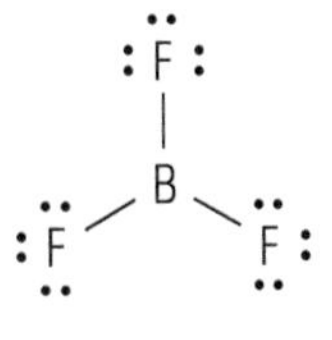

35. Draw the following compounds which exhibit exceptions to the octet rule:

   a. XeF_2

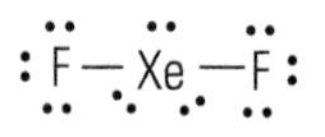

   $$:\ddot{F}-\ddot{X}e-\ddot{F}:$$

   b. ClF_5

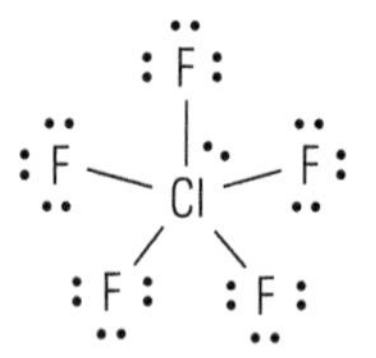

   (Lewis structure of ClF_5 with central Cl bonded to five F atoms)

   c. ClO_3^-

   (Lewis structure of ClO_3^- shown in brackets with negative charge)

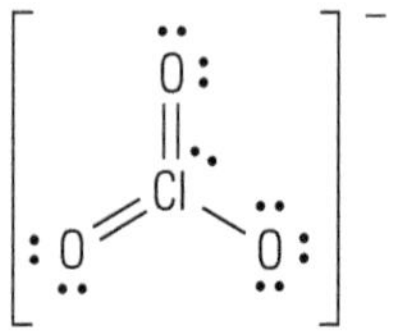

36. Write the Lewis structures and assign formal charges to the atoms in the following compounds:

   a. N_2H_4

   All atoms have a formal charge of zero.

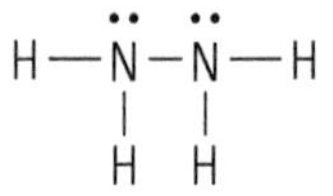

   (Lewis structure: H—N—N—H with H below each N)

   b. PO_4^{3-}

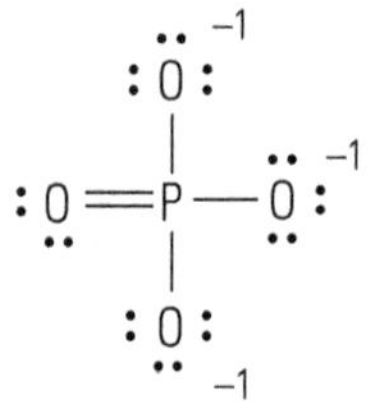

   (Lewis structure of phosphate with formal charges −1 on three oxygens)

   c. HNO_3

   (Lewis structure of nitric acid with formal charges −1 on oxygen and +1 on nitrogen)

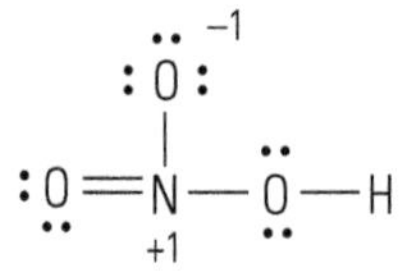

37. Write the Lewis structures and assign formal charges to the atoms in the following compounds:

a. BF_4^-

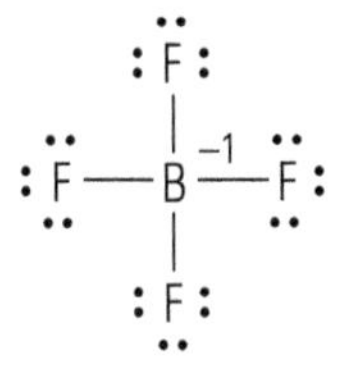

b. IF_5

All atoms have a formal charge of zero.

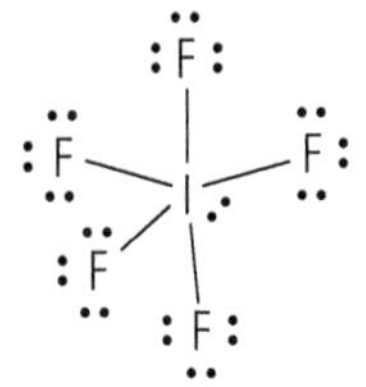

c. AlH_4^-

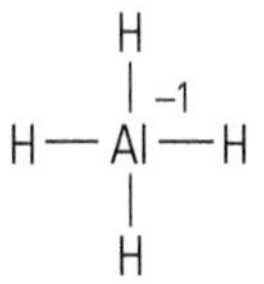

38. Write Lewis structures for the following and assign formal charges to all atoms. Expand octets where necessary to lower formal charges.

a. BrO_3^-

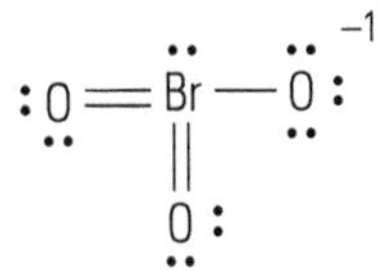

b. AsO_4^{3-}

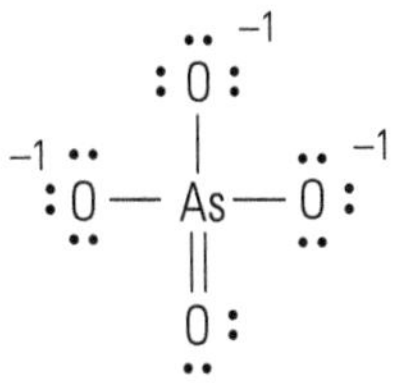

c. ClO_3^-

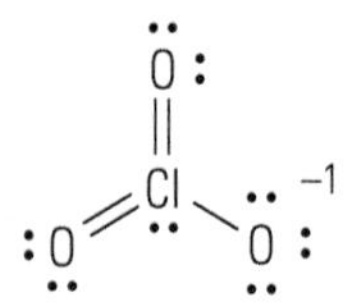

39. Write Lewis structures for the following and assign formal charges to all atoms. Expand octets where necessary to lower formal charges.

a. $SeOF_2$

All atoms have a formal charge of zero.

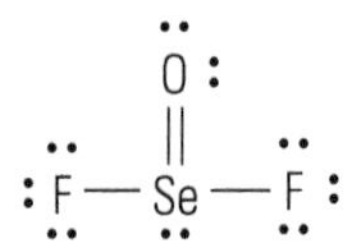

b. SO_4^{2-}

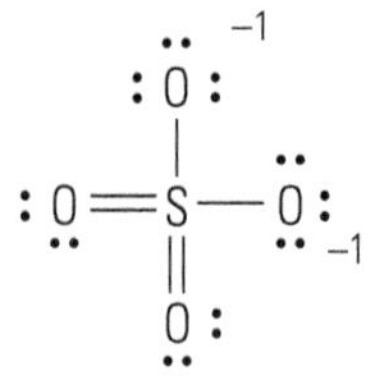

c. ClO_2^-

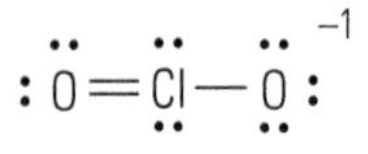

40. Using formal charge as a guide, determine which Lewis structure in the following set is more likely to be correct for HN_3 :

$H—N{=}N{=}N\!:$ is the best structure.

41. Using formal charge as a guide, determine which Lewis structure in the following set is more likely to be correct for **SCN^-** :

$$\left[\overset{-1}{:\!\ddot{S}} - \overset{0}{C} \equiv \overset{0}{N:} \right]^- \qquad \left[\overset{+1}{:S} \equiv \overset{0}{C} - \overset{-2}{\ddot{N}:} \right]^- \qquad \left[\overset{0}{:\!\ddot{S}} = \overset{0}{C} = \overset{-1}{\ddot{N}:} \right]^-$$

$$\left[:\!\ddot{S} = C = \ddot{N}: \right]^-$$ is the best structure as it places the negative formal charge on the most electronegative atom.

42. Using formal charge as a guide, determine which Lewis structure in the following set is more likely to be correct for **CH_2N_2** :

$$\begin{array}{c} H \\ | \\ H - \underset{-1}{C} - \underset{+1}{N} \equiv \underset{0}{N:} \\ \end{array} \qquad \begin{array}{c} \overset{0}{} \; H \\ | \\ H - \underset{0}{C} \underset{0}{=} N \underset{+1}{=} \ddot{N}: \\ \underset{-1}{} \end{array}$$

$$\begin{array}{c} H \\ | \\ H - C = N = \ddot{N}: \end{array}$$ is the best structure.

43. Using formal charge as a guide, determine which Lewis structure in the following set is more likely to be correct for **ClO_4^-** :

$$\left[\begin{array}{c} \overset{-1}{:\!\ddot{O}:} \\ | \overset{+3}{} \\ :\!\ddot{O} - \underset{-1}{Cl} - \ddot{O}: \\ | \\ :\!\underset{-1}{\ddot{O}}: \end{array} \right]^- \qquad \left[\begin{array}{c} \overset{0}{} \; \ddot{O}: \\ || \overset{0}{} \\ :\!\ddot{O} = Cl - \ddot{O}: \\ || \\ :\underset{0}{O} \end{array} \right]^- \qquad \left[\begin{array}{c} \overset{0}{} \; \ddot{O} \\ || \\ :\!\ddot{O} = Cl \overset{-1}{=} \ddot{O}: \\ || \\ :\underset{0}{O} \end{array} \right]^-$$

$$\left[\begin{array}{c} \ddot{O}: \\ || \\ :\!\ddot{O} = Cl - \ddot{O}: \\ || \\ :O \end{array} \right]^-$$ is the best structure.

VALENCE SHELL ELECTRON PAIR REPULSION THEORY (VSEPR)

44. What are the five basic electronic geometries and the number of electron groups which correspond to each?

2 electron groups – linear
3 electron groups – trigonal
4 electron groups – tetrahedral
5 electron groups – trigonal bipyramidal
6 electron groups – octahedral

45. What is the difference between electronic and molecular geometry? When are they the same? When are they different?

Electronic geometry refers to the 3-dimensional arrangement of all of the electrons on the central atom. This is the direct result of the application of the VSEPR model. Molecular geometry refers to the 3-dimnesional arrangement of the terminal atoms around the central atom. This is a derivative of the electronic geometry. These are the same as long as all electron groups on the central atom are bonding groups. When there is an admixture of bonding groups and lone pairs on the central atom, the molecular geometry will then be different from the electron geometry.

46. How many bonding groups and lone pairs are there on the central atom of a molecule with a tetrahedral molecular geometry?

There are four bonding electron groups and no lone pairs on a molecule with tetrahedral molecular geometry.

47. How many bonding groups and lone pairs are there on the central atom of a molecule with a see-saw molecular geometry?

There are four bonding electron groups and one lone pair on a molecule with see-saw molecular geometry.

48. How many bonding groups and lone pairs are there on the central atom of a molecule with a bent molecular geometry for which the bond angle is < 120°?

There are two bonding electron groups and one lone pair on a molecule with a trigonal bent molecular geometry.

49. How many bonding groups and lone pairs are there on the central atom of a molecule with a square planar molecular geometry?

There are four bonding electron groups and two lone pairs on a molecule with square planar molecular geometry.

50. How many bonding groups and lone pairs are there on the central atom of a molecule with a square pyramidal molecular geometry?

There are five bonding electron groups and one lone pair on a molecule with square pyramidal molecular geometry.

51. How many bonding groups and lone pairs are there on the central atom of a molecule with a pyramidal molecular geometry?

There are three bonding electron groups and one lone pair on a molecule with pyramidal molecular geometry.

52. How many bonding groups and lone pairs are there on the central atom of a molecule with a T-shaped molecular geometry?

There are three bonding electron groups and two lone pairs on a molecule with T-shaped molecular geometry.

53. How many bonding groups and lone pairs are there on the central atom of a molecule with a bent molecular geometry for which the bond angle is < 109.5°?

There are two bonding electron groups and two lone pairs on a molecule with tetrahedral bent molecular geometry.

54. Determine the molecular and electronic geometry and characteristic bond angle for each of the following:

a. PF_3

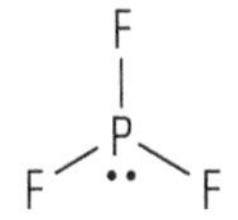

Electron groups = 4
Electronic geometry = tetrahedral
Molecular geometry = pyramidal
Bond angle < 109.5°

b. PF_5

Electron groups = 5
Electronic geometry = trigonal bipyramidal
Molecular geometry = trigonal bipyramidal
Bond angle = 120° & 90°

c. PF_6^-

Electron groups = 6
Electronic geometry = octahedral
Molecular geometry = octahedral
Bond angle = 90°

55. Determine the molecular and electronic geometry and characteristic bond angle for each of the following:

a. CH_2Cl_2

Electron groups = 4
Electronic geometry = tetrahedral
Molecular geometry = tetrahedral
Bond angle ~ 109.5°

b. $COCl_2$

Electron groups = 3
Electronic geometry = trigonal
Molecular geometry = trigonal
Bond angle ~ 120°

c. H_2S

Electron groups = 4
Electronic geometry = tetrahedral
Molecular geometry = tetrahedral bent
Bond angle < 109.5°

56. Determine the molecular and electronic geometry and characteristic bond angle for each of the following:

a. SiF_4

Electron groups = 4
Electronic geometry = tetrahedral
Molecular geometry = tetrahedral
Bond angle = 109.5°

b. SiF_5^-

Electron groups = 5
Electronic geometry = trigonal bipyramidal
Molecular geometry = trigonal bipyramidal
Bond angle = 120° & 90°

c. SiF_6^{2-}

Electron groups = 6
Electronic geometry = octahedral
Molecular geometry = octahedral
Bond angle = 90°

57. Sketch the 3-dimensional representations of the following using the solid and hatched wedge notation:

a.

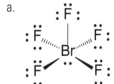

b.

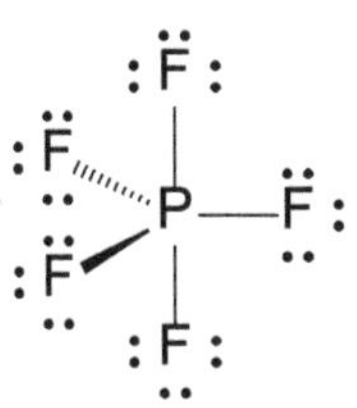

c.

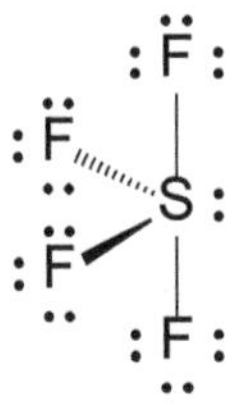

58. Sketch the 3-dimensional representations of the following using the solid and hatched wedge notation:

   a. SCl_6

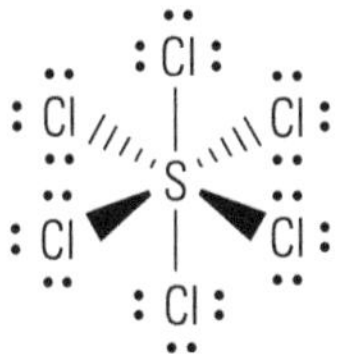

   b. BrF_3

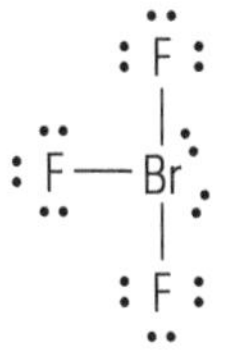

   c. CH_2Cl_2

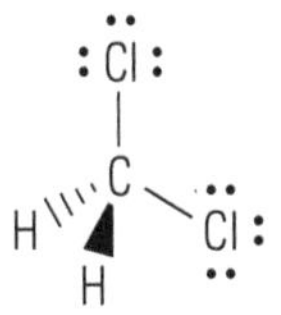

59. Arrange the following in order of increasing bond angle:

   a. SO_2

   b. SO_3

   c. SO_3^{2-}

d. SO_4^{2-}

$$SO_3^{2-} < SO_4^{2-} < SO_2 < SO_3$$

60. Arrange the following in order of increasing bond angle:
    a. ClO_2^-
    b. ClO_3^-
    c. ClO_4^-

$$ClO_2^- < ClO_3^- < ClO_4^-$$

BOND AND MOLECULAR POLARITY

61. What is meant by the term polar covalent bond?

    Separation of electric charge over a given distance is called an *electric dipole*. Covalent bonds which exhibit a measurable electric dipole (due to uneven sharing of bonding electron pairs) are referred as *polar covalent bonds*.

62. Is a $H - C$ bond covalent, polar covalent, or ionic? Why?

$$\Delta EN = EN_C - EN_H = 2.5 - 2.1 = 0.4$$

    We expect this bond to be covalent. The difference in electronegativity is ≤ 0.4, which means we do not expect there to be sufficient charge separation over the bond to result in a strong dipole.

63. Is a $H - N$ bond covalent, polar covalent, or ionic? Why?

$$\Delta EN = EN_N - EN_H = 3.0 - 2.1 = 0.9$$

    We expect this bond to be *polar covalent*. Because $0.4 < (\Delta EN = 0.9) < 2.0$ we expect there to be sufficient charge separation over the bond to result in a strong dipole.

64. Arrange the following bind types in order of increasing polarity:
    a. $Cl - O$
    b. $Cl - C$
    c. $Cl - P$
    d. $Cl - B$

    Bond polarity and ΔEN increase in the order a=b, c, d.

65. Arrange the following bind types in order of increasing polarity:
    a. $H - O$ - $\Delta EN = 1.4$

b. $Al - H$ - $\Delta EN = 0.6$

c. $Al - F$ - $\Delta EN = 2.5$

d. $Al - O$ - $\Delta EN = 2.0$

Bond polarity and ΔEN increase in the order b, a, d, c.

66. Categorize the following compounds as polar or nonpolar:
    a. SF_6 – nonpolar
    b. SF_4 – polar
    c. NCl_3 – nonpolar
    d. NF_3 – polar

67. Categorize the following compounds as polar or nonpolar:
    a. CH_2Cl_2 – polar
    b. $CHCl_3$ – polar
    c. CCl_4 – nonpolar
    d. CH_3Cl – polar

68. Categorize the following compounds as polar or nonpolar:
    a. BCl_3 – nonpolar
    b. $AsCl_3$ – polar
    c. SO_3 – nonpolar
    d. $AlCl_3$ – nonpolar

69. Categorize the following compounds as polar or nonpolar:
    a. CH_4 – nonpolar
    b. $SiCl_4$ – nonpolar
    c. BrF_5 – polar
    d. PCl_5 – nonpolar

VALENCE BOND THEORY

70. What hybridization is associated with each of the five electronic geometries?

Linear – sp
Trigonal – sp^2
Tetrahedral – sp^3
Trigonal bipyramidal – $sp^3 d$
Octahedral – $sp^3 d^2$

71. What characteristic bond angles are produced from the following orbital hybridizations:
    a. sp – 180°
    b. sp^2 – 120°
    c. sp^3 – 109.5°
    d. sp^3d – 120° (equatorial) and 90° (axial)
    e. sp^3d^2 – 90°

72. What is the hybridization on the central atom in each of the following compounds:
    a. BCl_3 – sp^2

    b. SiF_5^- – sp^3d

    c. SO_3 – sp^2

    d. SF_4 – sp^3d

73. What is the hybridization on the central atom in each of the following compounds:
    a. PF_6^- – sp^3d^2

    b. $AsCl_3$ – sp^3

    c. $COCl_2$ – sp^2

    d. $AlCl_3$ – sp^2

74. What is the hybridization on each carbon atom in ethylene, C_2H_4? Describe the bonding arrangement. How many π-bonds are present in this molecule? Where are they located?

    Each carbon atom has three sigma bonds (three electron groups) and therefore both of them are sp^2. There is one π-bond between the two carbons in this molecule.

75. What is the hybridization on each carbon atom in acetone, C_3H_6O? Describe the bonding arrangement. How many π-bonds are present in this molecule? Where are they located?

    The two outside carbons have four σ-bonds (four electron groups) and therefore these are sp^3. However, the middle carbon has three σ-bonds (three electron groups) and it is therefore sp^2. There is one π-bond between the middle carbon and oxygen.

76. What is the hybridization on each carbon atom in isopropyl alcohol, C_3H_7OH? Describe the bonding arrangement. How many π-bonds are present in this molecule? Where are they located?

We see from the Lewis structure that all of the carbon atoms are sp^3 with four electron groups. There are no π-bonds.

77. Predict the hybridization of each "non-hydrogen" atom in the following compounds:

a.

All the carbon atoms are sp^3 and the oxygen atom is also sp^3.

b.

All the carbon atoms are sp^2.

c.

The nitrogen is sp^3, the left-most carbon is sp^3, the right-most carbon is sp^2, the oxygen on the far right is sp^3 and the oxygen with the double bond is is sp^2.

MOLECULAR ORBITAL THEORY

78. Describe the principle difference between MO theory and VB theory.

Where VB theory combines wave-functions from atomic orbitals on the same atom to form hybrid orbitals, MO theory combines orbitals in the same way but from multiple atoms within a molecule such that the orbital and the electrons that occupy it are delocalized over the entire molecule.

79. What are bonding and antibonding orbitals and how do they arise in MO theory?

Again, when waves interact, they can do so constructively or destructively. When they are in phase, they interact constructively, building up electron density in the region between the two atomic nuclei. This is referred to as a *bonding molecular orbital* or simply a *bonding orbital*, in MO theory. Likewise, when the wave functions are out of phase they interact destructively, reducing the probability of finding an electron in the region between the nuclei.

This is referred to as an *antibonding orbital* and is characterized by a nodal plane perpendicular to the inter-nuclear axis. Note: the number of orbitals is always conserved.

80. What is bond order and what does it tell us?

The *bond order (BO)* is a number which describes whether a given set of occupied MO's is collectively lower in energy (stabilized) relative to the free (un-bonded) atoms.

81. Construct an MO diagram for the homonuclear diatomic molecule H_2. Use this diagram to determine the bond order of the following species and predict whether each will exist:

a. H_2 – $BO = 1$, exists.

b. H_2^+ – $BO = 0.5$, exists.

c. H_2^- – $BO = 0.5$ exists.

d. He_2^+ – $BO = 0.5$, exists.

e. He_2 – $BO = 0$, nonexistant.

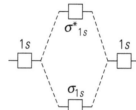

82. Determine the electron configurations of the following:

a. Li_2 – $\left(\sigma_{2s}\right)^2$

b. Li_2^+ – $\left(\sigma_{2s}\right)^1$

c. Li_2^- – $\left(\sigma_{2s}\right)^2\left(\sigma_{2s}^*\right)^1$

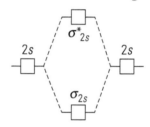

83. Determine the electron configurations of the following:

a. B_2 – $\left(\sigma_{2s}\right)^2\left(\sigma_{2s}^*\right)^2\left(\pi_{2p}\right)^2$

b. B_2^+ – $\left(\sigma_{2s}\right)^2\left(\sigma_{2s}^*\right)^2\left(\pi_{2p}\right)^1$

c. B_2^- – $\left(\sigma_{2s}\right)^2\left(\sigma_{2s}^*\right)^2\left(\pi_{2p}\right)^3$

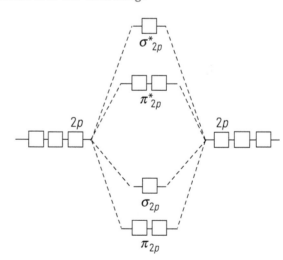

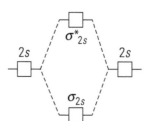

84. Determine the electron configurations of the following:

a. $N_2 - (\sigma_{2s})^2 (\sigma^*_{2s})^2 (\pi_{2p})^4 (\sigma_{2p})^2$

b. $N_2^+ - (\sigma_{2s})^2 (\sigma^*_{2s})^2 (\pi_{2p})^4 (\sigma_{2p})^1$

c. $N_2^- - (\sigma_{2s})^2 (\sigma^*_{2s})^2 (\pi_{2p})^4 (\sigma_{2p})^2 (\pi^*_{2p})^1$

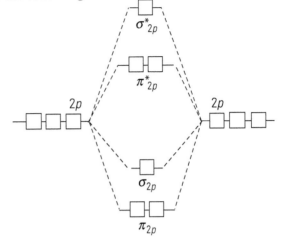

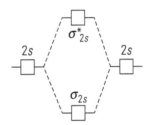

85. Determine the electron configurations of the following:

a. $F_2 - (\sigma_{2s})^2 (\sigma^*_{2s})^2 (\sigma_{2p})^2 (\pi_{2p})^4 (\pi^*_{2p})^4$

b. $F_2^+ - (\sigma_{2s})^2 (\sigma^*_{2s})^2 (\sigma_{2p})^2 (\pi_{2p})^4 (\pi^*_{2p})^3$

c. $F_2^- - (\sigma_{2s})^2 (\sigma^*_{2s})^2 (\sigma_{2p})^2 (\pi_{2p})^4 (\pi^*_{2p})^4 (\sigma^*_{2p})^1$

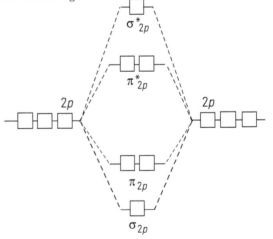

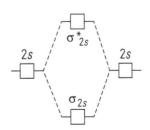

86. What are the bond orders for the species in problem 82? Arrange those that exist in order of increasing stability.
    a. Li_2 – $BO = 1$, exists.
    b. Li_2^+ – $BO = 0.5$, exists.
    c. Li_2^- – $BO = 0.5$, exists.

    $Li_2^-, Li_2^+ < Li_2$

87. What are the bond orders for the species in problem 83? Arrange those that exist in order of increasing stability.
    a. B_2 – $BO = 1$, exists.
    b. B_2^+ – $BO = 0.5$, exists.
    c. B_2^- – $BO = 1.5$, exists.

    $B_2^+ < B_2 < B_2^-$

88. What are the bond orders for the species in problem 84? Arrange those that exist in order of increasing stability.
    a. N_2 – $BO = 3$, exists.
    b. N_2^+ – $BO = 2.5$, exists.
    c. N_2^- – $BO = 2.5$, exists.

    $N_2^-, N_2^+ < N_2$

89. What are the bond orders for the species in problem 85? Arrange those that exist in order of increasing bond length.
    a. F_2 – $BO = 1$ exists.
    b. F_2^+ – $BO = 1.5$, exists.
    c. F_2^- – $BO = 0.5$, exists.

    $F_2^- < F_2 < F_2^+$

90. Use the following generic MO diagram to assess the following problems:

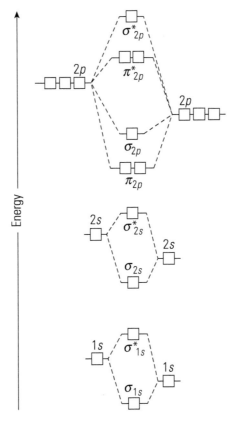

a. What is the bond order of *CO*? What is the HOMO? What is the LUMO? Is it paramagnetic?

$$BO = \frac{10-4}{2} = 3$$

$$HOMO = \sigma_{2p}$$

$$LUMO = \pi_{2p}^*$$

The molecule is diamagnetic.

b. What is the bond order of the hypothetical compound *BO*? Is it paramagnetic? What is the HOMO? What is the LUMO? Is it paramagnetic?

$$BO = \frac{9-4}{2} = 2.5$$

$$HOMO = \sigma_{2p}$$

$$LUMO = \pi_{2p}^*$$

The molecule is paramagnetic.

c. What is the bond order of CN^-? What is the HOMO? What is the LUMO? Is it paramagnetic?

$$BO = \frac{10-4}{2} = 3$$

$$HOMO = \sigma_{2p}$$

$$LUMO = \pi^*_{2p}$$

The molecule is diamagnetic.

d. What is the bond order of NF? What is the HOMO? What is the LUMO? Is it paramagnetic?

$$BO = \frac{10-6}{2} = 2$$

$$HOMO = \pi^*_{2p}$$

$$LUMO = \sigma^*_{2p}$$

The molecule is paramagnetic.

e. What is the bond order of NF^-? What is the HOMO? What is the LUMO? Is it paramagnetic?

$$BO = \frac{10-7}{2} = 1.5$$

$$HOMO = \pi^*_{2p}$$

$$LUMO = \sigma^*_{2p}$$

The molecule is paramagnetic.

KEY TERMS

Antibonding orbital   A molecular orbital which has one or more nodes in the bonding region between the bonding nuclei. Therefore, it has a destabilizing effect and weakens the bond if occupied by a pair of electrons.

Bond angle   The angle between two bond vectors.

Bond order   In MO theory this refers to a number which describes whether a given set of occupied MO's is collectively lower in energy (stabilized) relative to the free (un-bonded) atoms. It usually corresponds to the number (or multiplicity) of bonds between atoms (one for a single bond, two for a double bond, and three for a triple bond). However, fractional bond orders are possible. Nevertheless, the greater the bond order the shorter the bond length and the stronger the bond. Essentially, the greater the bond order, the more stable the molecule.

Bonding electron pair   In Lewis theory a bonding electron pair is one which is shared between two atoms and is the basis for a covalent bond.

Bonding orbital (MO)   A molecular orbital wherein there is an increase in electron density in the bonding region between two nuclei. Therefore, it has a stabilizing effect and strengthens the bond if occupied by a pair of electrons.

Bonding pair   In Lewis theory a bonding electron pair is one which is shared between two atoms and is the basis for a covalent bond.

Covalent bonding   When two nonmetals come together to form a bond they will do so by "sharing" electrons. Each nucleus in such a bond will exert an attractive force for the valence electrons of a neighboring atom. This has the effect of keeping the two atoms bound close together. Additionally, we say that the atoms in a covalent bond share a "pair" of valence electrons, each atom donating one electron to the bonding interaction.

Dipole moment   The product of the distance over which two opposite charges of equal magnitude are separated.

Double bond   When two pairs of bonding electrons are shared between the same two atoms this is referred to as a *double bond*. Double bonds are generally stronger than single bonds and they are also shorter.

Electron group   In VSEPR theory, an electron group is one or more pairs of electrons which occupy the same space. In other words, a double or a triple bond will be defined as a single electron group. It is the number of electron groups (EG) that will determine the electronic geometry in the VSEPR model.

Electronegativity   The relative attraction that a bonded atom has for shared, "bonding" electrons.

Electronic geometry   The 3-dimensional arrangement of all the electrons on the central atom. This is the direct result of the application of the VSEPR model.

Expanded octet   In Lewis theory, some elements can adopt *expanded octets*, meaning that they take on more than eight valence electrons. This is due to the fact that many elements have additional (empty) d orbitals which can contribute to their bonding structure. As such, elements in the 3rd row (or later rows) on the periodic table can accommodate up to 12 or more electrons in their Lewis structures.

Formal charge   A "fictional" charge assigned to each atom in a Lewis structure. Formal charge is calculated by assuming absolutely equal sharing of bonding electrons.

Free radical   When a Lewis structure has an odd number of valence electrons, it is called a *free radical*. Free radicals are characterized by "unpaired" electrons and are highly reactive.

Highest occupied molecular orbital (HOMO)   In MO theory this refers to the highest energy molecular orbital which is occupied by an electron.

Hybrid orbitals   In valence bond theory, hybrid orbitals are formed through mixing of the *s*, *p*, and *d* atomic orbitals on atom. In this way VB theory accounts for the observed geometry of molecules.

Incomplete octet   In Lewis theory, some elements do not adopt a complete set of eight valence electrons through bonding.

Ionic bonding   Ionic bonding is characterized by the complete transfer of one or more electrons from a metal to a nonmetal.

Lewis dot structure   A structural drawing wherein dots are used to depict electrons as well as the bonding arrangement between the atoms in a molecule.

Lewis theory   A chemical bonding theory which relies on an accounting of valence electrons to make predictions about bonding in compounds and molecules.

Lone pair   In Lewis theory, a lone pair refers to a pair of valence electrons which is not involved in bonding (also called a nonbonding pair).

Lowest unoccupied molecular orbital (LUMO)   In MO theory, this refers to the molecular orbital of lowest potential energy which is still unoccupied by electrons.

Metallic bonding   Metallic bonding occurs when metals bond to metals and is characterized by pooling of valence electrons over a large number of atoms. Metals are relatively large compared to nonmetals (recall trends in atomic radii from Chapter 7) and in addition their outer valence electrons are not held very strongly (metals tend to have lower ionization energies) and as such, they tend to share their valence electrons with other metal atoms. Unlike covalent bonding, this arrangement is not localized to a pair of atoms but rather delocalized over an entire sample of metal. Therefore, it is appropriate to consider atoms which make up a metal sample as "cationic cores" (the nuclei plus the core electrons) surrounded by a "sea" of valence electrons which are delocalized over the entire sample. It is this bonding arrangement which gives rise to the high electrical conductivity of metals.

Molecular geometry   In VSEPR theory, this term refers to the 3-dimensional arrangement of the terminal atoms around the central atom. This is a derivative of the electronic geometry.

Molecular orbital diagram   A qualitative description of molecular orbitals as linear combinations of atomic orbitals. These are represented according to relative potential energy levels along an energy coordinate, clearly depicting the relative stabilizing and destabilizing effects of the various combinations.

Molecular orbital theory   A quantum mechanical bonding theory wherein molecular orbitals are created from combinations of atomic orbitals from two or more different atoms such that the orbital and the electrons that occupy it are delocalized over the entire molecule. Where VB theory combines wave-functions from atomic orbitals on the same atom to form hybrid orbitals, MO theory combines orbitals in the same way but from multiple atoms within a molecule.

Molecular polarity   The degree to which there exists a net electric dipole over a molecule stemming from the presence and relative orientations of polar bonds within its structure.

Nonbonding electron pair   See "lone pair" above.

Octahedral   A term referring to molecular and electronic geometry in VSEPR theory wherein electron groups and/or terminal atoms occupy positions which correspond to the vertices of an imaginary octahedron. Octahedral geometry is associated with six electron groups on the central atom.

Octet rule   In Lewis theory, the octet rule states that atoms will gain, lose, or share electrons to attain a full valence shell of eight electrons referred to as an *octet* (or two in the case of Li, Be, and H, referred to as a *duet*).

Orbital hybridization   In Valence bond theory, this refers to the mixing of *s*, *p*, and *d* orbitals on a particular atom to form a new set of atomic orbitals, called *hybrid orbitals*.

Pi-Bond   From valence bond theory, a pi-bond is one in which two p-orbitals overlap in a side-to-side fashion. The combination of a σ- and π-bond is how VB theory accounts for double bonds.

Polar covalent bond   Covalent bonds which exhibit a measurable electric dipole (due to uneven sharing of bonding electron pairs).

Resonance   A concept in Lewis theory which refers to situations wherein more than one Lewis structure is necessary to depict a single molecule. These structures are called resonance structures.

Resonance hybrid   A molecular structure depicted by multiple Lewis structures simultaneously and described as an "average" of these resonance structures.

Resonance structures   A concept in Lewis theory which refers to situations wherein more than one Lewis structure is necessary to depict a single molecule. These structures are called resonance structures.

See-saw   A term which refers to a molecular geometry in VSEPR theory, referring specifically to a situation wherein there are five electron groups about a central atom (four bonding groups and one nonbonding). See-saw geometry is therefore a derivative of the trigonal bipyramidal electron geometry.

Sigma bond   In valence bond theory, this term refers to a bonding orbital which results from direct, "head-on" overlap between two atomic orbitals.

sp   This label refers to a type of hybrid atomic orbital in valence bond theory resulting from mixing one *s*-orbital and one *p*-orbital, creating a set of two *sp*-hybrid orbitals.

sp^2   This label refers to a type of hybrid atomic orbital in valence bond theory resulting from mixing one *s*-orbital and two *p*-orbitals, creating a set of three sp^2-hybrid orbitals.

sp^3   This label refers to a type of hybrid atomic orbital in valence bond theory resulting from mixing one *s*-orbital and three *p*-orbitals, creating a set of four sp^3-hybrid orbitals.

sp^3d   This label refers to a type of hybrid atomic orbital in valence bond theory resulting from mixing one *s*-orbital, three *p*-orbitals, and two *d*-orbitals, creating a set of five sp^3d-hybrid orbitals.

sp^3d^2   This label refers to a type of hybrid atomic orbital in valence bond theory resulting from mixing one *s*-orbital, three *p*-orbitals, and two *d*-orbitals, creating a set of six sp^3d^2-hybrid orbitals.

Spin-pair   A term describing a state wherein two electrons occupy an atomic or molecular orbital, adopting opposing spin states.

Triple bond   When three bonding pairs are shared between the same two atoms, this is referred to as a triple bond. Again, triple bonds generally have shorter bond lengths and are stronger than double bonds (which are shorter and stronger than single bonds).

Valence bond theory   The basic idea in valence bond theory is that electrons reside in quantum mechanical orbitals localized on individual atoms. These are the standard *s*, *p*, *d*, and *f* orbitals we learned in Chapter 7 and further, to maximize bonding, in valence bond theory the atomic orbitals on a given atom can mix to form new sets of hybrid combinations. These are termed hybrid orbitals.

Valence shell electron pair repulsion theory (VSEPR)   This theory is used in tandem with Lewis theory to predict molecular geometries. As the name implies, this theory assumes that electron pairs in the valence shell of the central atom of a molecule will exert an electrostatic repulsive force on each other. Owing to this, these electron pairs will naturally arrange themselves in a manner (or geometry) which minimizes these repulsions.

Intermolecular Forces and Phase Diagrams

9

KEY CONCEPTS

- Dispersion Forces
- Dipole-Dipole Interactions
- Hydrogen Bonding
- Ion-Dipole Forces
- The Influence of Intermolecular Forces on Physical Properties
- Phase Diagrams

INTERMOLECULAR FORCES

1. What are intermolecular forces and why are they important?

    Intermolecular forces are essentially responsible for holding condensed matter together and occur between atoms and molecules based on differences in charges, temporary charges, and partial charges. It is very important for us to understand why these forces exist as all living organisms are dependent on them. For example, intermolecular forces are responsible for holding the two strands of DNA together.

2. What are the major types of intermolecular forces discussed in this chapter?

    The major types of intermolecular forces discussed in this chapter include dispersion forces, dipole-dipole forces, hydrogen bonding, and ion-dipole interactions.

3. What are dispersion forces? Can you give an example of a molecule that experiences this type of intermolecular force?

    All atoms and molecules experience dispersion forces, which occur based on slight fluctuations in electron distribution within them. Based on probability given any point in time, the electrons will be unevenly distributed throughout the atom or molecule resulting in an electron rich region, leaving another region of the atom or molecule electron deficient. This unsymmetrical distribution of electrons can then result in an instantaneous temporary dipole in neighboring atoms or molecules. Hydrocarbons such as ethane, propane, and butane are all good examples of molecules that experience this type of intermolecular force.

4. Order the following noble gases in terms of increasing boiling points:

    $$Xe, Ne, Kr, and\ Ar$$

    All of the above elements experience dispersion forces, which increase in strength with increasing molar mass. Therefore, the relative boiling points also increase with increasing molar mass. Thus, the correct order in terms of increasing boiling points is:

    $$Ne < Ar < Kr < Xe$$

5. Order the following hydrocarbons in terms of increasing boiling points:

    $$CH_4, CH_3CH_2CH_2CH_3, CH_3CH_3, and\ CH_3CH_2CH_3$$

    All of the above hydrocarbons experience dispersion forces, which increase in strength with increasing molar mass. Therefore, the relative boiling points also increase with increasing molar mass. Thus, the correct order in terms of increasing boiling points is:

    $$CH_4 < CH_3CH_3 < CH_3CH_2CH_3 < CH_3CH_2CH_2CH_3$$

6. Which of the following molecules would you expect to have a higher boiling point and why?

$$H_3C \overset{CH_2}{\diagdown} CH_2 \overset{CH_2}{\diagdown} CH_3$$

$$H_3C - \overset{\overset{\displaystyle CH_3}{|}}{\underset{\underset{\displaystyle CH_3}{|}}{C}} - CH_3$$

Pentane (left molecule) has a higher boiling than neopentane (right molecule). Even though both molecules have the same molecular weight (72.17 g/mol), the major difference here is shape. Pentane (left molecule) has a larger surface area available to interact with neighboring molecules when compared to neopentane (right molecule). A larger surface area allows for greater interactions which translate into a higher boiling. In fact, the boiling of pentane is approximately 36 °C, while neopentane is closer to 9.5 °C.

7. What are dipole-dipole forces? Can you give an example of a molecule that experiences this type of intermolecular force?

Dipole-dipole forces exist in all polar molecules, which have a dipole, in which the molecule contains permanent electron rich and electron deficient regions. This gives rise to partially negative and partially positive "poles" of the molecule. Acetone and formaldehyde are both good examples of molecules that experience this type of intermolecular force (in addition to dispersion forces).

8. Which of the following molecules would you expect to have a higher boiling point and why?

$$H_3C \overset{CH_2}{\diagdown} CH_2 \overset{CH_3}{\diagup}$$

$$H_3C \overset{\overset{\displaystyle O}{\overset{\displaystyle \|}{C}}}{\diagup} \diagdown CH_3$$

Acetone (right molecule) has a higher boiling point than butane (left molecule). Even though both of these molecules experience dispersion forces and have similar molar masses of approximately 58.1 g/mol, acetone also has dipole-dipole forces. This is due to the fact that acetone has a permanent dipole and is therefore polar because of the presence of the highly electronegative oxygen atom. This makes a significant difference in boiling points (compare: −0.5 °C for butane and 56 °C for acetone).

9. What are miscible substances? Can you give an example?

Miscible substances are two substances that mix with one another without separating into two states of liquids. They form a homogenous mixture. Water (H_2O) and ethanol (CH_3CH_2OH) are miscible substances. Both substances are polar.

10. What are immiscible substances? Can you give an example?

Immiscible substances are two substances that do not mix with one another without separating into two states of liquids. They do not form a homogenous mixture (like oil and vinegar in salad dressing). Carbon tetrachloride (CCl_4) and water (H_2O) are immiscible substances. Carbon tetrachloride is nonpolar while water is polar.

11. What are amphiphilic molecules? Can you give an example?

Amphiphilic molecules are molecules that possess both nonpolar and polar properties. The molecules present in soap are amphiphilic molecules.

12. What is hydrogen bonding? Can you give an example of a molecule that experiences this type of intermolecular force?

Hydrogen bonding occurs when polar molecules contain hydrogen directly bound to very electronegative atoms, specifically nitrogen, oxygen, or fluorine. Water (H_2O) and ethanol (CH_3CH_2OH) are both good examples of molecules with hydrogen bonding (in addition to dispersion forces and dipole-dipole interactions).

13. Which of the following molecules would you expect to have a higher boiling point and why?

Pentanol (right molecule) has a higher boiling point than pentane (left molecule). While both molecules have dispersion forces, pentanol also experiences dipole-dipole interactions as well as hydrogen bonding. This dramatically increases the boiling point (compare 36 °C for pentane and greater than 130 °C for pentanol).

14. What are ion-dipole forces? Can you give an example of an ion(s) and molecule that experiences this type of intermolecular force?

Ion-dipole forces are intermolecular forces that occur between two different entities, such as a water molecule and some other molecule other than neighboring water (i.e. an ionic compound such as salt). If we were to mix sodium chloride in water, there are relatively strong interactions that would occur between these two entities. As the salt dissolves in water in a process known as solvation, ion-dipole forces takeover. The positively charged sodium cations interacts with the partially negatively charged oxygen atoms of water molecules and the negatively charged chloride ions interact with the partially positively charged hydrogen atoms in water.

15. Which kind of intermolecular forces are present in *He*?

Dispersion forces.

16. Which kind of intermolecular forces are present in NH_3?

Dispersion forces, dipole-dipole forces, and hydrogen bonding.

17. Which kind of intermolecular forces are present in *Kr*?

Dispersion forces.

18. Which kind of intermolecular forces are present in *HCl*?

Dispersion forces and dipole-dipole forces.

19. Which kind of intermolecular forces are present in CH_3OH?

Dispersion forces, dipole-dipole forces, and hydrogen bonding.

20. Which kind of intermolecular forces are present in $CH_3CH_2CH_3$?

Dispersion forces.

21. Which kind of intermolecular forces are present in H_2Se?

    Dispersion forces and dipole-dipole forces.

22. Which kind of intermolecular forces are present in CO?

    Dispersion forces and dipole-dipole forces.

23. Which kind of intermolecular forces are present in CCl_4?

    Dispersion forces.

24. Which kind of intermolecular forces are present in H_2O?

    Dispersion forces, dipole-dipole forces, and hydrogen bonding.

25. What are some of the characteristics that make water a rather unique substance necessary to sustain life and how is this related to intermolecular forces?

    Water has a bent geometry, and the highly polar O-H bonds give water a significant dipole moment. The two O-H bonds present in water allow for one water molecule to hydrogen bond with four other water molecules resulting in a somewhat uniquely intricate network. This extensive hydrogen bonding pattern allows water to be a liquid at room temperature, which is obviously very important in order to sustain life as it is the main solvent in living organisms allowing for nutrients to readily travel throughout the body. Water is also a very unique substance in that it is less dense in the solid phase than in the liquid phase, which is not the case with most substances. This is because this unique hydrogen bonding pattern allows water molecules to be regularly arranged resembling an "open-cage" structure containing lots of empty space making it less dense in the solid state versus the liquid. Thus, ice floats on top of the liquid water on a frozen lake, which is also an important fact as it relates to sustaining life because if solid ice sank to the bottom of a lake every time it froze, it would essentially eliminate all aquatic life in the lake.

PROPERTIES OF LIQUIDS ATTRIBUTED TO INTERMOLECULAR FORCES

26. Describe the process of vaporization (evaporation).

    Vaporization is a process which involves a substance changing from the liquid state to the gas state. This is an endothermic process.

27. Describe the process of condensation.

    Condensation is a process which involves a substance changing from the gas state to a liquid state. This is an exothermic process.

28. In volatile liquids, the intermolecular forces tend to be (weaker/stronger) and vaporize more readily, whereas nonvolatile liquids tend to have (weaker/stronger) intermolecular forces and fewer molecules escape the liquid phase.

    Weaker, stronger

29. Define heat of vaporization (ΔH^o_{vap}).

The heat of vaporization is the amount of heat energy required to vaporize one mole of a liquid to the gas state under standard conditions (units are generally given in kJ/mol).

30. Define dynamic equilibrium.

Dynamic equilibrium is the point at which the rate of condensation and evaporation become equal (occurring at the same time and same rate).

31. Define vapor pressure.

Vapor pressure is defined as the pressure of the vapor in dynamic equilibrium with its liquid, and is dependent on the intermolecular forces of the liquid at a given temperature. Essentially, vapor pressure is a measure of how easily molecules can escape the liquid state and go into the gas state.

32. What is a volatile liquid? What is a nonvolatile liquid?

The molecules of a volatile liquid have the propensity to escape the liquid phase and go into the gas phase, while a nonvolatile liquid does not.

33. What is the difference between the boiling point and normal boiling point of a liquid?

The boiling point is defined as the temperature at which a liquid's vapor pressure is equal to the external pressure, whereas the normal boiling point is the temperature at which a liquid's vapor pressure is 1 atm (atmospheric pressure at sea level). In the definition of normal boiling point, the external pressure is specified and therefore does not change with geographical location (which is not the case for boiling point).

34. What is a supercritical fluid? What is the critical temperature and critical pressure?

A supercritical fluid has properties of both liquids and gases and exists at specific temperature and pressure conditions. For a given liquid, the temperature and pressure at which a supercritical fluid is formed is called the critical temperature and the critical pressure, respectively.

35. What causes surface tension in a liquid?

Surface tension is the energy required to break the attractive interaction of molecules on the surface of the liquid. These attractive interactions at the surface exist due to the fact that surface molecules have fewer neighbors to interact with when compared to those present in the interior of the liquid. The effect of this on molecules present on the surface is an inward force of attraction between surface molecules that can act like an elastic skin layer giving rise to surface tension.

36. What is capillary action?

Capillary action is the ability of a liquid to flow up a narrow tube against gravity based on the attraction between the liquid molecules and the capillary tube (adhesive forces).

37. What is the difference between adhesive and cohesive forces?

The attractions between the molecules of a liquid and its container are known as adhesive forces, whereas the attractions between the molecules within the liquid are known as cohesive forces.

38. What causes a meniscus to form when a liquid is placed in a graduated cylinder?

A meniscus is a curve formed when a liquid is placed in a container (such as a graduated cylinder). With a liquid such as water, a concave "U" shape forms due to the attractive adhesive forces between the molecules and container. In some liquids with strong cohesive forces such as mercury, a convex meniscus can form.

39. What is the viscosity of a liquid?

The viscosity of a liquid is the resistance of the liquid to flow. The more viscous a liquid, the less readily it will flow.

40. Define miscibility and describe the difference between miscible and immiscible liquids.

Miscibility refers to the ability of substances to mix based largely on the polarity of the substance. Miscible liquids are able to mix, whereas immiscible liquids do not mix when combined. In general, polar liquids are miscible with other polar liquids, and nonpolar liquids are miscible with other nonpolar liquids. However, polar and nonpolar liquids are generally immiscible.

For questions 41–44, consider the following two substances:

41. Which of the two liquids above would have stronger intermolecular forces?

Water (left) has stronger intermolecular forces. It has dispersion forces, dipole-dipole interactions, and hydrogen bonding. Acetone (right) has dispersion forces and dipole-dipole interactions.

42. Which of the two liquids above would you expect to have a higher vapor pressure?

Acetone has a higher vapor pressure (weaker intermolecular forces when compared to water).

43. Which of the two liquids above would you expect to be more volatile?

Acetone is more volatile (weaker intermolecular forces when compared to water).

44. Which of the two liquids above would you expect to have a higher boiling point?

Water has a higher boiling point due to the stronger intermolecular forces present in water when compared to acetone.

For questions 45–48, consider the following two substances:

45. Which of the two liquids above would have stronger intermolecular forces?

Isopropanol (right) has stronger intermolecular forces. It has dispersion forces, dipole-dipole interactions, and hydrogen bonding. Diethyl ether (left) has dispersion forces and dipole-dipole interactions.

46. Which of the two liquids above would you expect to have a higher vapor pressure?

Diethyl ether has a higher vapor pressure (weaker intermolecular forces when compared to isopropanol).

47. Which of the two liquids above would you expect to be more volatile?

Diethyl ether is more volatile (weaker intermolecular forces when compared to isopropanol).

48. Which of the two liquids above would you expect to have a higher boiling point?

Isopropanol has a higher boiling point due to the stronger intermolecular forces present in isopropanol when compared to diethyl ether.

49. Are the vapor pressure of a particular liquid and temperature related? If so, what is the relationship?

Yes, the vapor pressure of a liquid and the temperature are in fact related. As the temperature increases, the vapor pressure also increases exponentially (not linearly). As the temperature decreases, the vapor pressure also decreases exponentially.

50. Consider two beakers of water, one containing 100 ml of water with a diameter of 8 cm and the other containing the same amount of water but with a diameter of 14 cm. From which beaker will the water evaporate faster? Is there a difference in the vapor pressure of the water between the two beakers?

The water in the beaker with the larger diameter (14 cm) will evaporate faster than the one with the smaller diameter (8 cm) because of the greater surface area associated with the larger one. There is no difference in the vapor pressure of the water between the two beakers because vapor pressure only depends on the substance and the temperature.

51. Consider two beakers with identical diameters (8 cm) containing the same amount of liquid (100 ml), one filled with water and the other containing acetone. Which liquid will evaporate faster? Is there a difference in the vapor pressure between the two liquids?

The acetone will evaporate faster than the water because of the weaker intermolecular forces associated with the acetone. Water can form hydrogen bonds, while acetone cannot. Acetone will have a higher vapor pressure when compared to the water at the same temperature.

52. One of the tubes below contains water and the other with mercury. Based on the shape of the meniscus, can you tell which one contains the water versus the mercury?

The tube on the left contains water with the concave meniscus due to the strong adhesive forces between the molecules and container, while the tube on the right contains mercury with a convex meniscus due to the stronger cohesive forces.

53. Shelby and Rusty are lab partners in their General Chemistry Laboratory class. As part of their experiment, they are required to fill a graduated cylinder with 25 ml of water. Shelby grabs a clean graduated cylinder, fills it with the required amount of water, and notices a nice concave meniscus. Rusty on the other hand unknowingly grabs a dirty graduated cylinder which has an oily residue lining on the inside of the cylinder. He fills it with the required amount of water and notices that the shape of his meniscus is not the same as Shelby's. What would you expect Rusty's meniscus to look like and why?

Shelby's clean graduated cylinder allows for strong adhesive forces between the water molecules and the cylinder resulting in a nice concave meniscus. Rusty's dirty cylinder containing the oily residue, however, interferes with these adhesive forces as water and oil do not mix (water is polar and oil is nonpolar). The result is essentially a flat meniscus as the water is unable to rise along the tube's interior (cohesive forces amongst the water molecules are stronger).

54. Are ethanol (CH_3CH_2OH) and water miscible substances? Explain.

Yes, they are both polar and are therefore miscible substances. Dispersion forces, dipole-dipole interactions, and hydrogen bonding exists between all molecules.

55. Are carbon tetrachloride (CCl_4) and water miscible substances? Explain.

No, carbon tetrachloride is nonpolar and water is polar. Therefore, they do not form a homogenous mixture and are immiscible substances.

56. Are *NaCl* and water miscible substances? Explain.

Yes, they are miscible substances. There are ion-dipole interactions present in this homogenous mixture between the Na^+ and Cl^- ions with water molecules.

PHASE DIAGRAMS

57. What is a phase diagram?

A phase diagram summarizes the various states of matter (solid, liquid, gas) using the relationship between temperature (x-axis) and pressure (y-axis). The lines on the phase diagram represent the temperature and pressure conditions in which two phases exist at equilibrium.

58. What is the significance of crossing a line in phase diagram?

Crossing a line in the phase diagram indicates a change in the state of matter.

Using the phase diagram depicted below, consider the following questions:

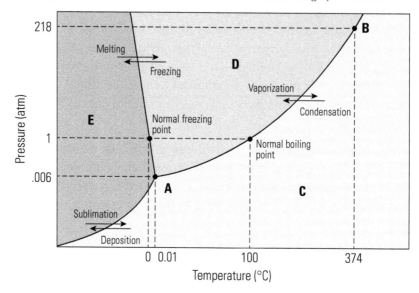

59. The gas phase is represented by which of the following letters?
    a. A
    b. B
    c. **C**
    d. D
    e. E

60. The solid phase is represented by which of the following letters?
    a. A
    b. B
    c. C
    d. D
    e. **E**

61. The liquid phase is represented by which of the following letters?
    a. A
    b. B
    c. C
    d. **D**
    e. E

62. The critical point is represented by which of the following letters?
    a. A
    b. **B**
    c. C
    d. D
    e. E

63. The triple point is represented by which of the following letters?
    a. A
    b. B
    c. C
    d. D
    e. E

KEY TERMS

Adhesive forces   A term used in the description of the phenomenon known as capillary action. Adhesive forces refers generically to the forces of attraction between the liquid and the walls of a tube or channel.

Amorphous solids   Solids which exhibit a random arrangement of molecules or atoms.

Amphiphilic molecules   Molecules that possess both nonpolar and polar properties.

Boiling point   The temperature at which a liquid's vapor pressure is equal to the external pressure.

Capillary action   The ability of a liquid to flow up a narrow tube against gravity. This is due to the attraction between the liquid and the tube, known as adhesive forces.

Cohesive forces   The attractive forces between the molecules in a liquid or solid (holding them in the liquid or solid state).

Condensation   The transition of a substance from the gaseous state to the liquid state.

Critical point   The conditions of temperature and pressure above which a substance will transition to a supercritical fluid.

Critical pressure   The pressure above which a fluid becomes supercritical.

Critical temperature   The temperature above which a fluid becomes supercritical.

Crystalline solid   A solid that has a highly ordered arrangement of its constituent atoms, ions, or molecules.

Dipole-dipole forces   The attractive, electrostatic forces which exist between the positive pole of an electric dipole and the negative pole of another. These forces are operative in all polar compounds.

Dispersion forces   Dispersion forces are present in all atoms and molecules and occur based on slight fluctuations in electron distribution. In other words, based on probability given any point in time, the electrons will be unevenly distributed throughout the atom or molecule resulting in an electron rich region, leaving another region of the atom or molecule electron deficient. This unsymmetrical distribution of electrons results in an instantaneous, temporary dipole (with slightly negative and positive regions), which can then induce temporary dipoles in neighboring atoms or molecules.

Dynamic equilibrium   A term describing a state wherein two competing processes achieve equal rates. As an example, when the rates of evaporation and condensation of a fluid in a closed container are equal, a dynamic steady state between the liquid and gas states in now in place. This system is now said to be in *dynamic equilibrium*.

Evaporation   The process wherein molecules on the surface of a liquid will transition to the gaseous state.

Fusion curve   The line on a phase diagram that separates the solid from the liquid phases.

Heat of vaporization   The heat required to vaporize one mole of a liquid under standard conditions.

Hydrogen bonding   Hydrogen bonding occurs when polar molecules contain hydrogen directly bound to very electronegative atoms, specifically nitrogen, oxygen, or fluorine. This intermolecular force is stronger than a regular dipole-dipole interaction and can be thought of as an exceptionally strong dipole-dipole interaction. This occurs due to the large electronegativity difference between hydrogen and any of these highly electronegative atoms. The result of such interactions is that hydrogen has a relatively large partial positive charge, while the nitrogen, oxygen, or fluorine atoms have a large partial negative charge.

Immiscible   A term describing pairs of liquids which do not mix with each other into a single liquid phase. For example, oil and water are immiscible.

Intermolecular forces   A generic term for the forces responsible for holding condensed matter together and that occur between atoms and molecules. These are essentially electrostatic forces arising from differences in ionic charges, temporary charges, and permanent partial charges.

Ion-dipole forces   The electrostatic attractive forces which occur between an ionic compound and a polar compound.

Meniscus   The "u-shape" adopted by liquids in a glass cylinder arising from the competing effects of adhesive and cohesive forces.

Miscible   A term referring to a pair of liquids which are capable of mixing into a single liquid phase.

Nonvolatile liquids   Nonvolatile liquids are characterized by intermolecular forces which are stronger and therefore fewer molecules escape the liquid phase.

Normal boiling point   The temperature at which a liquid's vapor pressure is 1 atm (atmospheric pressure at sea level).

Phase diagram   A chart which shows the pressure and temperature at which a substance exists in a distinct phase (solid, liquid, or gas). The lines or boundaries between phases in a phase diagram represent conditions at which the phases are in dynamic equilibrium.

Sublimation curve   The line in a phase diagram that represents the transition between solid and gas phases.

Supercritical fluid   There are specific temperature and pressure conditions at which the gas and liquid states comingle to form a supercritical fluid, which has properties of both liquids and gases.

Surface tension   The elastic nature of the surface of a liquid which arises from its tendency to minimize its surface area due to intermolecular forces.

Triple point   The temperature and pressure conditions in which all three states (solid, liquid, gas) coexist at equilibrium.

Vapor pressure   For a given substance, this is the pressure of the vapor in dynamic equilibrium with the liquid phase, and is dependent on the intermolecular forces of the liquid at a given temperature.

Vapor pressure curve   The line in a phase diagram which separates the gas and liquid phases.

Viscosity   The resistance of a liquid to flow.

Volatile liquids   Volatile liquids are characterized by intermolecular forces which are weak and therefore more molecules escape the liquid phase.

Volatility   The propensity of a liquid to evaporate.

CHAPTER 10

Chemical Equilibrium

KEY CONCEPTS

- Chemical Equilibrium
- The Law of Mass Action and the Equilibrium Constant, K
- Reactant and Product Favored Reactions
- Calculating Equilibrium Concentrations of Reactants and Products
- The Reaction Quotient, Q
- Le Châtelier's Principle
- Solubility Products, K_{sp}
- The Common Ion Effect

EQUILIBRIUM CONSTANT

1. When a reaction is at equilibrium, there is no change in the concentrations of the reactants or products. Why is this state considered dynamic?

    We define the term *dynamic equilibrium* in a chemical reaction as that state in which the rate of the forward reaction is equal to the rate of the reverse reaction. In other words, reactions are continuously proceeding in both the forward and reverse directions such that a dynamic steady state is established respecting product and reactant concentrations.

2. If a reaction proceeds to near completion, is K_c large or small?

    Because the product concentrations (or partial pressures) are in the numerator of the equilibrium constant expression, a large value of K_c represents a reaction that proceeds to near-complete conversion to product.

3. Write the equilibrium constant expression in terms of concentrations of reactants and products (K_c) as well as in terms of partial pressures (K_p) for the following reaction:

    $$CH_4(g) + 4\ F_2(g) \rightleftharpoons CF_4(g) + 4\ HF(g)$$

    $$K_c = \frac{[CF_4][HF]^4}{[CH_4][F_2]^4}$$

    $$K_p = \frac{P_{CF_4} \cdot P_{HF}^4}{P_{CH_4} \cdot P_{F_2}^4}$$

4. Write the equilibrium constant expression in terms of concentrations of reactants and products (K_c) as well as in terms of partial pressures (K_p) for the following reaction:

    $$2\ N_2(g) + 4\ H_2O(g) \rightleftharpoons 4\ H_2(g) + 4\ NO(g)$$

    $$K_c = \frac{[H_2]^4[NO]^4}{[N_2]^2[H_2O]^4},$$

    $$K_p = \frac{P_{H_2}^4 \cdot P_{NO}^4}{P_{N_2}^2 \cdot P_{H_2O}^4}$$

5. Write the equilibrium constant expression in terms of concentrations of reactants and products (K_c) as well as in terms of partial pressures (K_p) for the following reaction:

    $$4\ NH_3(g) + 3\ O_2(g) \rightleftharpoons 2\ N_2(g) + 6\ H_2O(g)$$

    $$K_c = \frac{[N_2]^2[H_2O]^6}{[NH_3]^4[O_2]^3}$$

    $$K_p = \frac{P_{N_2}^2 \cdot P_{H_2O}^6}{P_{NH_3}^4 \cdot P_{O_2}^3}$$

6. Write the equilibrium constant expression in terms of concentrations of reactants and products (K_c) as well as in terms of partial pressures (K_p) for the following reaction:

$$2 N_2(g) + 4 H_2O(g) \rightleftharpoons 4 H_2(g) + 4 NO(g)$$

$$K_c = \frac{[H_2]^4 [NO]^4}{[N_2]^2 [H_2O]^4}$$

$$K_p = \frac{P_{H_2}^4 \cdot P_{NO}^4}{P_{N_2}^2 \cdot P_{H_2O}^4}$$

7. Write the equilibrium constant expression in terms of concentrations of reactants and products (K_c) for the following reaction:

$$H_2O(l) + SO_3(g) \rightleftharpoons H_2SO_4(aq)$$

$$K_c = \frac{[H_2SO_4]}{[SO_3]}$$

8. Write the equilibrium constant expression in terms of concentrations of reactants and products (K_c) for the following reaction:

$$2 C(s) + O_2(g) \rightleftharpoons 2 CO(g)$$

$$K_c = \frac{[CO]^2}{[O_2]}$$

9. Classify the following reactions as product-favored or reactant-favored:

   a. $C_2H_2(g) + H_2O(g) \rightleftharpoons CH_3CHO(g)$ $\qquad K_c = 4.0 \times 10^{-4}$

   $K_c \ll 1$; Reactant-favored

   b. $PCl_3(g) + Cl_2(g) \rightleftharpoons PCl_5(g)$ $\qquad K_c = 23.0$

   $K_c \gg 1$; Product-favored

10. Classify the following reactions as product-favored or reactant-favored:

    a. $C(s) + 2 Cl_2(g) \rightleftharpoons CCl_4(g)$ $\qquad K_c = 8.3 \times 10^{10}$

    $K_c \gg 1$; Product-favored

    b. $CCl_4(g) + CH_4(g) \rightleftharpoons 2 CH_2Cl_2(g)$ $\qquad K_c = 0.95$

    $K_c \approx 1$; Neither reactant- nor product-favored.

11. At a particular temperature, $K'_c = 3.45 \times 10^{-9}$ for the following reaction:

$$C_2H_4(g) \rightleftharpoons C_2H_2(g) + H_2(g)$$

Given this information, what is the value of K_c for the following:

$$3\ C_2H_4(g) \rightleftharpoons 3\ C_2H_2(g) + 3\ H_2(g)$$

$$K_c = \left(K'_c\right)^3 = \left(3.45 \times 10^{-9}\right)^3 = 4.11 \times 10^{-26}$$

12. At a particular temperature, $K'_c = 3.45 \times 10^{-9}$ for the following reaction:

$$C_2H_4(g) \rightleftharpoons C_2H_2(g) + H_2(g)$$

Given this information, what is the value of K_c for the following:

$$C_2H_2(g) + H_2(g) \rightleftharpoons C_2H_4(g)$$

$$K_c = \frac{1}{K'_c} = \frac{1}{3.45 \times 10^{-9}} = 2.90 \times 10^8$$

13. At a particular temperature, $K'_c = 7.15 \times 10^{27}$ for the following reaction:

$$2\ CO(g) + O_2(g) \rightleftharpoons 2\ CO_2(g)$$

Given this information, what is the value of K_c for the following:

$$6\ CO_2(g) \rightleftharpoons 6\ CO(g) + 3\ O_2(g)$$

$$K_c = \frac{1}{\left(K'_c\right)^3} = \frac{1}{\left(7.15 \times 10^{27}\right)^3} = 2.74 \times 10^{-84}$$

14. At a particular temperature, $K'_c = 7.15 \times 10^{27}$ for the following reaction:

$$2\ CO(g) + O_2(g) \rightleftharpoons 2\ CO_2(g)$$

Given this information, what is the value of K_c for the following:

$$CO_2(g) \rightleftharpoons CO(g) + \frac{1}{2}O_2(g)$$

$$K_c = \frac{1}{\left(K'_c\right)^{1/2}} = \frac{1}{\left(7.15 \times 10^{27}\right)^{1/2}} = 1.18 \times 10^{-14}$$

15. Given the following (@ 298 K):

$$C(s) + 2 H_2(g) \rightleftharpoons CH_4(g) \qquad K_1 = 7.1 \times 10^8$$

$$C(s) + 2 Cl_2(g) \rightleftharpoons CCl_4(g) \qquad K_2 = 8.3 \times 10^{10}$$

$$H_2(g) + Cl_2(g) \rightleftharpoons 2 HCl(g) \qquad K_3 = 5.1 \times 10^{16}$$

Calculate the equilibrium constant, K_c, for the following reaction.

$$CH_4(g) + 4 Cl_2(g) \rightleftharpoons CCl_4(g) + 4 HCl(g) \qquad K_c = ?$$

$$CH_4(g) \rightleftharpoons \cancel{C(s)} + \cancel{2H_2(g)} \qquad K'_c = \frac{1}{7.1 \times 10^8}$$

$$\cancel{C(s)} + 2 Cl_2(g) \rightleftharpoons CCl_4(g) \qquad K''_c = 8.3 \times 10^{10}$$

$$+ \; \cancel{2H_2(g)} + 2 Cl_2(g) \rightleftharpoons 4 HCl(g) \qquad K'''_c = (5.1 \times 10^{16})^2$$

$$\overline{CH_4(g) + 4 Cl_2(g) \rightleftharpoons CCl_4(g) + 4 HCl(g)}$$

$$K_c = \frac{1}{7.1 \times 10^8} \times 8.3 \times 10^{10} \times (5.1 \times 10^{16})^2 = 3.04 \times 10^{35}$$

16. Given the following (@ 2000 K):

$$N_2O_4(g) \rightleftharpoons 2 NO_2(g) \qquad K_1 = 4.80 \times 10^4$$

$$N_2(g) + 2 O_2(g) \rightleftharpoons 2 NO_2(g) \qquad K_2 = 7.59 \times 10^{-9}$$

Calculate the equilibrium constant, K_c, for the following reaction.

$$N_2(g) + 2 O_2(g) \rightleftharpoons N_2O_4(g) \qquad K_c = ?$$

$$2 \cancel{NO_2}(g) \rightleftharpoons N_2O_4(g) \qquad K''_c = \frac{1}{4.80 \times 10^4}$$

$$+ \; N_2(g) + 2 O_2(g) \rightleftharpoons 2\cancel{NO_2}(g) \qquad K'''_c = 7.59 \times 10^{-9}$$

$$\overline{N_2(g) + 2 O_2(g) \rightleftharpoons N_2O_4(g)}$$

$$K_c = \frac{1}{4.8 \times 10^4} \times 7.59 \times 10^{-9} = 1.58 \times 10^{-13}$$

EQUILIBRIUM CONSTANT IN TERMS OF PARTIAL PRESSURE

17. Find K_c for the following reaction:

$$2\ NO(g) + O_2(g) \rightleftharpoons 2\ NO_2(g) \quad K_p = 1.95 \times 10^{12}\ (@\ 298\ K)$$

$$K_p = K_c(RT)^{\Delta n}$$

$$\Delta n = 2 - (2 + 1) = -1$$

$$K_c = \frac{K_p}{(RT)^{\Delta n}} = \frac{1.95 \times 10^{12}}{\left(\left(0.08206\dfrac{L \cdot atm}{mol \cdot K}\right)(298\ K)\right)^{-1}} = \mathbf{4.77 \times 10^{13}}$$

$$\boldsymbol{K_c = 4.77 \times 10^{13}}$$

18. Find K_c for the following reaction:

$$2\ CO(g) + O_2(g) \rightleftharpoons 2\ CO_2(g) \quad K_p = 1.38 \times 10^{90}\ (@\ 298\ K)$$

$$\Delta n = 2 - 2 - 1 = -1$$

$$K_c = \frac{K_p}{(RT)^{\Delta n}} = \frac{1.38 \times 10^{90}}{\left(\left(0.08206\dfrac{L \cdot atm}{mol \cdot K}\right)(298\ K)\right)^{-1}} = \mathbf{3.37 \times 10^{91}}$$

19. Find K_c for the following reaction:

$$CH_4(g) + H_2O(g) \rightleftharpoons CO(g) + 3\ H_2(g) \quad K_p = 1.98 \times 10^{32}\ (@\ 375\ K)$$

$$\Delta n = (3 + 1) - (1 + 1) = 2$$

$$K_c = \frac{K_p}{(RT)^{\Delta n}} = \frac{1.98 \times 10^{32}}{\left(\left(0.08206\dfrac{L \cdot atm}{mol \cdot K}\right)(375\ K)\right)^{2}} = \mathbf{2.09 \times 10^{29}}$$

20. Find K_p for the following reaction:

$$N_2(g) + 3\ H_2(g) \rightleftharpoons 2\ NH_3(g) \quad K_c = 3.78\ (@\ 600\ K)$$

$$\Delta n = (2) - (3 + 1) = -2$$

$$K_p = K_c(RT)^{\Delta n} = 3.78\left(\left(0.08206\dfrac{L \cdot atm}{mol \cdot K}\right)(600\ K)\right)^{-2} = \mathbf{1.56 \times 10^{-3}}$$

21. Find K_p for the following reaction:

$$2\ SO_2(g) + O_2(g) \rightleftharpoons 2\ SO_3(g) \quad K_c = 3.71 \times 10^8 \ (@\ 600\ K)$$

$$\Delta n = (2) - (2+1) = -1$$

$$K_p = K_c(RT)^{\Delta n} = 3.71 \times 10^8 \left[\left(0.08206 \frac{L \cdot atm}{mol \cdot K} \right)(600\ K) \right]^{-1} = \mathbf{7.54 \times 10^6}$$

22. For which of the following equilibria are the values of K_c and K_p the same?
    a. $H_2(g) + Cl_2(g) \rightleftharpoons 2HCl(g) \qquad \Delta n = (2) - (1+1) = 0$
    b. $C(s) + 2\ H_2(g) \rightleftharpoons CH_4(g)$
    c. $C_2H_4(g) \rightleftharpoons C_2H_2(g) + H_2(g)$

    $K_c = K_p$ when $\Delta n = 0$.

23. For which of the following equilibria are the values of K_c and K_p the same?
    a. $H_2O(g) + CO(g) \rightleftharpoons CO_2(g) + H_2(g) \qquad \Delta n = (1+1) - (1+1) = 0$
    b. $CCl_4(g) + CH_4(g) \rightleftharpoons 2\ CH_2Cl_2(g) \qquad \Delta n = (2) - (1+1) = 0$
    c. $4\ NH_3(g) + 3\ O_2(g) \rightleftharpoons 2\ N_2(g) + 6\ H_2O(g)$

    $K_c = K_p$ when $\Delta n = 0$.

HETEROGENEOUS EQUILIBRIA – SOLIDS AND LIQUIDS

24. Write the expression for K_c associated with the following reaction:

$$2\ HCl(aq) + CaCO_3(s) \rightleftharpoons CaCl_2(aq) + H_2O(l) + CO_2(g)$$

$$K_c = \frac{[CaCl_2][CO_2]}{[HCl]^2}$$

25. Write the expressions for K_p and K_c associated with the following reaction:

$$P_4(s) + 5O_2(g) \rightleftharpoons P_4O_{10}(s)$$

$$K_c = \frac{1}{[O_2]^5}$$

$$K_p = \frac{1}{P_{O_2}^5}$$

26. Write the expressions for K_p and K_c associated with the following reaction:

$$SnO_2(s) + 2\,H_2(g) \rightleftharpoons Sn(s) + 2\,H_2O(g)$$

$$K_c = \frac{[H_2O]^2}{[H_2]^2}$$

$$K_p = \frac{P_{H_2O}^2}{P_{H_2}^2}$$

27. Write the expressions for K_p and K_c associated with the following reaction:

$$CaCO_3(s) \rightleftharpoons CaO(s) + CO_2(g)$$

$$K_c = [CO_2]$$

$$K_p = P_{CO_2}$$

DETERMINING THE EQUILIBRIUM CONSTANT

28. A pure sample of ammonia gas is contained in a sealed reactor and heated to a particular temperature.

$$2\,NH_3(g) \rightleftharpoons N_2(g) + 3\,H_2(g)$$

At equilibrium, $[NH_3] = 0.418\ M$, $[N_2] = 0.282\ M$, and $[H_2] = 0.846\ M$. What is the value of K_c for this reaction?

$$K_c = \frac{[N_2][H_2]^3}{[NH_3]^2} = \frac{(0.282)(0.846)^3}{(0.418)^2} = \mathbf{0.977}$$

29. A pure sample of PCl_5 gas is contained in a sealed reactor and heated to a particular temperature.

$$PCl_5(g) \rightleftharpoons Cl_2(g) + PCl_3(g)$$

At equilibrium, $[PCl_5] = 0.0333\ M$, $[Cl_2] = 0.167\ M$, and $[PCl_3] = 0.167\ M$. What is the value of K_c for this reaction?

$$K_c = \frac{[PCl_3][Cl_2]}{[PCl_5]} = \frac{(0.167)(0.167)}{(0.0333)} = \mathbf{0.838}$$

30. A pure sample of SO_2Cl_2 gas is contained in a sealed reactor and heated to a particular temperature.

$$SO_2Cl_2(g) \rightleftharpoons SO_2(g) + Cl_2(g)$$

Initially, $[SO_2Cl_2] = 0.500\ M$. However, having established equilibrium, $[Cl_2] = 0.4075\ M$. Calculate the value of K_c for this reaction.

In this case, we construct a reaction table to determine expressions for the equilibrium concentrations of the components of the reaction mixture. These are inferred from the reaction stoichiometry as follows:

Concentration	$SO_2Cl_2(g) \rightleftharpoons SO_2(g) + Cl_2(g)$		
Initial	0.500	0	0
Change	$-x$	$+x$	$+x$
Equilibrium	**0.500 – x**	**x**	**x**

Since we know the equilibrium concentration of Cl_2 is 0.4075 M, we know:

$$x = 0.4075\ M$$

$$K_c = \frac{[SO_2][Cl_2]}{[SO_2Cl_2]} = \frac{(x)(x)}{(0.500-x)} = \frac{(0.4075)^2}{(0.500-0.4075)} = 1.80$$

$$\boldsymbol{K_c = 1.80}$$

31. Consider the following reaction equation:

$$2\,H_2S(g) \rightleftharpoons 2\,H_2(g) + S_2(g)$$

The initial partial pressure of H_2S is 0.345 *atm*, while the partial pressures of the products are zero initially. Having established equilibrium, $P_{S_2} = 0.00632\ atm$. Calculate the value of K_p for this reaction.

Concentration	$2\,H_2S(g) \rightleftharpoons 2\,H_2(g) + S_2(g)$		
Initial	0.345	0	0
Change	$-2x$	$+2x$	$+x$
Equilibrium	**0.345 – 2x**	**2x**	**x**

$$x = 0.00632\ atm$$

$$K_p = \frac{[P_{H2}]^2[P_{S2}]}{[P_{H2S}]^2} = \frac{(2x)^2(x)}{(0.345-2x)^2} = \frac{(0.01264)^2(0.00632)}{(0.345-0.01264)^2} = \frac{1.01\times10^{-6}}{0.1105} = 9.14\times10^{-6}$$

$$\boldsymbol{K_p = 9.14\times10^{-6}}$$

32. Consider the following reaction equation:

$$SO_2(g) + NO_2(g) \rightleftharpoons SO_3(g) + NO(g)$$

If 0.350 moles of SO_2 and 0.350 moles of NO_2 are delivered into a 1.00-L reactor at a particular temperature and having established equilibrium, calculate the value of K_c for this reaction, if it is determined that $[SO_3] = $ **0.214 M**.

Concentration	$SO_2(g) +$	$NO_2(g) \rightleftharpoons$	$SO_3(g) +$	$NO(g)$
Initial	0.350	0.350	0	0
Change	$-x$	$-x$	$+x$	$+x$
Equilibrium	**0.350 – x**	**0.350 – x**	**x**	**x**

$$[SO_3] = x = 0.214 \ M$$

$$K_c = \frac{[SO_3][NO]}{[SO_2][NO_2]} = \frac{x^2}{(0.350 - x)^2} = \frac{(0.214)^2}{(0.350 - 0.214)^2} = 2.48$$

$$\boldsymbol{K_c = 2.48}$$

33. Consider the following reaction equation:

$$CO(g) + H_2O(g) \rightleftharpoons CO_2(g) + H_2(g)$$

If 0.410 moles of CO_2 and 0.240 moles of H_2 are delivered into a 0.500-L reactor at a particular temperature and having established equilibrium, calculate the value of K_c for this reaction, if it is determined that $[CO] = $ **0.0960 M**.

Concentration	$CO(g) +$	$H_2O(g) \rightleftharpoons$	$CO_2(g) +$	$H_2(g)$
Initial	0	0	0.820	0.480
Change	$+x$	$+x$	$-x$	$-x$
Equilibrium	**x**	**x**	**0.820 – x**	**0.480 – x**

$$x = 0.0960 \ atm$$

$$K_c = \frac{[CO_2][H_2]}{[H_2O][CO]} = \frac{(0.820 - x)(0.480 - x)}{x^2} = \frac{(0.820 - 0.0960)(0.480 - 0.0960)}{(0.0960)^2} = 30.2$$

$$\boldsymbol{K_c = 30.2}$$

THE REACTION QUOTIENT

34. Consider the following hypothetical reaction:

$$A(g) \rightleftharpoons 2\, B(g)$$

If the value of K_c at a particular temperature is 15, is the reaction at equilibrium if the concentrations of the gases A and B are $[A] = 0.10\, M$ and $[B] = 1.50\, M$? If not, which direction will the reaction proceed to establish equilibrium?

$$Q_c = \frac{[B]^2}{[A]} = \frac{(1.50)^2}{0.10} = \mathbf{22.5}$$

Since $Q_c > K_c$, the reaction will need to diminish the value of Q_c in order to establish equality with K_c (equilibrium). Hence, *the reaction will shift toward the reactant* (with concomitant depletion of product).

35. Consider the following hypothetical reaction:

$$A(g) + B(g) \rightleftharpoons 2\, C(g)$$

If the value of K_c at a particular temperature is 2.3×10^{-2}, is the reaction at equilibrium if the concentrations of the gases A, B, and C are $[A] = 0.250\, M$, $[B] = 0.377\, M$, and $[C] = 0.0652\, M$? If not, which direction will the reaction proceed to establish equilibrium?

$$Q_c = \frac{[C]^2}{[A][B]} = \frac{(0.0652)^2}{(0.250)(0.377)} = \mathbf{4.51 \times 10^{-2}}$$

$$Q_c > K_c$$

Therefore, the reaction will proceed to the left (toward reactants) as it establishes equilibrium.

36. Consider the following reaction:

$$2\, SO_2(g) + O_2(g) \rightleftharpoons 2\, SO_3(g)$$

Calculate the value of Q_c if the reaction mixture contains 3.25 g SO_2, 4.87 g O_2, and 3.70 g SO_3 contained in a 0.500-L reactor. If $K_c = 250$, is the reaction at equilibrium? If not, which direction will the reaction proceed in order to establish equilibrium?

$$[SO_3] = \frac{\left(\dfrac{3.70\ g\ SO_3}{80.06\ g/mol} \right)}{0.500\ L} = 0.0924\ M$$

$$[O_2] = \frac{\left(\dfrac{4.87\ g\ O_2}{32.00\ g/mol} \right)}{0.500\ L} = 0.3044\ M$$

$$[SO_2] = \frac{\left(\dfrac{3.25\ g\ SO_2}{64.06\ g/mol} \right)}{0.500\ L} = 0.1015\ M$$

$$Q_c = \frac{[SO_3]^2}{[SO_2]^2[O_2]} = \frac{(0.0924)^2}{(0.1015)^2(0.3044)} = \mathbf{2.72}$$

$$Q_c < K_c$$

Therefore, the reaction will proceed to the right (toward products) as it establishes equilibrium.

37. Consider the following reaction:

$$I_2(g) + Cl_2(g) \rightleftharpoons 2\ ICl(g) \qquad K_p = 82$$

If the reaction mixture is described by the partial pressure P_{I_2} = 0.210 *atm*, P_{Cl_2} = 0.185 *atm*, and P_{ICl} = **2.01** *atm* , is the reaction at equilibrium? If not, will the product need to be depleted or produced in order to establish equilibrium?

$$Q_p = \frac{P_{ICl}^2}{P_{I_2} \cdot P_{Cl_2}} = \frac{(2.01)^2}{(0.210)(0.185)} = \mathbf{104}$$

The reaction is not at equilibrium since $Q_p \neq K_p$. Further, since $Q_p > K_p$, the reaction must proceed to the left (toward reactants) as it establishes equilibrium.

DETERMINING EQUILIBRIUM CONCENTRATIONS

38. Consider the following hypothetical reaction:

$$A(g) \rightleftharpoons 2\ B(g)$$

The value of K_c at a particular temperature for this reaction is 15. Assuming the initial concentration of A was $[A]$ = **0.200** *M* , construct a reaction table and determine the equilibrium concentration of B.

Concentration	$A(g) \rightleftharpoons 2\ B(g)$	
Initial	0.200	0
Change	$-x$	$+2x$
Equilibrium	**0.200 − x**	**2x**

$$K_c = 15 = \frac{[B]^2}{[A]} = \frac{(2x)^2}{(0.200 - x)}$$

$$3.0 - 15x = 4x^2$$

$$4x^2 + 15x - 3.0 = 0$$

$$x = \frac{-15 \pm \sqrt{(15)^2 - 4(4)(-3.0)}}{2(4)}$$

$$x = \frac{-15 \pm \sqrt{273}}{8}$$

$$x = \frac{-15 \pm 16.52}{8} = 0.19 \quad or \quad -3.94$$

Therefore:

$$x = 0.19 \; M$$

$$[B] = 2x = 2(0.19) = 0.38 \; M$$

39. Consider the following hypothetical reaction:

$$A(g) + B(g) \rightleftharpoons 2\,C(g)$$

If the value of K_c at a particular temperature is 2.3×10^{-2} and the initial concentrations of reactants are $[A] = 0.100 \; M$ and $[B] = 0.100 \; M$, what is the equilibrium concentration of C?

Concentration	$A(g)$	+	$B(g)$	$\rightleftharpoons$	$2\,C(g)$
Initial	0.100		0.100		0
Change	$-x$		$-x$		$+2x$
Equilibrium	**0.100 – x**		**0.100 – x**		**2x**

$$K_c = 2.3 \times 10^{-2} = \frac{[C]^2}{[A][B]} = \frac{(2x)^2}{(0.100 - x)^2}$$

$$\sqrt{2.3 \times 10^{-2}} = \frac{2x}{0.100 - x}$$

$$0.100\sqrt{2.3 \times 10^{-2}} - x\sqrt{2.3 \times 10^{-2}} = 2x$$

$$0.100\sqrt{2.3 \times 10^{-2}} = \left(2 + \sqrt{2.3 \times 10^{-2}}\right)x$$

$$x = \frac{0.100\sqrt{2.3 \times 10^{-2}}}{\left(2 + \sqrt{2.3 \times 10^{-2}}\right)} = \frac{0.01517}{2.1517} = 0.00705$$

$$[C] = 2x = 2(0.00705) = 0.0141 \; M$$

40. Consider the following reaction (@ 925 K):

$$CO(g) + H_2O(g) \rightleftharpoons CO_2(g) + H_2(g) \qquad K_c = 1.34$$

If 0.250 moles of CO and 0.250 moles of H_2O are initially placed in a 0.500-L reactor and allowed to reach equilibrium, what are the equilibrium concentrations of the products and reactants?

$$[CO] = \frac{0.250 \ mol \ CO}{0.500 \ L} = 0.500 \ M$$

$$[H_2O] = \frac{0.250 \ mol \ H_2O}{0.500 \ L} = 0.500 \ M$$

Concentration	$CO(g)$	$+$	$H_2O(g)$	$\rightleftharpoons$	$CO_2(g)$	$+$	$H_2(g)$
Initial	0.500		0.500		0		0
Change	$-x$		$-x$		$+x$		$+x$
Equilibrium	**0.500 – x**		**0.500 – x**		**x**		**x**

$$K_c = \frac{[CO_2][H_2]}{[H_2O][CO]} = \frac{(x)(x)}{(0.500-x)(0.500-x)} = \frac{x^2}{(0.500-x)^2}$$

$$\sqrt{K_c} = \frac{x}{(0.500-x)}$$

$$(0.500-x)\sqrt{K_c} = x$$

$$0.500\sqrt{K_c} - x\sqrt{K_c} = x$$

$$0.500\sqrt{K_c} = \left(1+\sqrt{K_c}\right)x$$

$$x = \frac{0.500\sqrt{K_c}}{\left(1+\sqrt{K_c}\right)} = \frac{0.500(1.158)}{(1+1.158)} = \frac{0.579}{2.158} = 0.268$$

$$[CO] = [H_2O] = 0.500 - x = 0.500 - 0.268 = \textbf{0.232 M}$$

$$[CO_2] = [H_2] = x = \textbf{0.268 M}$$

41. Consider the following reaction (@ 800 K):

$$COCl_2(g) \rightleftharpoons CO(g) + Cl_2(g) \qquad K_c = 6.16 \times 10^{-2}$$

If 0.350 moles of $COCl_2$ is initially placed in a 0.250-L reactor, heated to 800 K, and allowed to reach equilibrium, what are the equilibrium concentrations of the products and the reactant?

$$[COCl_2] = \frac{0.350 \; mol \; COCl_2}{0.250 \; L} = 1.40 \; M$$

Concentration	$COCl_2(g)$	$\rightleftharpoons$	$CO(g)$	+	$Cl_2(g)$
Initial	1.40		0		0
Change	$-x$		$+x$		$+x$
Equilibrium	**1.40 – x**		**x**		**x**

$$K_c = \frac{[Cl_2][CO]}{[COCl_2]} = \frac{(x)(x)}{(1.40 - x)}$$

$$1.40K_c - xK_c = x^2$$

$$x^2 + xK_c - 1.40K_c = 0$$

$$x = \frac{-K_c \pm \sqrt{K_c^2 - 4(1)(-1.40K_c)}}{2(1)}$$

$$x = \frac{-0.0616 \pm \sqrt{0.0616^2 - 4(1)(-1.40 \times 0.0616)}}{2} = \frac{-0.0616 \pm \sqrt{0.3488}}{2}$$

$$x = \frac{-0.0616 \pm \sqrt{0.3488}}{2} = \frac{-0.0616 \pm 0.5906}{2} = 0.265 \; or \; -0.326$$

Therefore, because we cannot have a negative concentration:

$$x = 0.265$$

$$[COCl_2] = 1.40 - x = 1.40 - 0.265 = \textbf{1.135 } \textbf{\textit{M}}$$

$$[CO] = [Cl_2] = \textbf{0.265 } \textbf{\textit{M}}$$

42. Consider the following reaction (@ 375 K):

$$C_2H_2(g) + H_2O(g) \rightleftharpoons CH_3CHO(g) \qquad K_c = 4.0 \times 10^{-4}$$

If 0.100 moles of C_2H_2 and 0.250 moles of H_2O are initially placed in a 0.300-L reactor and allowed to reach equilibrium, what are the equilibrium concentrations of the product and the reactants?

$$[C_2H_2] = \frac{0.100 \ mol \ C_2H_2}{0.300 \ L} = 0.333 \ M$$

$$[H_2O] = \frac{0.250 \ mol \ C_2H_2}{0.300 \ L} = 0.833 \ M$$

Concentration	$C_2H_2(g)$	$+$	$H_2O(g)$	$\rightleftharpoons$	$CH_3CHO(g)$
Initial	0.333		0.833		0
Change	$-x$		$-x$		$+x$
Equilibrium	**0.333 – x**		**0.833 – x**		**x**

$$K_c = \frac{[CH_3CHO]}{[C_2H_2][H_2O]} = \frac{x}{(0.333-x)(0.833-x)} \approx \frac{x}{(0.333)(0.833)} = \frac{x}{0.2774}$$

$$x = 0.2774K_c = 0.2774\left(4.0\times10^{-4}\right) = 1.11\times10^{-4} \ M$$

$$[CH_3CHO] = 1.11\times10^{-4} \ M$$

$$[C_2H_2] = 0.333 \ M$$

$$[H_2O] = 0.833 \ M$$

43. Consider the following reaction (@ 1100 K):

$$CO(g) + H_2O(g) \rightleftharpoons CO_2(g) + H_2(g) \qquad K_c = 0.458$$

If 14.01 g of CO and 4.504 g of H_2O are initially placed in a 1.00-L reactor and allowed to reach equilibrium, what are the equilibrium concentrations of the products and the reactants?

$$[CO] = \frac{\left(\frac{14.01 \ g \ CO}{28.01 \ g/mol}\right)}{1.00 \ L} = 0.500 \ M$$

$$[H_2O] = \frac{\left(\frac{4.504 \ g \ H_2O}{18.02 \ g/mol}\right)}{1.00 \ L} = 0.250 \ M$$

Concentration	$CO(g)$	$+$	$H_2O(g)$	$\rightleftharpoons$	$CO_2(g)$	$+$	$H_2(g)$
Initial	0.500		0.250		0		0
Change	$-x$		$-x$		$+x$		$+x$
Equilibrium	**0.500 – x**		**0.250 – x**		**x**		**x**

$$K_c = \frac{[CO_2][H_2]}{[H_2O][CO]} = \frac{(x)(x)}{(0.500-x)(0.250-x)} = \frac{x^2}{x^2 - 0.750x + 0.125}$$

$$\left(x^2 - 0.750x + 0.125\right)K_c = x^2$$

$$0.458x^2 - 0.3435x + 0.05725 = x^2$$

$$0.542x^2 + 0.3435x - 0.05725 = 0$$

$$x = \frac{-0.3435 \pm \sqrt{0.3435^2 - 4(0.542)(-0.05725)}}{2(0.542)} = \frac{-0.3435 \pm \sqrt{0.2421}}{1.084} = \frac{-0.3435 \pm 0.4920}{1.084}$$

$$x = 0.137 \; or \; -0.771$$

Therefore (we ignore the result which gives negative concentrations):

$$[CO_2] = [H_2] = \textbf{0.137 M}$$

$$[CO] = 0.500 - x = 0.500 - 0.137 = \textbf{0.363 M}$$

$$[H_2O] = 0.250 - x = 0.250 - 0.137 = \textbf{0.113 M}$$

44. Consider the following reaction (@ 1000 K):

$$COCl_2(g) \rightleftharpoons CO(g) + Cl_2(g) \qquad K_c = 1.59$$

If initially the reactor contains $COCl_2$ at a partial pressure of $P_{COCl_2} = 0.880 \; atm$, what are the equilibrium partial pressures of the products and the reactant? (Hint: You will need to know K_p for this problem.)

$$K_p = K_c(RT)^{\Delta n}$$

$$\Delta n = (1+1) - 1 = 1$$

$$K_p = K_c(RT)^1 = (1.59)\left(0.08206\frac{L \cdot atm}{mol \cdot K}\right)(1000 \; K) = 130.5$$

$$K_p = 130.5$$

Concentration	$COCl_2(g)$	$\rightleftharpoons$	$CO(g)$	$+$	$Cl_2(g)$
Initial	0.880		0		0
Change	$-x$		$+x$		$+x$
Equilibrium	**0.880 – x**		**x**		**x**

$$K_p = \frac{P_{Cl_2} \cdot P_{CO}}{P_{COCl_2}} = \frac{(x)(x)}{(0.880-x)} = \frac{x^2}{(0.880-x)} = 130.5$$

$$x^2 = 114.84 - 130.5x$$

$$x^2 + 130.5x - 114.84 = 0$$

$$x = \frac{-130.5 \pm \sqrt{130.5^2 - 4(1)(-114.84)}}{2(1)} = \frac{-130.5 \pm \sqrt{17489.61}}{2} = \frac{-130.5 \pm 132.25}{2}$$

$$x = 0.875 \ \ or \ -131.4$$

The second solution gives negative values for the partial pressures of the products at equilibrium; as such, we dispense with it.

$$P_{COCl_2} = 0.880 - x = 0.880 - 0.875 = \textbf{0.005 atm}$$

$$P_{Cl_2} = P_{CO} = \textbf{0.875 atm}$$

45. Consider the following reaction (@800 K):

$$COCl_2(g) \rightleftharpoons CO(g) + Cl_2(g) \qquad K_c = 6.16 \times 10^{-2}$$

Assuming a reactor contained all 3 gaseous components, all with partial pressures of 0.250 atm, what partial pressures will the reactant and products have at equilibrium? (Hint: You will need to know K_p for this problem.)

$$K_p = K_c (RT)^{\Delta n}$$

$$\Delta n = (1+1) - 1 = 1$$

$$K_p = K_c (RT)^1 = \left(6.16 \times 10^{-2}\right)\left(0.08206 \frac{L \cdot atm}{mol \cdot K}\right)(800 \ K) = 4.04$$

$$K_p = 4.04$$

Next, we will need to determine which direction the reaction will proceed in establishing equilibrium.

$$Q_p = \frac{P_{Cl_2} \cdot P_{CO}}{P_{COCl_2}} = \frac{(0.250)(0.250)}{(0.250)} = 0.250$$

Since $Q_p < K_p$, the reaction will proceed to the right (formation of products and depletion of reactants):

Concentration	$COCl_2(g)$	$\rightleftharpoons$	$CO(g)$	+	$Cl_2(g)$
Initial	0.250		0.250		0.250
Change	$-x$		$+x$		$+x$
Equilibrium	**0.250 − x**		**0.250 + x**		**0.250 + x**

$$K_p = \frac{P_{Cl_2} \cdot P_{CO}}{P_{COCl_2}} = \frac{(0.250+x)(0.250+x)}{(0.250-x)} = \frac{x^2+0.500x+0.0625}{(0.250-x)} = 4.04$$

$$x^2 + 0.500x + 0.0625 = -4.04x + 1.01$$

$$x^2 + 4.54x - 0.9475 = 0$$

$$x = \frac{-4.54 \pm \sqrt{4.54^2 - 4(1)(-0.9475)}}{2(1)} = \frac{-4.54 \pm \sqrt{24.402}}{2} = \frac{-4.54 \pm 4.940}{2}$$

$$x = 0.20 \ \ or \ -4.74$$

The second solution gives negative values for the partial pressures of the products at equilibrium; as such, we dispense with it.

$$P_{COCl_2} = 0.250 - x = 0.250 - 0.20 = \textbf{0.05 atm}$$

$$P_{Cl_2} = P_{CO} = 0.250 + 0.20 = \textbf{0.45 atm}$$

46. Consider the following reaction (@ 425 K):

$$NH_3(g) + H_2S(g) \rightleftharpoons NH_4HS(g) \qquad K_c = 323$$

If 1.703 g **NH_3**, 3.408 g **H_2S**, and 25.05 g **NH_4HS** are initially placed in a 1.00-L reactor and allowed to reach equilibrium, what is the concentration of **H_2S** at equilibrium?

$$[NH_3] = \frac{\left(\dfrac{1.703 \ g \ NH_3}{17.034 \ g/mol}\right)}{1.00 \ L} = 0.100 \ M$$

$$[H_2S] = \frac{\left(\dfrac{3.408 \ g \ H_2S}{34.076 \ g/mol}\right)}{1.00 \ L} = 0.100 \ M$$

$$[NH_4HS] = \frac{\left(\dfrac{25.05 \ g \ NH_4HS}{51.11 \ g/mol}\right)}{1.00 \ L} = 0.490 \ M$$

$$Q_c = \frac{[NH_4HS]}{[NH_3][H_2S]} = \frac{(0.490)}{(0.100)(0.100)} = 49$$

Since $Q_c < K_c$, the reaction will proceed to the right (formation of product and depletion of reactants):

Concentration	$NH_3(g)$	$+$	$H_2S(g)$	$\rightleftharpoons$	$NH_4HS(g)$
Initial	0.100		0.100		0.490
Change	$-x$		$-x$		$+x$
Equilibrium	**0.100 − x**		**0.100 − x**		**0.490 + x**

$$K_c = \frac{[NH_4HS]}{[NH_3][H_2S]} = \frac{(0.490 + x)}{(0.100 - x)^2} = \frac{(0.490 + x)}{x^2 - 0.200x + 0.0100} = 323$$

$$0.490 + x = 323\left(x^2 - 0.200x + 0.0100\right)$$

$$0.490 + x = 323x^2 - 64.6x + 3.23$$

$$323x^2 - 65.6x + 2.74 = 0$$

$$x = \frac{65.6 \pm \sqrt{65.6^2 - 4(323)(2.74)}}{2(323)} = \frac{65.6 \pm \sqrt{763.28}}{646} = \frac{65.6 \pm 27.63}{646}$$

$$x = 0.0588 \ or \ 0.1443$$

The second solution gives negative values for the partial pressures of the reactants at equilibrium; as such, we dispense with it.

$$[H_2S] = 0.100 - x = 0.100 - 0.0588 = \textbf{0.041 M}$$

LE CHÂTELIER'S PRINCIPLE

47. Consider the following endothermic reaction:

$$CH_4(g) + 2\ H_2S(g) \rightleftharpoons CS_2(g) + 4\ H_2(g) \quad \Delta H > 0$$

Assuming the reaction is at equilibrium, in which direction will the reaction shift in response to each of the following stresses?

a. Increase in P_{CS_2}

According to Le Châtelier, if additional product is added to the reaction mixture (at equilibrium), the reaction will shift to minimize this change. As such, the reaction will shift to the left, depleting the product (CS_2 and H_2).

b. Decrease in $[H_2S]$

According to Le Châtelier, if reactant is removed from the reaction mixture (at equilibrium), the reaction will shift to minimize this change. As such, the reaction will shift to the left, depleting the products, resulting in an increase in the concentrations of the reactants.

c. Increased Temperature

Since the reaction is endothermic, we can think of heat as a reactant. Therefore, heating the reaction mixture will result in a shift to the right, according to Le Châtelier.

d. Increased Volume

The expansion of the reaction mixture would result in decreased partial pressures of all components. According to Le Châtelier, the reaction will respond to minimize this decrease in partial pressure if possible. Since the left side of the equation has fewer moles of gas particles than the right, the reaction will shift right, resulting in the formation of products. This would increase the number of gaseous molecules in the system, which increases the pressure.

48. Consider the following endothermic reaction:

$$COCl_2(g) \rightleftharpoons CO(g) + Cl_2(g) \quad \Delta H > 0$$

Assuming the reaction is at equilibrium, in which direction will the reaction shift in response to each of the following stresses?

a. Increase in P_{COCl_2}

According to Le Châtelier, if additional reactant is added to the reaction mixture (at equilibrium), the reaction will shift to minimize this change. As such, the reaction will shift to the right.

b. Decrease in P_{Cl_2}

According to Le Châtelier, if product is removed from the reaction mixture (at equilibrium), the reaction will shift to minimize this change. As such, the reaction will shift to the right.

c. Decreased Temperature

Since the reaction is endothermic, we can think of heat as a reactant. Therefore, cooling the reaction mixture is analogous to depleting or removing a reactant. The reaction will shift to the left, according to Le Châtelier.

d. Decreased Volume

The compression of the reaction mixture would result in increased partial pressures of all components. According to Le Châtelier, the reaction will respond to minimize this increase in partial pressure. Since the left side of the equation has fewer moles of gas particles than the right, the reaction will shift left, resulting in the depletion of products. This would diminish the number of gaseous molecules in the system, which reduces the pressure.

49. Consider the following exothermic reaction:

$$CO(g) + H_2O(g) \rightleftharpoons CO_2(g) + H_2(g) \quad \Delta H < 0$$

Assuming the reaction is at equilibrium, in which direction will the reaction shift in response to each of the following stresses?

a. Increase in $[H_2O]$

According to Le Châtelier, if additional reactant is added to the reaction mixture (at equilibrium), the reaction will shift to minimize this change. As such, the reaction will shift to the right.

b. Decrease in P_{CO}

According to Le Châtelier, if reactant is removed from the reaction mixture (at equilibrium), the reaction will shift to minimize this change. As such, the reaction will shift to the left.

c. Decreased Temperature

Since the reaction is exothermic, we can think of heat as a product. Therefore, cooling the reaction mixture is analogous to depleting or removing product. The reaction will shift to the right, according to Le Châtelier.

d. Increased Volume

The expansion of the reaction mixture would result in decreased partial pressures of all components. According to Le Châtelier, the reaction will respond to minimize this decrease in partial pressure if possible. However, since the left side of the equation has an equal number of moles of gas particles as the right, the reaction will not be affected by a change in volume.

50. Consider the following exothermic reaction:

$$CO(g) + 2\ H_2(g) \rightleftharpoons CH_3OH(l) \quad \Delta H < 0$$

Assuming the reaction is at equilibrium, in which direction will the reaction shift in response to each of the following stresses?

a. Decrease in $[H_2]$

According to Le Châtelier, if reactant is removed from the reaction mixture (at equilibrium), the reaction will shift to minimize this change. As such, the reaction will shift to the left.

b. Increase in P_{CO}

According to Le Châtelier, if additional reactant is added to the reaction mixture (at equilibrium), the reaction will shift to minimize this change. As such, the reaction will shift to the right.

c. Decreased Temperature

Since the reaction is exothermic, we can think of heat as a product. Therefore, cooling the reaction mixture is analogous to depleting or removing product. The reaction will shift to the right, according to Le Châtelier.

d. Decreased Volume

The compression of the reaction mixture would result in increased partial pressures of all gaseous components. According to Le Châtelier, the reaction will respond to minimize this increase in partial pressure. Since the right side of the equation has fewer moles of gas particles than the left, the reaction will shift right, resulting in the depletion of reactants. This would diminish the number of gaseous molecules in the system, which reduces the pressure.

SOLUBILITY PRODUCT - K_{SP}

51. Write the expression for the solubility product, K_{sp}, for each of the following compounds:

a. $Al(OH)_3$

Write the balanced equation describing the dissolution of the compound in water:

$$Al(OH)_3(s) \rightleftharpoons Al^{3+}(aq) + 3\ OH^-(aq)$$

From this we can write the K_{sp} expression:

$$K_{sp} = [Al^{3+}][OH^-]^3$$

b. CaF_2

Write the balanced equation describing the dissolution of the compound in water:

$$CaF_2(s) \rightleftharpoons Ca^{2+}(aq) + 2\ F^-(aq)$$

From this we can write the K_{sp} expression:

$$K_{sp} = [Ca^{2+}][F^-]^2$$

c. $PbCl_2$

Write the balanced equation describing the dissolution of the compound in water:

$$PbCl_2(s) \rightleftharpoons Pb^{2+}(aq) + 2\ Cl^-(aq)$$

From this we can write the K_{sp} expression:

$$K_{sp} = [Pb^{2+}][Cl^-]^2$$

d. $CoCO_3$

Write the balanced equation describing the dissolution of the compound in water:

$$CoCO_3(s) \rightleftharpoons Co^{2+}(aq) + CO_3^{2-}(aq)$$

From this we can write the K_{sp} expression:

$$K_{sp} = \left[Co^{2+} \right]\left[CO_3^{2-} \right]$$

52. Write the expression for the solubility product, K_{sp}, for each of the following compounds:

a. $BaCrO_4$

Write the balanced equation describing the dissolution of the compound in water:

$$BaCrO_4(s) \rightleftharpoons Ba^{2+}(aq) + CrO_4^{2-}(aq)$$

From this we can write the K_{sp} expression:

$$K_{sp} = \left[Ba^{2+} \right]\left[CrO_4^{2-} \right]$$

b. $Ca_3(PO_4)_2$

Write the balanced equation describing the dissolution of the compound in water:

$$Ca_3(PO_4)_2(s) \rightleftharpoons 3\ Ca^{2+}(aq) + 2\ PO_4^{3-}(aq)$$

From this we can write the K_{sp} expression:

$$K_{sp} = \left[Ca^{2+} \right]^3\left[PO_4^{3-} \right]^2$$

c. $Mg(OH)_2$

Write the balanced equation describing the dissolution of the compound in water:

$$Mg(OH)_2(s) \rightleftharpoons Mg^{2+}(aq) + 2\ OH^-(aq)$$

From this we can write the K_{sp} expression:

$$K_{sp} = \left[Mg^{2+} \right]\left[OH^- \right]^2$$

d. $SrSO_4$

Write the balanced equation describing the dissolution of the compound in water:

$$SrSO_4(s) \rightleftharpoons Sr^{2+}(aq) + SO_4^{2-}(aq)$$

From this we can write the K_{sp} expression:

$$K_{sp} = \left[Sr^{2+} \right]\left[SO_4^{2-} \right]$$

53. Use the K_{sp} values in Appendix III to determine the molar solubilities of the following compounds in pure water:

a. $Al(OH)_3$

Concentration	$Al(OH)_3(s)$	$\rightleftharpoons$ $Al^{3+}(aq)$	+ $3\,OH^-(aq)$
Initial	N/A	0	0
Change	N/A	+x	+3x
Equilibrium	N/A	x	3x

$$K_{sp} = \left[Al^{3+} \right]\left[OH^- \right]^3 = (x)(3x)^3 = (x)\left(27x^3\right) = 27x^4 = 1.3 \times 10^{-33}$$

$$x = \sqrt[4]{\frac{1.3 \times 10^{-33}}{27}} = 2.6 \times 10^{-9} \; moles/liter$$

b. CaF_2

Concentration	$CaF_2(s)$	$\rightleftharpoons$ $Ca^{2+}(aq)$	+ $2\,F^-(aq)$
Initial	N/A	0	0
Change	N/A	+x	+2x
Equilibrium	N/A	x	2x

$$K_{sp} = \left[Ca^{2+} \right]\left[F^- \right]^2 = (x)(2x)^2 = (x)\left(4x^2\right) = 4x^3 = 1.5 \times 10^{-10}$$

$$x = \sqrt[3]{\frac{1.5 \times 10^{-10}}{4}} = 3.35 \times 10^{-4} \; moles/liter$$

c. *PbCl$_2$*

Concentration	$PbCl_2(s)$	$\rightleftharpoons$	$Pb^{2+}(aq)$	+	$2\ Cl^-(aq)$
Initial	N/A		0		0
Change	N/A		$+x$		$+2x$
Equilibrium	N/A		x		$2x$

$$K_{sp} = \left[Pb^{2+} \right]\left[Cl^- \right]^2 = (x)(2x)^2 = (x)\left(4x^2 \right) = 4x^3 = 1.2 \times 10^{-5}$$

$$x = \sqrt[3]{\frac{1.2 \times 10^{-5}}{4}} = 1.4 \times 10^{-2}\ \textbf{\textit{moles/liter}}$$

d. *CoCO$_3$*

Concentration	$CoCO_3(s)$	$\rightleftharpoons$	$Co^{2+}(aq)$	+	$CO_3^{2-}(aq)$
Initial	N/A		0		0
Change	N/A		$+x$		$+x$
Equilibrium	N/A		x		x

$$K_{sp} = \left[Co^{2+} \right]\left[CO_3^{2-} \right] = (x)(x) = x^2 = 5.0 \times 10^{-9}$$

$$x = \sqrt{5.0 \times 10^{-9}}$$

$$x = 7.1 \times 10^{-5}\ \textbf{\textit{moles/liter}}$$

54. Use the K_{sp} values in Appendix III to determine the molar solubilities of the following compounds in pure water:

a. *BaCrO$_4$*

Concentration	$BaCrO_4(s)$	$\rightleftharpoons$	$Ba^{2+}(aq)$	+	$CrO_3^{2-}(aq)$
Initial	N/A		0		0
Change	N/A		$+x$		$+x$
Equilibrium	N/A		x		x

$$K_{sp} = \left[Ba^{2+} \right]\left[CrO_4^{2-} \right] = 1.2 \times 10^{-10}$$

$$x^2 = 1.2 \times 10^{-10}$$

$$x = 1.1 \times 10^{-5}\ \textbf{\textit{moles/liter}}$$

b. $Ca_3(PO_4)_2$

Concentration	$Ca_3(PO_4)_2(s)$	$\rightleftharpoons$	$3\,Ca^{2+}(aq)$	$+$	$2\,PO_4^{3-}(aq)$
Initial	N/A		0		0
Change	N/A		$+3x$		$+2x$
Equilibrium	N/A		$3x$		$2x$

$$K_{sp} = \left[Ca^{2+}\right]^3\left[PO_4^{3-}\right]^2 = (3x)^3(2x)^2 = \left(27x^3\right)\left(4x^2\right) = 108x^5$$

$$108x^5 = 2.1\times 10^{-33}$$

$$x^5 = \frac{2.1\times 10^{-33}}{108} = 1.94\times 10^{-35}$$

$$x = 1.14\times 10^{-7}\ \textit{moles}/\textit{liter}$$

c. $Mg(OH)_2$

Concentration	$Mg(OH)_2(s)$	$\rightleftharpoons$	$Mg^{2+}(aq)$	$+$	$2\,OH^-(aq)$
Initial	N/A		0		0
Change	N/A		$+x$		$+2x$
Equilibrium	N/A		x		$2x$

$$K_{sp} = \left[Mg^{2+}\right]\left[OH^-\right]^2 = (x)(2x)^2 = 4x^3 = 2.1\times 10^{-13}$$

$$x = \sqrt[3]{\frac{2.1\times 10^{-13}}{4}} = 3.74\times 10^{-5}\ \textit{moles}/\textit{liter}$$

d. PbI_2

Concentration	$PbI_2(s)$	$\rightleftharpoons$	$Pb^{2+}(aq)$	$+$	$2\,I^-(aq)$
Initial	N/A		0		0
Change	N/A		$+x$		$+2x$
Equilibrium	N/A		x		$2x$

$$K_{sp} = \left[Pb^{2+}\right]\left[I^-\right]^2 = (x)(2x)^2 = (x)\left(4x^2\right) = 4x^3 = 9.8\times 10^{-9}$$

$$x = \sqrt[3]{\frac{9.8\times 10^{-9}}{4}} = 1.35\times 10^{-3}\ \textit{moles}/\textit{liter}$$

55. Determine the molar solubility of calcium sulfate in the following solvents or solutions:

a. Pure water

Concentration	$CaSO_4(s)$	$\rightleftharpoons$	$Ca^{2+}(aq)$	+	$SO_4^{2-}(aq)$
Initial	N/A		0		0
Change	N/A		+x		+x
Equilibrium	N/A		x		x

$$K_{sp} = \left[Ca^{2+} \right]\left[SO_4^{2-} \right] = (x)(x) = x^2 = 7.1 \times 10^{-5}$$

$$x = \sqrt{7.1 \times 10^{-5}}$$

$$x = 8.4 \times 10^{-3} \text{ moles/liter}$$

b. 0.100 M $Ca(NO_3)_2$

Concentration	$CaSO_4(s)$	$\rightleftharpoons$	$Ca^{2+}(aq)$	+	$SO_4^{2-}(aq)$
Initial	N/A		0.100		0
Change	N/A		+x		+x
Equilibrium	N/A		0.100 + x		x

$$K_{sp} = \left[Ca^{2+} \right]\left[SO_4^{2-} \right] = (0.100 + x)(x) = 7.1 \times 10^{-5}$$

$$0.100 + x \approx 0.100$$

$$(0.100 + x)(x) \approx (0.100)(x) = 0.100x = 7.1 \times 10^{-5}$$

$$x = \frac{7.1 \times 10^{-5}}{0.100} = 7.1 \times 10^{-4} \text{ moles/liter}$$

$$x = 7.1 \times 10^{-4} \text{ moles/liter}$$

c. 0.200 M Na_2SO_4

Concentration	$CaSO_4(s)$	$\rightleftharpoons$	$Ca^{2+}(aq)$	+	$SO_4^{2-}(aq)$
Initial	N/A		0		0.200
Change	N/A		+x		+x
Equilibrium	N/A		x		0.200 + x

$$K_{sp} = \left[Ca^{2+} \right]\left[SO_4^{2-} \right] = (x)(0.200 + x) = 7.1 \times 10^{-5}$$

$$0.200 + x \approx 0.200$$

$$(x)(0.200 + x) \approx (x)(0.200) = 0.200x = 7.1 \times 10^{-5}$$

$$x = \frac{7.1 \times 10^{-5}}{0.200} = 3.6 \times 10^{-4} \ moles/liter$$

$$x = \mathbf{3.6 \times 10^{-4}} \ \mathbf{moles/liter}$$

56. Determine the molar solubility of magnesium fluoride in the following solvents or solutions:
    a. Pure water

Concentration	$MgF_2(s)$	$\rightleftharpoons$	$Mg^{2+}(aq)$	+	$2F^-(aq)$
Initial	N/A		0		0
Change	N/A		$+x$		$+2x$
Equilibrium	N/A		x		$2x$

$$K_{sp} = \left[Mg^{2+}\right]\left[F^-\right]^2 = (x)(2x)^2 = 4x^3 = 2.1 \times 10^{-13}$$

$$x = \sqrt[3]{\frac{2.1 \times 10^{-13}}{4}} = 3.7 \times 10^{-5} \ moles/liter$$

$$x = \mathbf{3.7 \times 10^{-5}} \ \mathbf{moles/liter}$$

b. 0.200 M $Mg(NO_3)_2$

Concentration	$MgF_2(s)$	$\rightleftharpoons$	$Mg^{2+}(aq)$	+	$2F^-(aq)$
Initial	N/A		0.200		0
Change	N/A		$+x$		$+2x$
Equilibrium	N/A		$0.200 + x$		$2x$

$$K_{sp} = \left[Mg^{2+}\right]\left[F^-\right]^2 = (0.200 + x)(2x)^2 = 2.1 \times 10^{-13}$$

$$0.200 + x \approx 0.200$$

$$(0.200 + x)(2x)^2 \approx (0.200)(2x)^2 = 0.800x^2 = 2.1 \times 10^{-13}$$

$$x = \sqrt{\frac{2.1 \times 10^{-13}}{0.800}} = 5.12 \times 10^{-7}$$

$$x = 5.1 \times 10^{-7} \ \textit{moles/liter}$$

c.   0.270 M *NaF*

Concentration	$MgF_2(s)$	$\rightleftharpoons$	$Mg^{2+}(aq)$	$+$	$2\,F^-(aq)$
Initial	N/A		0		0.270
Change	N/A		$+x$		$+2x$
Equilibrium	N/A		x		$0.270+2x$

$$K_{sp} = \left[Mg^{2+} \right]\left[F^- \right]^2 = (x)(0.270 + 2x)^2 = 2.1 \times 10^{-13}$$

$$0.270 + 2x \approx 0.270$$

$$(x)(0.270 + 2x)^2 \approx (x)(0.270)^2 = 0.0729x = 2.1 \times 10^{-13}$$

$$x = \frac{2.1 \times 10^{-13}}{0.0729} = 2.88 \times 10^{-12}$$

$$x = 2.88 \times 10^{-12} \ \textit{moles/liter}$$

KEY TERMS

Chemical equilibrium   The state in a chemical reaction wherein the concentrations of the reactants and products no longer have a drive to change. This is due to equal rates of the forward and reverse reactions.

Chemical kinetics   A term for the study of chemical reaction rates.

Common ion effect   When a compound is dissolved in a solution which already contains one of its constituent ions, its solubility in that solution will be diminished to a degree dictated by the value of K_{sp} and the initial concentration of the common ion. This is a phenomenon known as the common ion effect. The solubility of an ionic compound will be lower in a solution which contains a common ion than it otherwise would be in pure water.

Dynamic equilibrium   A term describing a state wherein two competing processes achieve equal rates.

Endothermic reaction   Chemical reactions which have a positive enthalpy of reaction (reactions which absorb heat).

Exothermic reaction   Chemical reactions which have a negative enthalpy of reaction (reactions which release heat).

Law of mass action   In a chemical system, at a given temperature, a state is, or will be, reached in which the ratio of the reactant and product concentrations maintains a constant value.

Le Châtelier's principle   When a chemical system at equilibrium is perturbed, the system will shift in the direction which minimizes the perturbation.

Reaction quotient   The ratio of the product and reactant molar concentrations (or partial pressures) each raised to their respective stoichiometric coefficient at a given point in a chemical reaction.

Reaction rate   The velocity at which a reaction proceeds from the reactants to products and is defined as the change in concentration of reactants and/or products per unit time.

Reversible reaction   A reaction which can proceed in either the forward or reverse direction.

Solubility product   For ionic compounds sparingly soluble in water, the solubility product is the product of the concentrations of its constituent ions in solution.

Acids, Bases, and Buffers

KEY CONCEPTS

- Arrhenius Acids and Bases
- Brønsted-Lowry Acids and Bases
- Lewis Acids and Bases
- Conjugate Acid/Base Pairs
- Acid Formulas and Nomenclature
- K_a, K_b, and K_w
- The pH and pOH scales
- Acid/Base Titrations and Titration Curves
- Strong and Weak Acids and Bases
- Buffers

ACIDS AND BASES – DEFINITIONS

1. What is the definition of an Arrhenius acid and an Arrhenius base?

   An Arrhenius acid produces H^+ ions in aqueous solution while an Arrhenius base produces OH^- ions in aqueous solution.

2. For each of the following, identify which are Arrhenius acids and which are Arrhenius bases.
   a. HCl – acid
   b. $NaOH$ – base
   c. $HC_2H_3O_2$ – acid
   d. KOH – base

3. What is the definition of a Brønsted-Lowry acid and a Brønsted-Lowry base?

   A Brønsted-Lowry acid is a proton donor, while a Brønsted-Lowry base is a proton acceptor.

4. Identify the Brønsted-Lowry acid and Brønsted-Lowry base in each of the following reactions.
   a. $HBr\ (aq) + H_2O\ (l) \rightarrow H_3O^+\ (aq) + Br^-\ (aq)$

      HBr is the acid (proton donor) and H_2O is the base (proton acceptor).

   b. $NH_3\ (aq) + H_2O\ (l) \rightleftharpoons NH_4^+\ (aq) + OH^-\ (aq)$

      H_2O is the acid (proton donor) and NH_3 is the base (proton acceptor).

   c. $HI\ (aq) + H_2O\ (l) \rightarrow H_3O^+\ (aq) + I^-\ (aq)$

      HI is the acid (proton donor) and H_2O is the base (proton acceptor).

   d. $CH_3NH_2\ (aq) + H_2O\ (l) \rightleftharpoons CH_3NH_3^+\ (aq) + OH^-\ (aq)$

      H_2O is the acid (proton donor) and CH_3NH_2 is the base (proton acceptor).

5. What is an amphoteric substance? Give an example.

   An amphoteric substance is defined as any substance that can act like either an acid or a base. Water is a good example.

6. What are conjugate acid-base pairs?

   Conjugate acid-base pairs are two substances that are related to one another by the simple transferring of a proton.

7. What are the conjugate acids for each of the following bases?
   a. ClO_4^- – $HClO_4$
   b. HCO_3^- – H_2CO_3
   c. NH_3 – NH_4^+
   d. OH^- – H_2O

8. What are the conjugate bases for each of the following acids?
    a. $H_3O^+ - H_2O$
    b. $H_2SO_4 - HSO_4^-$
    c. $HCl - Cl^-$
    d. $HI - I^-$

ACIDS AND BASES – NOMENCLATURE

9. What is a binary acid?

    A binary acid contains hydrogen and a nonmetal.

10. What is an oxyacid acid?

    An oxyacid is composed of hydrogen and an oxyanion (anion containing a nonmetal and oxygen).

11. What are the names of the following acids?
    a. $HClO$ – hypochlorus acid
    b. HCl – hydrochloric acid
    c. H_2SO_3 – sulfurous acid
    d. HBr – hydrobromic acid

12. What are the names of the following acids?
    a. $HClO_4$ – perchloric acid
    b. HF – hydrofluoric acid
    c. H_2SO_4 – sulfuric acid
    d. $HClO_2$ – chlorus acid

13. Write the formulas for each of the following acids:
    a. Phosphoric acid – H_3PO_4
    b. Hydroiodic acid – HI
    c. Chloric acid – $HClO_3$
    d. Acetic acid – $HC_2H_3O_2$

14. What are the names of the following bases?
    a. $NaOH$ – sodium hydroxide
    b. $Ba(OH)_2$ – barium hydroxide
    c. KOH – potassium hydroxide
    d. $RbOH$ – rubidium hydroxide

15. Write the formulas for each of the following bases:
    a. Magnesium hydroxide – $Mg(OH)_2$
    b. Lithium hydroxide – $LiOH$
    c. Ammonia – NH_3
    d. Calcium hydroxide – $Ca(OH)_2$

AUTOIONIZATION OF WATER AND SCALES USED TO QUANTIFY ACIDITY AND BASICITY

16. What is the autoionization of water?

The autoionization of water is a process in which water self-ionizes as follows:

$$H_2O \, (l) + H_2O \, (l) \rightleftharpoons H_3O^+ \, (aq) + OH^- \, (aq)$$

Notice that while one of the water reactants is acting like an acid (proton donor), the other water reactant is acting like a base (proton acceptor). The ability of water to act like either an acid or base makes it an amphoteric substance.

17. What is the ion product constant for water?

The ion product constant for water (K_w) is the equilibrium constant for the autoionization of water, and can be expressed as follows:

$$H_2O \, (l) \rightleftharpoons H^+ \, (aq) + OH^- \, (aq)$$
$$K_w = [H^+][OH^-]$$

At 25°C, $K_w = 1.0 \times 10^{-14}$

18. In an acidic solution at 25 °C, which of the following is true?
   a. $[H^+] < [OH^-]$
   b. $[H^+] = [OH^-]$
   c. $[H^+] > [OH^-]$
   d. $[H^+] = [OH^-] = 1.0 \times 10^{-14} \, M$

   $[H^+] > [OH^-]$

19. In a basic solution at 25 °C, which of the following is true?
   a. $[H^+] < [OH^-]$
   b. $[H^+] = [OH^-]$
   c. $[H^+] > [OH^-]$
   d. $[H^+] = [OH^-] = 1.0 \times 10^{-14} \, M$

   $[H^+] < [OH^-]$

20. In neutral solution at 25 °C, which of the following is true?
   a. $[H^+] < [OH^-]$
   b. $[H^+] = [OH^-]$
   c. $[H^+] > [OH^-]$
   d. $[H^+] = [OH^-] = 1.0 \times 10^{-14} \, M$

   $[H^+] = [OH^-]$

21. Calculate the hydronium ion concentration for each solution at 25°C and determine whether it is acidic, basic, or neutral: (at 25 °C, $K_w = 1.0 \times 10^{-14}$).

a. $[OH^-] = 1.0 \times 10^{-7}$ M

$$K_w = 1.0 \times 10^{-14} = [H^+][OH^-]$$

$$[H^+] = \frac{1.0 \times 10^{-14}}{[OH^-]} = \frac{1.0 \times 10^{-14}}{\left[1.0 \times 10^{-7}\right]} = 1.0 \times 10^{-7} \ M$$

Therefore, the solution is neutral; $[H^+] = [OH^-]$.

b. $[OH^-] = 6.3 \times 10^{-8}$ M

$$K_w = 1.0 \times 10^{-14} = [H^+][OH^-]$$

$$[H^+] = \frac{1.0 \times 10^{-14}}{[OH^-]} = \frac{1.0 \times 10^{-14}}{\left[6.3 \times 10^{-8}\right]} = 1.6 \times 10^{-7} \ M$$

Therefore, the solution is slightly acidic; $[H^+] > [OH^-]$.

c. $[OH^-] = 4.1 \times 10^{-2}$ M

$$K_w = 1.0 \times 10^{-14} = [H^+][OH^-]$$

$$[H^+] = \frac{1.0 \times 10^{-14}}{[OH^-]} = \frac{1.0 \times 10^{-14}}{\left[4.1 \times 10^{-2}\right]} = 2.4 \times 10^{-13} \ M$$

Therefore, the solution is very basic; $[H^+] \ll [OH^-]$.

d. $[OH^-] = 2.3 \times 10^{-10}$ M

$$K_w = 1.0 \times 10^{-14} = [H^+][OH^-]$$

$$[H^+] = \frac{1.0 \times 10^{-14}}{[OH^-]} = \frac{1.0 \times 10^{-14}}{\left[2.3 \times 10^{-10}\right]} = 4.3 \times 10^{-5} \ M$$

Therefore, the solution is acidic; $[H^+] > [OH^-]$.

22. Calculate the hydroxide ion concentration for each solution at 25 °C and determine whether it is acidic, basic, or neutral: (at 25 °C, $K_w = 1.0 \times 10^{-14}$).

a. $[H^+] = 3.4 \times 10^{-4}$ M

$$K_w = 1.0 \times 10^{-14} = [H^+][OH^-]$$

$$[OH^-] = \frac{1.0 \times 10^{-14}}{[H^+]} = \frac{1.0 \times 10^{-14}}{\left[3.4 \times 10^{-4}\right]} = 2.9 \times 10^{-11} \ M$$

Therefore, the solution is acidic; $[H^+] > [OH^-]$.

b. $[H^+] = 8.5 \times 10^{-11}$ M

$K_w = 1.0 \times 10^{-14} = [H^+][OH^-]$

$[OH^-] = \dfrac{1.0 \times 10^{-14}}{[H^+]} = \dfrac{1.0 \times 10^{-14}}{\left[8.5 \times 10^{-11}\right]} = 1.2 \times 10^{-4}$ M

Therefore, the solution is basic; $[H^+] < [OH^-]$.

c. $[H^+] = 5.2 \times 10^{-3}$ M

$K_w = 1.0 \times 10^{-14} = [H^+][OH^-]$

$[OH^-] = \dfrac{1.0 \times 10^{-14}}{[H^+]} = \dfrac{1.0 \times 10^{-14}}{\left[5.2 \times 10^{-3}\right]} = 1.9 \times 10^{-12}$ M

Therefore, the solution is very acidic; $[H^+] \gg [OH^-]$.

d. $[H^+] = 9.8 \times 10^{-5}$ M

$K_w = 1.0 \times 10^{-14} = [H^+][OH^-]$

$[OH^-] = \dfrac{1.0 \times 10^{-14}}{[H^+]} = \dfrac{1.0 \times 10^{-14}}{\left[9.8 \times 10^{-5}\right]} = 1.0 \times 10^{-10}$ M

Therefore, the solution is acidic; $[H^+] > [OH^-]$.

23. Define pH and pOH.

The pH is the negative log of the hydronium ion concentration and the pOH is the negative log of the hydroxide ion concentration as follows:

$$pH = -\log[H_3O^+]$$

$$pOH = -\log[OH^-]$$

24. Calculate the pH and pOH for each of the solutions listed in question 21.

a. $[OH^-] = 1.0 \times 10^{-7}$ M

$pOH = -\log[OH^-] = -\log\left(1.0 \times 10^{-7}\right) = 7.00$

$pH = 14.00 - pOH = 14.00 - 7.00 = 7.00$

b. $[OH^-] = 6.3 \times 10^{-8}$ M

$pOH = -\log[OH^-] = -\log\left(6.3 \times 10^{-8}\right) = 7.20$

$pH = 14.00 - pOH = 14.00 - 7.20 = 6.80$

c. $[OH^-] = 4.1 \times 10^{-2}$ M

$pOH = -\log[OH^-] = -\log\left(4.1 \times 10^{-2}\right) = 1.39$

$pH = 14.00 - pOH = 14.00 - 1.39 = 12.61$

d. $[OH^-] = 2.3 \times 10^{-10}$ M

$pOH = -\log[OH^-] = -\log\left(2.3 \times 10^{-10}\right) = 9.64$

$pH = 14.00 - pOH = 14.00 - 9.64 = 4.36$

25. Calculate the pH and pOH for each of the solutions listed in question 22.

a. $[H^+] = 3.4 \times 10^{-4}$ M

$pH = -\log[H^+] = -\log\left(3.4 \times 10^{-4}\right) = 3.47$

$pOH = 14.00 - pH = 14.00 - 3.47 = 10.53$

b. $[H^+] = 8.5 \times 10^{-11}$ M

$pH = -\log[H^+] = -\log\left(8.5 \times 10^{-11}\right) = 10.07$

$pOH = 14.00 - pH = 14.00 - 10.07 = 3.93$

c. $[H^+] = 5.2 \times 10^{-3}$ M

$pH = -\log[H^+] = -\log\left(5.2 \times 10^{-3}\right) = 2.28$

$pOH = 14.00 - pH = 14.00 - 2.28 = 11.72$

d. $[H^+] = 9.8 \times 10^{-5}$ M

$pH = -\log[H^+] = -\log\left(9.8 \times 10^{-5}\right) = 4.01$

$pOH = 14.00 - pH = 14.00 - 4.01 = 9.99$

ACID AND BASE TITRATIONS: A COMMON LABORATORY TECHNIQUE

26. What is a titration reaction? Define titrant and analyte.

A titration reaction is a common laboratory technique involving the addition of a solution of known concentration to another solution of unknown concentration (i.e. acid-base reactions or neutralization reactions). This can be done in order to determine the concentration of the unknown substance. The solution of known concentration is called the titrant, while the substance of unknown concentration is the analyte.

27. What is a burette?

A burette is a device used in chemistry to dispense precise amounts of chemical solutions (see figure 11.5).

28. What is the difference between the equivalence and endpoints in an acid-base neutralization reaction during titration? What is an indicator, and why is it used in these types of reactions?

The equivalence point is the point at which the number of moles of added OH^- ions equals the number of H^+ ions present, while the endpoint is the point at which a color change is observed with the help of an indicator. An indicator is a dye that changes color based on the acidity/basicity of the solution, which helps us know that we have reached the endpoint. In theory, the equivalence point and endpoint should be very close to one another; however, the pH at which different indicators undergo a color change varies from one indicator to another.

29. Complete and balance the following acid-base equation:

$$HCl\ (aq) + NaOH\ (aq) \rightarrow H_2O\ (l) + NaCl\ (aq)$$

30. Complete and balance the following acid-base equation:

$$H_2SO_4\ (aq) + 2\ LiOH\ (aq) \rightarrow 2\ H_2O\ (l) + Li_2SO_4\ (aq)$$

31. Complete and balance the following acid-base equation:

$$H_3PO_4\ (aq) + 3\ NaOH\ (aq) \rightarrow 3\ H_2O\ (l) + Na_3PO_4\ (aq)$$

32. Complete and balance the following acid-base equation:

$$2\ HCl\ (aq) + Ca(OH)_2\ (aq) \rightarrow 2\ H_2O\ (l) + CaCl_2\ (aq)$$

33. A 30.0 ml sample of *HCl* (unknown concentration) is titrated with a 0.100 M *NaOH* solution. The equivalence point is reached after 38.2 ml of the *NaOH* solution is added. What is the concentration of the *HCl* sample?

$$HCl\ (aq) + NaOH\ (aq) \rightarrow H_2O\ (l) + NaCl\ (aq)$$

$$38.2\ ml\ NaOH \times \frac{1\ L}{1{,}000\ ml} \times \frac{0.100\ mols\ NaOH}{1\ L\ Sol'n} \times \frac{1\ mol\ HCl}{1\ mol\ NaOH} \times \frac{1}{0.0300\ L\ Sol'n} = \textbf{0.127 M HCl}$$

34. What is the volume of a 0.127 M *HCl* solution if it requires 38.2 ml of a 0.100 M *NaOH* solution to reach the equivalence point?

$$HCl \ (aq) + NaOH \ (aq) \rightarrow H_2O \ (l) + NaCl \ (aq)$$

$$38.2 \ ml \ NaOH \times \frac{1 \ L}{1,000 \ ml} \times \frac{0.100 \ mols \ NaOH}{1 \ L \ Sol'n} \times \frac{1 \ mol \ HCl}{1 \ mol \ NaOH} \times \frac{1 \ L \ Sol'n}{0.127 \ mols \ HCl} \times \frac{1,000 \ ml}{1 \ L}$$

= **30.1 *ml HCl***

Notice this is the same volume of *HCl* used in question 33 (~30.0 ml-slightly off due to rounding and significant figures). To get the exact number (30.0 ml *HCl*), use 0.12733 M for the concentration of *HCl*, which would be the correct answer to question 33 if expressed to 5 significant figures.

35. A 19.3 ml sample of H_2SO_4 (unknown concentration) is titrated with a 0.320 M *NaOH* solution. The equivalence point is reached after 24.6 ml of the *NaOH* solution is added. What is the concentration of the H_2SO_4 sample?

$$H_2SO_4 \ (aq) + 2NaOH \ (aq) \rightarrow 2H_2O \ (l) + Na_2SO_4 \ (aq)$$

$$24.6 \ ml \ NaOH \times \frac{1 \ L}{1,000 \ ml} \times \frac{0.320 \ mols \ NaOH}{1 \ L \ Sol'n} \times \frac{1 \ mol \ H_2SO_4}{2 \ mol \ NaOH} \times \frac{1}{0.0193 \ L \ Sol'n} = \textbf{0.204 } \textbf{\textit{M H}}_2\textbf{\textit{SO}}_4$$

36. What is the volume of a 0.204 M H_2SO_4 solution if it requires 24.6 ml of a 0.320 M *NaOH* solution to reach the equivalence point?

$$H_2SO_4 \ (aq) + 2NaOH \ (aq) \rightarrow 2H_2O \ (l) + Na_2SO_4 \ (aq)$$

$$24.6 \ ml \ NaOH \times \frac{1 \ L}{1,000 \ ml} \times \frac{0.320 \ mols \ NaOH}{1 \ L \ Sol'n} \times \frac{1 \ mol \ H_2SO_4}{2 \ mol \ NaOH} \times \frac{1 \ L \ Sol'n}{0.204 \ mols \ H_2SO_4} \times \frac{1,000 \ ml}{1 \ L}$$

= **19.3 *ml H*$_2$*SO*$_4$**

Notice this is the same volume of H_2SO_4 used in question 35 (19.3 ml H_2SO_4).

37. A 12.8 ml sample of H_3PO_4 (unknown concentration) is titrated with a 0.250 M *KOH* solution. The equivalence point is reached after 28.7 ml of the *KOH* solution is added. What is the concentration of the H_3PO_4 sample?

$$H_3PO_4 \ (aq) + 3KOH \ (aq) \rightarrow 3H_2O \ (l) + K_3PO_4 \ (aq)$$

$$28.7 \ ml \ KOH \times \frac{1 \ L}{1,000 \ ml} \times \frac{0.250 \ mols \ KOH}{1 \ L \ Sol'n} \times \frac{1 \ mol \ H_3PO_4}{3 \ mol \ KOH} \times \frac{1}{0.0128 \ L \ Sol'n}$$

= **0.187 *M H*$_3$*PO*$_4$**

38. What is the volume of a 0.187 M H_3PO_4 solution if it requires 28.7 ml of a 0.250 M *KOH* solution to reach the equivalence point?

$$H_3PO_4 \ (aq) + 3KOH \ (aq) \rightarrow 3H_2O \ (l) + K_3PO_4 \ (aq)$$

$$28.7 \ ml \ KOH \times \frac{1 \ L}{1,000 \ ml} \times \frac{0.250 \ mols \ KOH}{1 \ L \ Sol'n} \times \frac{1 \ mol \ H_3PO_4}{3 \ mol \ KOH} \times \frac{1 \ L \ Sol'n}{0.187 \ mols \ H_3PO_4} \times \frac{1,000 \ ml}{1 \ L}$$

$$= \textbf{12.8 ml } \boldsymbol{H_3PO_4}$$

Notice this is the same volume of H_3PO_4 used in question 37 (12.8 ml H_3PO_4).

39. A 22.0 ml sample of $HClO_4$ (unknown concentration) is titrated with a 0.200 M *NaOH* solution. The equivalence point is reached after 34.2 ml of the *NaOH* solution is added. What is the concentration of the $HClO_4$ sample?

$$HClO_4 \ (aq) + NaOH \ (aq) \rightarrow H_2O \ (l) + NaClO_4 \ (aq)$$

$$34.2 \ ml \ NaOH \times \frac{1 \ L}{1,000 \ ml} \times \frac{0.200 \ mols \ NaOH}{1 \ L \ Sol'n} \times \frac{1 \ mol \ HClO_4}{1 \ mol \ NaOH} \times \frac{1}{0.0220 \ L \ Sol'n} = \textbf{0.311 } \boldsymbol{M \ HClO_4}$$

40. A 25.0 ml sample of *HCl* (unknown concentration) is titrated with a 0.150 M $Ca(OH)_2$ solution. The equivalence point is reached after 22.5 ml of the $Ca(OH)_2$ solution is added. What is the concentration of the *HCl* sample?

$$2HCl \ (aq) + Ca(OH)_2 \ (aq) \rightarrow 2H_2O \ (l) + CaCl_2 \ (aq)$$

$$22.5 \ ml \ Ca(OH)_2 \times \frac{1 \ L}{1,000 \ ml} \times \frac{0.150 \ mols \ Ca(OH)_2}{1 \ L \ Sol'n} \times \frac{2 \ mol \ HCl}{1 \ molCa(OH)_2} \times \frac{1}{0.0250 \ L \ Sol'n}$$

$$= \textbf{0.270 } \boldsymbol{M \ HCl}$$

41. Below are the titrations curves of a strong base being added to either a strong or weak acid. Which one is which, and why?

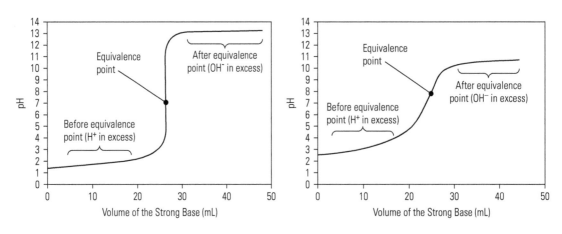

The titration curve on the left is of a strong acid, while the one on the right is of a weak acid. Strong acids tend to have a low starting pH value (< 2.00) as we would expect, while weaker acids have higher pH values prior to the titration (> 2.00). Also, strong acids being titrated with a strong base have an equivalence point of approximately 7.00 and a relatively steeper curve, while weaker acids being titrated with a strong base have a slightly basic equivalence point (~8.00) and a more gradual curve.

ACID STRENGTH

42. What is the major distinction between strong and weak acids?

    Strong acids completely dissociate into ions when dissolved in water (and are therefore strong electrolytes), while weak acids only partially ionize when dissolved in water (and are therefore weak electrolytes).

43. What is the pH of a 0.25 M solution of the strong acid HCl?

    Since strong acids completely ionize, we assume that we have 0.25 M H^+ ions in solution in this case; therefore, we determine the pH as follows:

    $$pH = -\log [H^+] = -\log 0.25 = 0.60$$

44. What is the pH of a 0.10 M solution of the strong acid $HClO_4$?

    Since strong acids completely ionize, we assume that we have 0.10 M H^+ ions in solution in this case; therefore, we determine the pH as follows:

    $$pH = -\log [H^+] = -\log 0.10 = 1.00$$

45. What is the pH of a 0.02 M solution of the strong acid HNO_3?

    Since strong acids completely ionize, we assume that we have 0.02 M H^+ ions in solution in this case; therefore, we determine the pH as follows:

    $$pH = -\log [H^+] = -\log 0.02 = 1.70$$

46. What is the hydronium ion concentration in a HCl solution (strong acid) with a pH value of 1.55?

    $$pH = -\log [H^+]$$

    $$[H^+] = antilog \, (-pH) = antilog \, (-1.55) = \mathbf{2.8 \times 10^{-2} \, M}$$

47. What is the hydronium ion concentration in a HI solution (strong acid) with a pH value of 2.59?

    $$pH = -\log [H^+]$$

    $$[H^+] = antilog \, (-pH) = antilog \, (-2.59) = \mathbf{2.6 \times 10^{-3} \, M}$$

48. What mass (grams) of the strong acid *HCl* is present in a 0.35 L solution with a pH value of 1.85?

$$pH = -\log [H^+]$$

$$[H^+] = antilog\,(-pH) = antilog\,(-1.85) = 1.4 \times 10^{-2}\ M\ HCl$$

$$mols\ HCl = \left(1.4 \times 10^{-2}\ M\ HCl\right) \times (0.35\ L\ Sol'n) = 4.9 \times 10^{-3}\ mols\ HCl$$

$$4.9 \times 10^{-3}\ mols\ HCl \times \frac{36.46\ g\ HCl}{mols\ HCl} = \mathbf{0.18\ grams\ HCl}$$

49. What mass (grams) of the strong acid *HI* is present in a 0.20 L solution with a pH value of 1.26?

$$pH = -\log [H^+]$$

$$[H^+] = antilog\,(-pH) = antilog\,(-1.26) = 5.5 \times 10^{-2}\ M\ HI$$

$$mols\ HI = \left(5.5 \times 10^{-2}\ M\ HI\right) \times (0.20\ L\ Sol'n) = 1.1 \times 10^{-2}\ mols\ HI$$

$$1.1 \times 10^{-2}\ mols\ HI \times \frac{127.91\ g\ HI}{mols\ HI} = \mathbf{1.4\ grams\ HI}$$

50. What is the acid ionization constant (K_a)?

The acid ionization constant (K_a) is the equilibrium constant for the ionization reaction of acids, which is very useful for calculations involving weak acids.

51. Write the K_a expression for the generic weak acid *HA*.

The acid ionization constant (K_a) can be expressed as follows for the generic weak acid *HA*:

$$HA\ (aq) \rightleftharpoons H^+\ (aq) + A^-\ (aq)$$

$$K_a = \frac{[H^+][A^-]}{[HA]}$$

52. What is percent ionization, and how do we calculate it when dealing with weak acids?

Percent ionization is the ratio of the ionized acid concentration (denoted as *x* below) to the initial acid concentration multiplied by 100% as follows:

$$Percent\ Ionization = \frac{x\ (change)}{[Initial\ Acid\ Concentration]} \times 100\%$$

53. When doing calculations involving weak acids ánd acid ionization constants, when can you use the "simplifying" assumption (i.e. assume that the change, or *x*, is small), and when can you not?

We can simplify our calculations when the change (or percent ionization) is less than 5% of the initial acid concentration. If the percent ionization is greater 5%, then we would use the quadratic equation as follows:

$$x = \frac{-b \pm \sqrt{b^2 - 4ac}}{2a}.$$

54. Calculate the pH of a 0.50 M nitrous acid solution ($K_a = 4.6 \times 10^{-4}$).

$$HNO_2\,(aq) \rightleftharpoons H^+\,(aq) + NO_2^-\,(aq)$$

Concentration	$HNO_2\,(aq) \rightleftharpoons$	$H^+\,(aq) +$	$NO_2^-\,(aq)$
Initial	0.50	0.00	0.00
Change	$-x$	$+x$	$+x$
Equilibrium	$0.50 - x$	x	x

$$K_a = \frac{\left[H^+\right]\left[NO_2^-\right]}{\left[HNO_2\right]}$$

$$4.6 \times 10^{-4} = \frac{[x][x]}{[0.50 - x]}$$

$$4.6 \times 10^{-4} = \frac{[x][x]}{[0.50 - \cancel{x}]}$$

$$4.6 \times 10^{-4} = \frac{[x]^2}{[0.50]}$$

$$x = \sqrt{\left(4.6 \times 10^{-4}\right) \times (0.50)} = 1.5 \times 10^{-2}\ M$$

Percent ionization $= \dfrac{x}{0.50\ M} \times 100 = \dfrac{1.5 \times 10^{-2}\ M}{0.50\ M} \times 100\% = 3.0\%$

Our assumption (simplification) is valid, thus we can now calculate the pH:

$$pH = -\log\left(1.5 \times 10^{-2}\right) = \textbf{1.82}$$

55. Calculate the pH of a 0.30 M hydrofluoric acid solution ($K_a = 3.5 \times 10^{-4}$).

$$HF\,(aq) \rightleftharpoons H^+\,(aq) + F^-\,(aq)$$

Concentration	$HF\,(aq) \rightleftharpoons$	$H^+\,(aq) +$	$F^-\,(aq)$
Initial	0.30	0.00	0.00
Change	$-x$	$+x$	$+x$
Equilibrium	$0.30 - x$	x	x

$$K_a = \frac{[H^+][F^-]}{[HF]}$$

$$3.5 \times 10^{-4} = \frac{[x][x]}{[0.30 - x]}$$

$$3.5 \times 10^{-4} = \frac{[x][x]}{[0.30 - \cancel{x}]}$$

$$3.5 \times 10^{-4} = \frac{[x]^2}{[0.30]}$$

$$x = \sqrt{\left(3.5 \times 10^{-4}\right) \times (0.30)} = 1.0 \times 10^{-2} \ M$$

Percent ionization $= \dfrac{x}{0.30 \ M} \times 100 = \dfrac{1.0 \times 10^{-2} \ M}{0.30 \ M} \times 100\% = 3.3\%$

Our assumption (simplification) is valid, thus we can now calculate the pH:

$$pH = -\log\left(1.0 \times 10^{-2}\right) = \mathbf{2.00}$$

56. Calculate the pH of a 0.25 M acetic acid solution ($K_a = 1.8 \times 10^{-5}$).

$$HC_2H_3O_2(aq) \rightleftharpoons H^+(aq) + C_2H_3O_2^-(aq)$$

Concentration	$HC_2H_3O_2(aq) \rightleftharpoons$	$H^+(aq) +$	$C_2H_3O_2^-(aq)$
Initial	0.25	0.00	0.00
Change	$-x$	$+x$	$+x$
Equilibrium	$0.25 - x$	x	x

$$K_a = \frac{\left[H^+\right]\left[C_2H_3O_2^-\right]}{\left[HC_2H_3O_2\right]}$$

$$1.8 \times 10^{-5} = \frac{[x][x]}{[0.25 - x]}$$

$$1.8 \times 10^{-5} = \frac{[x][x]}{[0.25 - \cancel{x}]}$$

$$1.8 \times 10^{-5} = \frac{[x]^2}{[0.25]}$$

$$x = \sqrt{\left(1.8 \times 10^{-5}\right) \times (0.25)} = 2.1 \times 10^{-3} \ M$$

Percent ionization $= \dfrac{x}{0.25 \ M} \times 100 = \dfrac{2.1 \times 10^{-3} \ M}{0.25 \ M} \times 100\% = 0.84\%$

Our assumption (simplification) is valid, thus we can now calculate the pH:

$$pH = -\log\left(2.1 \times 10^{-3}\right) = \mathbf{2.68}$$

57. Calculate the pH of a 0.65 M formic acid solution ($K_a = 1.8 \times 10^{-4}$).

$$HCHO_2 (aq) \rightleftharpoons H^+ (aq) + CHO_2^- (aq)$$

Concentration	$HCHO_2 (aq) \rightleftharpoons H^+ (aq) + CHO_2^- (aq)$		
Initial	0.65	0.00	0.00
Change	$-x$	$+x$	$+x$
Equilibrium	$0.65 - x$	x	x

$$K_a = \frac{\left[H^+ \right] \left[CHO_2^- \right]}{\left[HCHO_2 \right]}$$

$$1.8 \times 10^{-4} = \frac{[x][x]}{[0.65 - x]}$$

$$1.8 \times 10^{-4} = \frac{[x][x]}{[0.65 - \cancel{x}]}$$

$$1.8 \times 10^{-4} = \frac{[x]^2}{[0.65]}$$

$$x = \sqrt{\left(1.8 \times 10^{-4} \right) \times (0.65)} = 1.1 \times 10^{-2}\ M$$

$$\text{Percent ionization} = \frac{x}{0.65\ M} \times 100 = \frac{1.1 \times 10^{-2}\ M}{0.65\ M} \times 100\% = 1.7\%$$

Our assumption (simplification) is valid, thus we can now calculate the pH:

$$pH = -\log \left(1.1 \times 10^{-2} \right) = \mathbf{1.96}$$

58. Calculate the pH of a 0.80 M nitrous acid solution ($K_a = 4.6 \times 10^{-4}$).

$$HNO_2 (aq) \rightleftharpoons H^+ (aq) + NO_2^- (aq)$$

Concentration	$HNO_2 (aq) \rightleftharpoons H^+ (aq) + NO_2^- (aq)$		
Initial	0.80	0.00	0.00
Change	$-x$	$+x$	$+x$
Equilibrium	$0.80 - x$	x	x

$$K_a = \frac{[H^+][NO_2^-]}{[HNO_2]}$$

$$4.6 \times 10^{-4} = \frac{[x][x]}{[0.80 - x]}$$

$$4.6 \times 10^{-4} = \frac{[x][x]}{[0.80 - \cancel{x}]}$$

$$4.6 \times 10^{-4} = \frac{[x]^2}{[0.80]}$$

$$x = \sqrt{\left(4.6 \times 10^{-4}\right) \times (0.80)} = 1.9 \times 10^{-2} \ M$$

Percent ionization $= \dfrac{x}{0.80 \ M} \times 100 = \dfrac{1.9 \times 10^{-2} \ M}{0.80 \ M} \times 100\% = 2.4 \ \%$

Our assumption (simplification) is valid, thus we can now calculate the pH:

$$pH = -\log\left(1.9 \times 10^{-2}\right) = \mathbf{1.72}$$

59. Calculate the pH of a 0.50 M hydrofluoric acid solution ($K_a = 3.5 \times 10^{-4}$).

$$HF(aq) \rightleftharpoons H^+(aq) + F^-(aq)$$

Concentration	$HF(aq) \rightleftharpoons H^+(aq) + F^-(aq)$		
Initial	0.50	0.00	0.00
Change	$-x$	$+x$	$+x$
Equilibrium	$0.50 - x$	x	x

$$K_a = \frac{[H^+][F^-]}{[HF]}$$

$$3.5 \times 10^{-4} = \frac{[x][x]}{[0.50 - x]}$$

$$3.5 \times 10^{-4} = \frac{[x][x]}{[0.50 - \cancel{x}]}$$

$$3.5 \times 10^{-4} = \frac{[x]^2}{[0.50]}$$

$$x = \sqrt{\left(3.5 \times 10^{-4}\right) \times (0.50)} = 1.3 \times 10^{-2} \ M$$

Percent ionization $= \dfrac{x}{0.50 \ M} \times 100 = \dfrac{1.3 \times 10^{-2} \ M}{0.50 \ M} \times 100\% = 2.6\%$

Our assumption (simplification) is valid, thus we can now calculate the pH:

$$pH = -\log\left(1.3 \times 10^{-2}\right) = \mathbf{1.89}$$

60. Calculate the pH of a 0.10 M nitrous acid solution ($K_a = 4.6 \times 10^{-4}$).

$$HNO_2(aq) \rightarrow H^+(aq) + NO_2^-(aq)$$

Concentration	$HNO_2(aq) \rightarrow$	$H^+(aq) +$	$NO_2^-(aq)$
Initial	0.10	0.00	0.00
Change	$-x$	$+x$	$+x$
Equilibrium	$0.10 - x$	x	x

$$K_a = \frac{\left[H^+\right]\left[NO_2^-\right]}{\left[HNO_2\right]}$$

$$4.6 \times 10^{-4} = \frac{[x][x]}{[0.10 - x]}$$

$$4.6 \times 10^{-4} = \frac{[x][x]}{[0.10 - \cancel{x}]}$$

$$4.6 \times 10^{-4} = \frac{[x]^2}{[0.10]}$$

$$x = \sqrt{\left(4.6 \times 10^{-4}\right) \times (0.10)} = 6.8 \times 10^{-3} \ M$$

Percent ionization $= \dfrac{x}{0.10 \ M} \times 100 = \dfrac{6.8 \times 10^{-3} \ M}{0.10 \ M} \times 100\% = 6.8\%$

Our assumption (simplification) is NOT valid this time; therefore we need to use the quadratic formula to solve this problem:

$$4.6 \times 10^{-4} = \frac{[x]^2}{[0.10 - x]}$$

$$\left(4.6 \times 10^{-4}\right)(0.10 - x) = x^2$$

$$4.6 \times 10^{-5} - \left(4.6 \times 10^{-4}\right)x = x^2$$

$$x^2 + \left(4.6 \times 10^{-4}\right)x - 4.6 \times 10^{-5} = 0$$

$$x = \frac{-b \pm \sqrt{b^2 - 4ac}}{2a}$$

$$x = \frac{-\left(4.6 \times 10^{-4}\right) \pm \sqrt{\left(4.6 \times 10^{-4}\right)^2 - 4(1)\left(-4.6 \times 10^{-5}\right)}}{2(1)}$$

$$x = \frac{-\left(4.6 \times 10^{-4}\right) \pm 0.0136}{2(1)}$$

$$x = -0.0070 \ or \ x = 0.0066$$

$$pH = -\log 0.0066 = \textbf{2.18}$$

61. Calculate the pH of a 0.050 M hydrofluoric acid solution ($K_a = 3.5 \times 10^{-4}$).

$$HF(aq) \rightleftharpoons H^+ (aq) + F^- (aq)$$

Concentration	$HF(aq) \rightleftharpoons$	$H^+ (aq) +$	$F^- (aq)$
Initial	0.050	0.00	0.00
Change	$-x$	$+x$	$+x$
Equilibrium	$0.050 - x$	x	x

$$K_a = \frac{[H^+][F^-]}{[HF]}$$

$$3.5 \times 10^{-4} = \frac{[x][x]}{[0.050 - x]}$$

$$3.5 \times 10^{-4} = \frac{[x][x]}{[0.050 - \cancel{x}]}$$

$$3.5 \times 10^{-4} = \frac{[x]^2}{[0.050]}$$

$$x = \sqrt{\left(3.5 \times 10^{-4}\right) \times (0.050)} = 4.2 \times 10^{-3} \ M$$

$$\text{Percent ionization} = \frac{x}{0.050 \ M} \times 100 = \frac{4.2 \times 10^{-3} \ M}{0.050 \ M} \times 100\% = 8.4\%$$

Our assumption (simplification) is NOT valid this time; therefore, we need to use the quadratic formula to solve this problem:

$$3.5 \times 10^{-4} = \frac{[x]^2}{[0.050 - x]}$$

$$\left(3.5 \times 10^{-4}\right)(0.050 - x) = x^2$$

$$1.75 \times 10^{-5} - \left(3.5 \times 10^{-4}\right)x = x^2$$

$$x^2 + \left(3.5 \times 10^{-4}\right)x - 1.75 \times 10^{-5} = 0$$

$$x = \frac{-b \pm \sqrt{b^2 - 4ac}}{2a}$$

$$x = \frac{-\left(3.5 \times 10^{-4}\right) \pm \sqrt{\left(3.5 \times 10^{-4}\right)^2 - 4(1)\left(-1.75 \times 10^{-5}\right)}}{2(1)}$$

$$x = \frac{-\left(3.5 \times 10^{-4}\right) \pm 0.00837}{2(1)}$$

$$x = -0.0044 \ or \ x = 0.0040$$

$$pH = -\log 0.0040 = \mathbf{2.40}$$

62. Calculate the pH of a 0.010 M nitrous acid solution ($K_a = 4.6 \times 10^{-4}$).

$$HNO_2(aq) \rightleftharpoons H^+(aq) + NO_2^-(aq)$$

Concentration	$HNO_2(aq)$	$\rightleftharpoons$	$H^+(aq)$	$+$	$NO_2^-(aq)$
Initial	0.010		0.00		0.00
Change	$-x$		$+x$		$+x$
Equilibrium	$0.010 - x$		x		x

$$K_a = \frac{[H^+][NO_2^-]}{[HNO_2]}$$

$$4.6 \times 10^{-4} = \frac{[x][x]}{[0.010 - x]}$$

$$4.6 \times 10^{-4} = \frac{[x][x]}{[0.010 - \cancel{x}]}$$

$$4.6 \times 10^{-4} = \frac{[x]^2}{[0.010]}$$

$$x = \sqrt{\left(4.6 \times 10^{-4}\right) \times (0.010)} = 2.1 \times 10^{-3} \ M$$

$$\text{Percent ionization} = \frac{x}{0.010 \ M} \times 100 = \frac{2.1 \times 10^{-3} \ M}{0.010 \ M} \times 100\% = 21\%$$

Our assumption (simplification) is NOT valid this time; therefore, we need to use the quadratic formula to solve this problem:

$$4.6 \times 10^{-4} = \frac{[x]^2}{[0.010 - x]}$$

$$\left(4.6 \times 10^{-4}\right)(0.010 - x) = x^2$$

$$4.6 \times 10^{-6} - \left(4.6 \times 10^{-4}\right)x = x^2$$

$$x^2 + \left(4.6 \times 10^{-4}\right)x - 4.6 \times 10^{-6} = 0$$

$$x = \frac{-b \pm \sqrt{b^2 - 4ac}}{2a}$$

$$x = \frac{-\left(4.6 \times 10^{-4}\right) \pm \sqrt{\left(4.6 \times 10^{-4}\right)^2 - 4(1)\left(-4.6 \times 10^{-6}\right)}}{2(1)}$$

$$x = \frac{-\left(4.6 \times 10^{-4}\right) \pm 0.00431}{2(1)}$$

$$x = -0.0024 \; or \; x = 0.0019$$

$$pH = -\log 0.0019 = \mathbf{2.72}$$

63. Calculate the percent ionization of a 1.0 M solution of acetic acid ($K_a = 1.8 \times 10^{-5}$).

$$HC_2H_3O_2(aq) \rightleftharpoons H^+(aq) + C_2H_3O_2^-(aq)$$

Concentration	$HC_2H_3O_2(aq) \rightleftharpoons$	$H^+(aq) +$	$C_2H_3O_2^-(aq)$
Initial	1.0	0.00	0.00
Change	$-x$	$+x$	$+x$
Equilibrium	$1.0 - x$	x	x

$$K_a = \frac{[H^+][C_2H_3O_2^-]}{[HC_2H_3O_2]}$$

$$1.8 \times 10^{-5} = \frac{[x][x]}{[1.0 - x]}$$

$$1.8 \times 10^{-5} = \frac{[x][x]}{[1.0 - \!\!\!\!-x]}$$

$$1.8 \times 10^{-5} = \frac{[x]^2}{[1.0]}$$

$$x = \sqrt{\left(1.8 \times 10^{-5}\right) \times (1.0)} = 4.2 \times 10^{-3} \ M$$

Percent ionization $= \dfrac{x}{1.0 \ M} \times 100 = \dfrac{4.2 \times 10^{-3} \ M}{1.0 \ M} \times 100\% = \mathbf{0.42\%}$

64. Calculate the percent ionization of a 1.0 M solution of formic acid ($K_a = 1.8 \times 10^{-4}$).

$$HCHO_2 (aq) \rightleftharpoons H^+ (aq) + CHO_2^- (aq)$$

Concentration	$HCHO_2 (aq) \rightleftharpoons$	$H^+ (aq) +$	$CHO_2^- (aq)$
Initial	1.0	0.00	0.00
Change	$-x$	$+x$	$+x$
Equilibrium	$1.0 - x$	x	x

$$K_a = \frac{[H^+][CHO_2^-]}{[HCHO_2]}$$

$$1.8 \times 10^{-4} = \frac{[x][x]}{[1.0 - x]}$$

$$1.8 \times 10^{-4} = \frac{[x][x]}{[1.0 \cancel{-x}]}$$

$$1.8 \times 10^{-4} = \frac{[x]^2}{[1.0]}$$

$$x = \sqrt{\left(1.8 \times 10^{-4}\right) \times (1.0)} = 1.3 \times 10^{-2} \ M$$

Percent ionization $= \dfrac{x}{1.0 \ M} \times 100 = \dfrac{1.3 \times 10^{-2} \ M}{1.0 \ M} \times 100\% = \mathbf{1.3\%}$

65. Calculate the percent ionization of a 0.10 M solution of acetic acid ($K_a = 1.8 \times 10^{-5}$).

$$HC_2H_3O_2 (aq) \rightleftharpoons H^+ (aq) + C_2H_3O_2^- (aq)$$

Concentration	$HC_2H_3O_2 (aq) \rightleftharpoons$	$H^+ (aq) +$	$C_2H_3O_2^- (aq)$
Initial	0.10	0.00	0.00
Change	$-x$	$+x$	$+x$
Equilibrium	$0.10 - x$	x	x

$$K_a = \frac{[H^+][C_2H_3O_2^-]}{[HC_2H_3O_2]}$$

$$1.8 \times 10^{-5} = \frac{[x][x]}{[0.10 - x]}$$

$$1.8 \times 10^{-5} = \frac{[x][x]}{[0.10 -\!\!\!\!\!\times]}$$

$$1.8 \times 10^{-5} = \frac{[x]^2}{[0.10]}$$

$$x = \sqrt{\left(1.8 \times 10^{-5}\right) \times (0.10)} = 1.3 \times 10^{-3} \ M$$

Percent ionization $= \dfrac{x}{0.10 \ M} \times 100 = \dfrac{1.3 \times 10^{-3} \ M}{0.10 \ M} \times 100\% = \mathbf{1.3\%}$

66. What are polyprotic acids?

Polyprotic acids have more than one ionizable proton, and therefore have more than one K_a value (i.e. K_{a1} and K_{a2} etc.).

67. For the most part, what assumption can we generally make when dealing with polyprotic acids and why?

We can generally focus on Ka_1 only as Ka_2 (and Ka_3 if it applies) generally tend to be negligible (not always the case, such as dilute solutions of certain acids). This is in part due to the fact that polyprotic acids ionizes in successive steps, and the formation of hydronium ions in the first step inhibits their formation in the second (and third step if it applies) as Le Châtelier's principle would predict. Therefore, we can determine the pH of most solutions of polyprotic acids by just using the K_{a1} value.

68. Define monoprotic, diprotic, and triprotic acids. Give an example for each.

Monoprotic acids (i.e. HCl) have one ionizable proton, diprotic acids (i.e. H_2SO_4) have two ionizable protons, and triprotic acids (i.e. H_3PO_4) have three ionizable protons.

69. Calculate the pH of a 0.20 M carbonic acid solution ($K_{a1} = 4.3 \times 10^{-7}$ and $K_{a2} = 5.6 \times 10^{-11}$).

$$H_2CO_3 \, (aq) \rightleftharpoons H^+ \, (aq) + HCO_3^- \, (aq)$$

Concentration	$H_2CO_3 \, (aq) \rightarrow H^+ \, (aq) + HCO_3^- \, (aq)$		
Initial	0.20	0.00	0.00
Change	$-x$	$+x$	$+x$
Equilibrium	$0.20 - x$	x	x

$$K_a = \frac{[H^+][HCO_3^-]}{[H_2CO_3]}$$

$$4.3 \times 10^{-7} = \frac{[x][x]}{[0.20 - x]}$$

$$4.3 \times 10^{-7} = \frac{[x][x]}{-[0.20 - x]}$$

$$4.3 \times 10^{-7} = \frac{[x]^2}{[0.20]}$$

$$x = \sqrt{\left(4.3 \times 10^{-7}\right) \times (0.20)} = 2.9 \times 10^{-4} \ M$$

Percent ionization $= \dfrac{x}{0.20 \ M} \times 100 = \dfrac{2.9 \times 10^{-4} \ M}{0.20 \ M} \times 100\% = 0.15\%$

Our assumption (simplification) is valid, thus we can now calculate the pH:

$$pH = -\log\left(2.9 \times 10^{-4}\right) = \mathbf{3.54}$$

*Note-K_{a2} is very small (5.6×10^{-11}) and is essentially negligible in this example. Therefore, we determine the pH by just using the K_{a1} value here.

70. Below are titration curves of a diprotic and triprotic acid titrated with a strong base. Which one is which, and how can you tell?

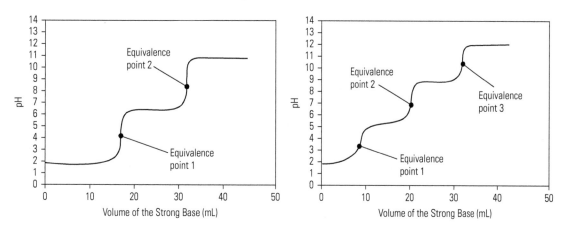

The titration curve on the left is of a diprotic acid being titrated with a strong base, while the one on the right is of a triprotic acid being titrated with a strong base. The diprotic acid has two equivalency points as expected, while the triprotic acid has three.

71. Which acid would you expect to be stronger, H_2S or HCl?

HCl is a stronger acid due to the presence of the electronegative chlorine atom which results in a very polarized bond.

72. Which acid would you expect to be stronger, H_2Se or HBr?

HBr is a stronger acid due to the presence of the electronegative bromine atom which results in a very polarized bond.

73. Which acid would you expect to be stronger, HF or HI?

HI is a much stronger acid (acidic strength increases as you go down column 7A) because hydrogen is released easier with larger atoms.

74. Which acid would you expect to be stronger, $HClO$ or $HClO_4$?

$HClO_4$ is a much stronger acid (more oxygen atoms translates into stronger oxyacids).

BASE STRENGTH

75. What is the major distinction between strong and weak bases?

Strong bases completely dissociate into ions when dissolved in water, while weak bases only partially ionize when dissolved in water.

76. What is the pH of a 0.20 M solution of the strong base $NaOH$?

Since strong bases completely ionize, we assume that we have 0.20 M OH^- ions in solution in this case; therefore, we determine the pOH as follows:

$$pOH = -\log [OH^-] = -\log 0.20 = 0.70$$

From here, we can calculate the pH:

$$pH = 14.00 - pOH = 13.33$$

77. What is the pH of a 0.15 M solution of the strong base KOH?

Since strong bases completely ionize, we assume that we have 0.15 M OH^- ions in solution in this case; therefore, we determine the pOH as follows:

$$pOH = -\log [OH^-] = -\log 0.15 = 0.82$$

From here, we can calculate the pH:

$$pH = 14.00 - pOH = 13.18$$

78. What is the pH of a 0.050 M solution of the strong base $Sr(OH)_2$?

Since strong bases completely ionize, we assume that we have 2 × (0.05 M) OH^- ions in solution in this case; therefore, we determine the pOH as follows:

$$pOH = -\log [OH^-] = -\log 0.10 = 1.00$$

From here, we can calculate the pH:

$$pH = 14.00 - pOH = 13.00$$

79. What is the hydroxide ion concentration in a *NaOH* solution with a pH value of 11.25?

$$pOH = 14.00 - pH = 2.75$$

$$pOH = -\log [OH^-]$$

$$[OH^-] = antilog\ (-pOH) = antilog\ (-2.75) = 1.8 \times 10^{-3}\ M$$

80. What is the hydroxide ion concentration in a *LiOH* solution with a pH value of 9.10?

$$pOH = 14.00 - pH = 4.90$$

$$pOH = -\log [OH^-]$$

$$[OH^-] = antilog\ (-pOH) = antilog\ (-4.90) = 1.3 \times 10^{-5}\ M$$

81. What is the hydroxide ion concentration *Ca(OH)$_2$* solution with a pH value of 12.25?

$$pOH = 14.00 - pH = 1.75$$

$$pOH = -\log [OH^-]$$

$$[OH^-] = antilog\ (-pOH) = antilog\ (-1.75) = 1.8 \times 10^{-2}\ M$$

*Note – While the hydroxide ion concentration here is 1.8×10^{-2} M, the concentration of the *Ca(OH)$_2$* solution would be 9.0×10^{-3} M.

82. What is the hydroxide ion concentration *Ba(OH)$_2$* solution with a pH value of 13.15?

$$pOH = 14.00 - pH = 0.85$$

$$pOH = -\log [OH^-]$$

$$[OH^-] = antilog\ (-pOH) = antilog\ (-0.85) = 0.14\ M$$

*Note – While the hydroxide ion concentration here is 0.14 M, the concentration of the *Ba(OH)$_2$* solution would be 0.07 M.

83. What is the pH of a solution that is 2.8% *NaOH* by mass and has a density of 1.02 g/ml?

$$\frac{2.8\ g\ NaOH}{100\ g\ Sol'n} \times \frac{1.02\ g\ Sol'n}{ml\ Sol'n} \times \frac{1\ mol\ NaOH}{40.00\ g\ NaOH} \times \frac{1,000\ ml}{1\ L} = 0.71\ M\ NaOH$$

$$pOH = -\log [OH^-] = -\log [0.71] = 0.15$$

$$pH = 14.00 - pOH = 13.85$$

84. What is the pH of a solution that is 1.5% *LiOH* by mass and has a density of 1.02 g/ml?

$$\frac{1.5\ g\ LiOH}{100\ g\ Sol'n} \times \frac{1.02\ g\ Sol'n}{ml\ Sol'n} \times \frac{1\ mol\ LiOH}{23.95\ g\ LiOH} \times \frac{1,000\ ml}{1\ L} = 0.64\ M\ LiOH$$

$$pOH = -\log[OH^-] = -\log [0.64] = 0.19$$

$$pH = 14.00 - pOH = 13.81$$

85. What is the base ionization constant (K_b)?

The base ionization constant (K_b) is the equilibrium constant for the ionization reaction of bases, which is very useful for calculations involving weak bases.

86. Write the K_b expression for the generic weak base B.

$$B\,(aq) + H_2O\,(l) \rightleftharpoons BH^+\,(aq) + OH^-\,(aq)$$

$$K_b = \frac{[BH^+][OH^-]}{[B]}$$

87. Calculate the pH of a 0.50 M ammonia solution $(K_b = 1.8 \times 10^{-5})$.

$$NH_3\,(aq) + H_2O\,(l) \rightleftharpoons NH_4^+\,(aq) + OH^-\,(aq)$$

Concentration	$NH_3\,(aq) + H_2O\,(l) \rightleftharpoons$	$NH_4^+\,(aq) +$	$OH^-\,(aq)$
Initial	0.050	0.00	0.00
Change	$-x$	$+x$	$+x$
Equilibrium	$0.50 - x$	x	x

$$K_b = \frac{[NH_4^+][OH^-]}{[NH_3]}$$

$$1.8 \times 10^{-5} = \frac{[x][x]}{[0.50 - x]}$$

$$1.8 \times 10^{-5} = \frac{[x][x]}{[0.50 - \cancel{x}]}$$

$$1.8 \times 10^{-5} = \frac{[x]^2}{[0.50]}$$

$$x = \sqrt{\left(1.8 \times 10^{-5}\right) \times (0.50)} = 3.0 \times 10^{-3}\ M$$

$$\text{Percent ionization} = \frac{x}{0.50\ M} \times 100 = \frac{3.0 \times 10^{-3}\ M}{0.50\ M} \times 100\% = 0.60\%$$

Our assumption (simplification) is valid, thus we can now calculate the pOH and then the pH:

$$pOH = -\log\left(3.0 \times 10^{-3}\right) = 2.52$$

$$pH = 14.00 - pOH = \mathbf{11.48}$$

88. Calculate the pH of a 0.25 M hydrogen carbonate solution ($K_b = 2.3 \times 10^{-8}$).

$$HCO_3^- \ (aq) + H_2O \ (l) \rightleftharpoons H_2CO_3 \ (aq) + OH^- \ (aq)$$

Concentration	$HCO_3^- \ (aq) + H_2O \ (l) \rightleftharpoons H_2CO_3 \ (aq) + OH^- \ (aq)$		
Initial	0.25	0.00	0.00
Change	$-x$	$+x$	$+x$
Equilibrium	$0.25 - x$	x	x

$$K_b = \frac{[H_2CO_3][OH^-]}{[HCO_3^-]}$$

$$2.3 \times 10^{-8} = \frac{[x][x]}{[0.25 - x]}$$

$$2.3 \times 10^{-8} = \frac{[x][x]}{[0.25 - \cancel{x}]}$$

$$2.3 \times 10^{-8} = \frac{[x]^2}{[0.25]}$$

$$x = \sqrt{\left(2.3 \times 10^{-8}\right) \times (0.25)} = 7.6 \times 10^{-5} \ M$$

$$\text{Percent ionization} = \frac{x}{0.25 \ M} \times 100 = \frac{7.6 \times 10^{-5} \ M}{0.25 \ M} \times 100\% = 0.030\%$$

Our assumption (simplification) is valid, thus we can now calculate the pOH and then the pH:

$$pOH = -\log\left(7.6 \times 10^{-5}\right) = 4.12$$

$$pH = 14.00 - pOH = \textbf{9.88}$$

89. Calculate the pH of a 0.30 M methylamine solution ($K_b = 4.4 \times 10^{-4}$).

$$CH_3NH_2 \ (aq) + H_2O \ (l) \rightleftharpoons CH_3NH_3^+ \ (aq) + OH^- \ (aq)$$

Concentration	$CH_3NH_2 \ (aq) + H_2O \ (l) \rightleftharpoons CH_3NH_3^+ \ (aq) + OH^- \ (aq)$		
Initial	0.30	0.00	0.00
Change	$-x$	$+x$	$+x$
Equilibrium	$0.30 - x$	x	x

$$K_b = \frac{[CH_3NH_3^+][OH^-]}{[CH_3NH_2]}$$

$$4.4 \times 10^{-4} = \frac{[x][x]}{[0.30 - x]}$$

$$4.4 \times 10^{-4} = \frac{[x][x]}{[0.30 - \cancel{x}]}$$

$$4.4 \times 10^{-4} = \frac{[x]^2}{[0.30]}$$

$$x = \sqrt{\left(4.4 \times 10^{-4}\right) \times (0.30)} = 1.1 \times 10^{-2} \ M$$

$$\text{Percent ionization} = \frac{x}{0.30 \ M} \times 100 = \frac{1.1 \times 10^{-2} \ M}{0.30 M} \times 100\% = 3.7\%$$

Our assumption (simplification) is valid, thus we can now calculate the pOH and then the pH:

$$pOH = -\log\left(1.1 \times 10^{-2}\right) = 1.96$$

$$pH = 14.00 - pOH = \mathbf{12.04}$$

90. Calculate the pH of a 0.45 M carbonate solution ($K_b = 1.8 \times 10^{-4}$).

$$CO_3^{2-} \ (aq) + H_2O \ (l) \rightleftharpoons HCO_3^- \ (aq) + OH^- \ (aq)$$

Concentration	$CO_3^{2-} \ (aq) + H_2O \ (l) \rightleftharpoons HCO_3^- \ (aq) + OH^- \ (aq)$		
Initial	0.45	0.00	0.00
Change	$-x$	$+x$	$+x$
Equilibrium	$0.45 - x$	x	x

$$K_b = \frac{[HCO_3^-][OH^-]}{[CO_3^{2-}]}$$

$$1.8 \times 10^{-4} = \frac{[x][x]}{[0.45 - x]}$$

$$1.8 \times 10^{-4} = \frac{[x][x]}{[0.45 - \cancel{x}]}$$

$$1.8 \times 10^{-4} = \frac{[x]^2}{[0.45]}$$

$$x = \sqrt{\left(1.8 \times 10^{-4}\right) \times (0.45)} = 9.0 \times 10^{-3} \ M$$

$$\text{Percent ionization} = \frac{x}{0.45 \ M} \times 100 = \frac{9.0 \times 10^{-3} \ M}{0.45 \ M} \times 100\% = 2.0\%$$

Our assumption (simplification) is valid, thus we can now calculate the pOH and then the pH:

$$pOH = -\log\left(9.0 \times 10^{-3}\right) = 2.05$$

$$pH = 14.00 - pOH = \textbf{11.95}$$

91. Calculate the pH of a 1.0 M ethylamine solution ($K_b = 5.6 \times 10^{-4}$).

$$C_2H_5NH_2 \ (aq) + H_2O \ (l) \rightleftharpoons C_2H_5NH_3^+ \ (aq) + OH^- \ (aq)$$

Concentration	$C_2H_5NH_2 \ (aq) + H_2O \ (l) \rightleftharpoons$	$C_2H_5NH_3^+ \ (aq) +$	$OH^- \ (aq)$
Initial	1.0	0.00	0.00
Change	$-x$	$+x$	$+x$
Equilibrium	$1.0 - x$	x	x

$$K_b = \frac{[C_2H_5NH_3^+][OH^-]}{[C_2H_5NH_2]}$$

$$5.6 \times 10^{-4} = \frac{[x][x]}{[1.0 - x]}$$

$$5.6 \times 10^{-4} = \frac{[x][x]}{[1.0 - \cancel{x}]}$$

$$5.6 \times 10^{-4} = \frac{[x]^2}{[1.0]}$$

$$x = \sqrt{\left(5.6 \times 10^{-4}\right) \times (1.0)} = 2.4 \times 10^{-2} \ M$$

Percent ionization $= \dfrac{x}{1.0 \ M} \times 100 = \dfrac{2.4 \times 10^{-2} \ M}{1.0 \ M} \times 100\% = 2.4\%$

Our assumption (simplification) is valid, thus we can now calculate the pOH and then the pH:

$$pOH = -\log\left(2.4 \times 10^{-2}\right) = 1.62$$

$$pH = 14.00 - pOH = \textbf{12.38}$$

92. Calculate the pH of a 1.5×10^{-2} M ammonia solution ($K_b = 1.8 \times 10^{-5}$).

$$NH_3 \ (aq) + H_2O \ (l) \rightleftharpoons NH_4^+ \ (aq) + OH^- \ (aq)$$

Concentration	$NH_3 \ (aq) + H_2O \ (l) \rightleftharpoons$	$NH_4^+ \ (aq) +$	$OH^- \ (aq)$
Initial	0.015	0.00	0.00
Change	$-x$	$+x$	$+x$
Equilibrium	$0.015 - x$	x	x

$$K_b = \frac{[NH_4^+][OH^-]}{[NH_3]}$$

$$1.8 \times 10^{-5} = \frac{[x][x]}{[0.015 - x]}$$

$$1.8 \times 10^{-5} = \frac{[x][x]}{[0.015 - \cancel{x}]}$$

$$1.8 \times 10^{-5} = \frac{[x]^2}{[0.015]}$$

$$x = \sqrt{\left(1.8 \times 10^{-5}\right) \times (0.015)} = 5.2 \times 10^{-4} \ M$$

$$\text{Percent ionization} = \frac{x}{0.015 \ M} \times 100 = \frac{5.2 \times 10^{-4} \ M}{0.015 \ M} \times 100\% = 3.5\%$$

Our assumption (simplification) is valid, thus we can now calculate the pOH and then the pH:

$$pOH = -\log\left(5.2 \times 10^{-4}\right) = 3.28$$

$$pH = 14.00 - pOH = \textbf{10.72}$$

93. Calculate the pH of a 0.85 M hydrogen carbonate solution ($K_b = 2.3 \times 10^{-8}$).

$$HCO_3^- \ (aq) + H_2O \ (l) \rightleftharpoons H_2CO_3 \ (aq) + OH^- \ (aq)$$

Concentration	HCO_3^- (aq) + H_2O (l) $\rightleftharpoons$ H_2CO_3 (aq) + OH^- (aq)		
Initial	0.85	0.00	0.00
Change	$-x$	$+x$	$+x$
Equilibrium	$0.85 - x$	x	x

$$K_b = \frac{[H_2CO_3][OH^-]}{[HCO_3^-]}$$

$$2.3 \times 10^{-8} = \frac{[x][x]}{[0.85 - x]}$$

$$2.3 \times 10^{-8} = \frac{[x][x]}{[0.85 - \cancel{x}]}$$

$$2.3 \times 10^{-8} = \frac{[x]^2}{[0.85]}$$

$$x = \sqrt{\left(2.3 \times 10^{-8}\right) \times (0.85)} = 1.4 \times 10^{-4} \ M$$

$$\text{Percent ionization} = \frac{x}{0.85 \; M} \times 100 = \frac{1.4 \times 10^{-4} \; M}{0.85 \; M} \times 100\% = 0.016\%$$

Our assumption (simplification) is valid, thus we can now calculate the pOH and then the pH:

$$pOH = -\log\left(1.4 \times 10^{-4}\right) = 3.85$$

$$pH = 14.00 - pOH = \textbf{10.15}$$

94. Calculate the pH of a 0.50 M ethylamine solution ($K_b = 5.6 \times 10^{-4}$).

$$C_2H_5NH_2 \; (aq) + H_2O \; (l) \rightleftharpoons C_2H_5NH_3^+ \; (aq) + OH^- \; (aq)$$

Concentration	$C_2H_5NH_2 \; (aq) + H_2O \; (l) \rightleftharpoons C_2H_5NH_3^+ \; (aq) + OH^- \; (aq)$		
Initial	0.50	0.00	0.00
Change	$-x$	$+x$	$+x$
Equilibrium	$0.50 - x$	x	x

$$K_b = \frac{[C_2H_5NH_3^+][OH^-]}{[C_2H_5NH_2]}$$

$$5.6 \times 10^{-4} = \frac{[x][x]}{[0.50 - x]}$$

$$5.6 \times 10^{-4} = \frac{[x][x]}{[0.50 -\!\!\!\!\!\times]}$$

$$5.6 \times 10^{-4} = \frac{[x]^2}{[0.50]}$$

$$x = \sqrt{\left(5.6 \times 10^{-4}\right) \times (0.50)} = 1.7 \times 10^{-2} \; M$$

$$\text{Percent ionization} = \frac{x}{0.50 \; M} \times 100 = \frac{1.7 \times 10^{-2} \; M}{0.50 \; M} \times 100\% = 3.4\%$$

Our assumption (simplification) is valid, thus we can now calculate the pOH and then the pH:

$$pOH = -\log\left(1.7 \times 10^{-2}\right) = 1.80$$

$$pH = 14.00 - pOH = \textbf{12.20}$$

95. Calculate the pH of a 0.35 M carbonate solution ($K_b = 1.8 \times 10^{-4}$).

$$CO_3^{2-}\ (aq) + H_2O\ (l) \rightleftharpoons HCO_3^-\ (aq) + OH^-\ (aq)$$

Concentration	$CO_3^{2-}\ (aq) + H_2O\ (l) \rightleftharpoons HCO_3^-\ (aq) + OH^-\ (aq)$		
Initial	0.35	0.00	0.00
Change	$-x$	$+x$	$+x$
Equilibrium	$0.35 - x$	x	x

$$K_b = \frac{[HCO_3^-][OH^-]}{[CO_3^{2-}]}$$

$$1.8 \times 10^{-4} = \frac{[x][x]}{[0.35 - x]}$$

$$1.8 \times 10^{-4} = \frac{[x][x]}{[0.35 - \cancel{x}]}$$

$$1.8 \times 10^{-4} = \frac{[x]^2}{[0.35]}$$

$$x = \sqrt{\left(1.8 \times 10^{-4}\right) \times (0.35)} = 7.9 \times 10^{-3}\ M$$

Percent ionization $= \dfrac{x}{0.35\ M} \times 100 = \dfrac{7.9 \times 10^{-3}\ M}{0.35\ M} \times 100\% = 2.3\%$

Our assumption (simplification) is valid, thus we can now calculate the pOH and then the pH:

$$pOH = -\log\left(7.9 \times 10^{-3}\right) = 2.10$$

$$pH = 14.00 - pOH = \mathbf{11.90}$$

96. Morphine is a narcotic pain reliever commonly used to treat moderate to severe pain and is a weak base ($K_b = 1.6 \times 10^{-6}$). What is the pH of a 0.25 M solution of morphine?

To solve this problem, we will let "M" represent morphine and "HM^+" be the protonated form of morphine in the following equation:

$$M\ (aq) + H_2O\ (l) \rightleftharpoons HM^+\ (aq) + OH^-\ (aq)$$

Concentration	$M\ (aq) + H_2O\ (l) \rightleftharpoons HM^+\ (aq) + OH^-\ (aq)$		
Initial	0.25	0.00	0.00
Change	$-x$	$+x$	$+x$
Equilibrium	$0.25 - x$	x	x

$$K_b = \frac{[HM^+][OH^-]}{[M]}$$

$$1.6 \times 10^{-6} = \frac{[x][x]}{[0.25 - x]}$$

$$1.6 \times 10^{-6} = \frac{[x][x]}{[0.25 - \cancel{x}]}$$

$$1.6 \times 10^{-6} = \frac{[x]^2}{[0.25]}$$

$$x = \sqrt{\left(1.6 \times 10^{-6}\right) \times (0.25)} = 6.3 \times 10^{-4}\ M$$

Percent ionization $= \dfrac{x}{0.25\ M} \times 100 = \dfrac{6.3 \times 10^{-4}\ M}{0.25\ M} \times 100\% = 0.25\%$

Our assumption (simplification) is valid, thus we can now calculate the pOH and then the pH:

$$pOH = -\log\left(6.3 \times 10^{-4}\right) = 3.20$$

$$pH = 14.00 - pOH = \mathbf{10.80}$$

97. Nicotine is a highly addictive drug and is a weak base ($K_b = 1.0 \times 10^{-6}$). What is the pH of a 0.85 M solution of nicotine?

To solve this problem, we will let "N" represent nicotine and "HN^+" be the protonated form of nicotine in the following equation:

$$N\ (aq) + H_2O\ (l) \rightleftharpoons HN^+\ (aq) + OH^-\ (aq)$$

Concentration	$N\ (aq) + H_2O\ (l) \rightleftharpoons HN^+\ (aq) + OH^-\ (aq)$		
Initial	0.85	0.00	0.00
Change	$-x$	$+x$	$+x$
Equilibrium	$0.85 - x$	x	x

$$K_b = \frac{[HM^+][OH^-]}{[M]}$$

$$1.0 \times 10^{-6} = \frac{[x][x]}{[0.85 - x]}$$

$$1.0 \times 10^{-6} = \frac{[x][x]}{[0.85 - \cancel{x}]}$$

$$1.0 \times 10^{-6} = \frac{[x]^2}{[0.85]}$$

$$x = \sqrt{\left(1.0 \times 10^{-6}\right) \times (0.85)} = 9.2 \times 10^{-4} \ M$$

Percent ionization $= \dfrac{x}{0.85 \ M} \times 100 = \dfrac{9.2 \times 10^{-4} \ M}{0.85 \ M} \times 100\% = 0.11\%$

Our assumption (simplification) is valid, thus we can now calculate the pOH and then the pH:

$$pOH = -\log\left(9.2 \times 10^{-4}\right) = 3.04$$

$$pH = 14.00 - pOH = \mathbf{10.96}$$

98. Calculate the percent ionization of a 0.10 M solution of ammonia ($K_b = 1.8 \times 10^{-5}$).

$$NH_3 \ (aq) + H_2O \ (l) \rightleftharpoons NH_4^+ \ (aq) + OH^- \ (aq)$$

Concentration	$NH_3 \ (aq) + H_2O \ (l) \rightleftharpoons NH_4^+ \ (aq) + OH^- \ (aq)$		
Initial	0.10	0.00	0.00
Change	$-x$	$+x$	$+x$
Equilibrium	$0.10 - x$	x	x

$$K_b = \frac{[NH_4^+][OH^-]}{[NH_3]}$$

$$1.8 \times 10^{-5} = \frac{[x][x]}{[0.10 - x]}$$

$$1.8 \times 10^{-5} = \frac{[x][x]}{[0.10 - \cancel{x}]}$$

$$1.8 \times 10^{-5} = \frac{[x]^2}{[0.10]}$$

$$x = \sqrt{\left(1.8 \times 10^{-5}\right) \times (0.10)} = 1.3 \times 10^{-3} \ M$$

Percent ionization $= \dfrac{x}{0.10 \ M} \times 100 = \dfrac{1.3 \times 10^{-3} \ M}{0.10 \ M} \times 100\% = \mathbf{1.3\%}$

99. Calculate the percent ionization of a 1.5 M solution of ammonia ($K_b = 1.8 \times 10^{-5}$).

$$NH_3 \ (aq) + H_2O \ (l) \rightleftharpoons NH_4^+ \ (aq) + OH^- \ (aq)$$

Concentration	$NH_3\,(aq) + H_2O\,(l) \rightleftharpoons NH_4^+\,(aq) + OH^-\,(aq)$		
Initial	1.5	0.00	0.00
Change	$-x$	$+x$	$+x$
Equilibrium	$1.5 - x$	x	x

$$K_b = \frac{[NH_4^+][OH^-]}{[NH_3]}$$

$$1.8 \times 10^{-5} = \frac{[x][x]}{[1.5 - x]}$$

$$1.8 \times 10^{-5} = \frac{[x][x]}{[1.5 - \cancel{x}]}$$

$$1.8 \times 10^{-5} = \frac{[x]^2}{[1.5]}$$

$$x = \sqrt{\left(1.8 \times 10^{-5}\right) \times (1.5)} = 5.2 \times 10^{-3}\ M$$

$$\text{Percent ionization} = \frac{x}{1.5\ M} \times 100 = \frac{5.2 \times 10^{-3}\ M}{1.5\ M} \times 100\% = \mathbf{0.35\%}$$

100. Calculate the percent ionization of a 0.45 M solution of methylamine ($K_b = 4.4 \times 10^{-4}$).

$$CH_3NH_2\,(aq) + H_2O\,(l) \rightleftharpoons CH_3NH_3^+\,(aq) + OH^-\,(aq)$$

Concentration	$CH_3NH_2\,(aq) + H_2O\,(l) \rightleftharpoons CH_3NH_3^+\,(aq) + OH^-\,(aq)$		
Initial	0.45	0.00	0.00
Change	$-x$	$+x$	$+x$
Equilibrium	$0.45 - x$	x	x

$$K_b = \frac{[CH_3NH_3^+][OH^-]}{[CH_3NH_2]}$$

$$4.4 \times 10^{-4} = \frac{[x][x]}{[0.45 - x]}$$

$$4.4 \times 10^{-4} = \frac{[x][x]}{[0.45 - \cancel{x}]}$$

$$4.4 \times 10^{-4} = \frac{[x]^2}{[0.45]}$$

$$x = \sqrt{\left(4.4 \times 10^{-4}\right) \times (0.45)} = 1.4 \times 10^{-2} \ M$$

Percent ionization $= \dfrac{x}{0.45 \ M} \times 100 = \dfrac{1.4 \times 10^{-2} \ M}{0.45M} \times 100\% = \mathbf{3.11\%}$

BUFFERS

101.   What are buffers? Give an example of a buffer.

Buffers are solutions that resist drastic changes in pH by neutralizing added acid or base, thereby allowing them to maintain a relatively small specific pH range. Human blood is a good example of a buffer.

102.   What is the normal pH range of human blood? How is this pH range maintained?

Human blood contains a mixture of carbonic acid (weak acid) and the bicarbonate ion (conjugate base), which is a buffer system allowing it to maintain a constant pH of approximately ~7.26–7.42.

103.   What are acidic and basic buffers and how are they made?

Acidic buffers are composed of a weak acid and its conjugate base, while a basic buffer contains a weak base and its conjugate acid.

104.   What is the common ion effect?

The common ion effect can be observed when a solution contains two substances that share a common ion. This effect follows Le Châtelier's principle of shifting equilibrium in response to added acid or base in this case.

105.   Explain why you would NOT use strong acids or bases to make a buffer.

Strong acids and bases are not used for a buffer system because they ionize completely. A buffer needs to contain both the weak acid and its conjugate base (or weak base and conjugate acid) for it to be effective at resisting dramatic pH changes. This can only occur with partial (not complete) ionization of either acid or base. Thus, weak acids and bases are used in buffer systems.

106.   Consider the following generic acidic buffer system containing approximately equal amounts of acid (HA) and conjugate base (A^-):

$$HA \ (aq) \rightleftharpoons H^+(aq) + A^- \ (aq)$$

Based on Le Châtelier's principle, describe how added *acid* would affect this equilibrium and how this buffer system would minimize a dramatic change in pH. Does the pH go up or down?

Added acid would react with the conjugate base (A^-) to make more acid (HA). The pH may drop, but only slightly as the added acid would be effectively neutralized by the presence of the conjugate base.

107. Consider the following generic acidic buffer system containing approximately equal amounts of acid (HA) and conjugate base (A^-):

$$HA\,(aq) \rightleftharpoons H^+(aq) + A^-\,(aq)$$

Based on Le Châtelier's principle, describe how added *base* would affect this equilibrium and how this buffer system would minimize a dramatic change in pH. Does the pH go up or down?

Added base would react with the acid (HA) to make more conjugate base (A^-). The pH may go up but only slightly, as the added base would be effectively neutralized by the presence of the acid.

108. What is the pH of a buffer system containing 0.25 M $HCHO_2$ and 0.20 M $NaCHO_2$? The K_a value for formic acid is 1.8×10^{-4}.

$$HCHO_2\,(aq) \rightleftharpoons H^+\,(aq) + CHO_2^-\,(aq)$$

Concentration	$HCHO_2\,(aq) \rightleftharpoons$	$H^+\,(aq) +$	$CHO_2^-\,(aq)$
Initial	0.25	0.00	0.20
Change	$-x$	$+x$	$+x$
Equilibrium	$0.25 - x$	x	$0.20 + x$

$$K_a = \frac{[H^+][CHO_2^-]}{[HCHO_2]}$$

$$1.8 \times 10^{-4} = \frac{[x][0.20 + x]}{[0.25 - x]}$$

$$1.8 \times 10^{-4} = \frac{[x][0.20 + \cancel{x}]}{[0.25 - \cancel{x}]}$$

$$1.8 \times 10^{-4} = \frac{x\,(0.20)}{0.25}$$

$$x = \frac{\left(1.8 \times 10^{-4}\right) \times (0.25)}{0.20} = 2.3 \times 10^{-4}\ M$$

$$\text{Percent ionization} = \frac{x}{0.25\ M} \times 100 = \frac{2.3 \times 10^{-4}\ M}{0.25\ M} \times 100\% = 0.092\%$$

Our assumption (simplification) is valid, thus we can now calculate the pH:

$$pH = -\log\left(2.3 \times 10^{-4}\right) = \textbf{3.64}$$

109. What is the pH of a buffer system containing 0.10 M $HC_2H_3O_2$ and 0.15 M $NaC_2H_3O_2$? The K_a value for acetic acid is 1.8×10^{-5}.

$$HC_2H_3O_2\,(aq) \rightleftharpoons H^+\,(aq) + C_2H_3O_2^-\,(aq)$$

Concentration	$HC_2H_3O_2\,(aq) \rightleftharpoons H^+\,(aq) + C_2H_3O_2^-\,(aq)$		
Initial	0.10	0.00	0.15
Change	$-x$	$+x$	$+x$
Equilibrium	$0.10 - x$	x	$0.15 + x$

$$K_a = \frac{[H^+][C_2H_3O_2^-]}{[HC_2H_3O_2]}$$

$$1.8 \times 10^{-5} = \frac{[x][0.15 + x]}{[0.10 - x]}$$

$$1.8 \times 10^{-5} = \frac{[x][0.15 + \cancel{x}]}{[0.10 - \cancel{x}]}$$

$$1.8 \times 10^{-5} = \frac{x\,(0.15)}{0.10}$$

$$x = \frac{\left(1.8 \times 10^{-5}\right) \times (0.10)}{0.15} = 1.2 \times 10^{-5}\ M$$

$$\text{Percent ionization} = \frac{x}{0.10\ M} \times 100 = \frac{1.2 \times 10^{-5}\ M}{0.10\ M} \times 100\% = 0.012\%$$

Our assumption (simplification) is valid, thus we can now calculate the pH:

$$pH = -\log\left(1.2 \times 10^{-5}\right) = \mathbf{4.92}$$

110. What is the pH of a buffer system containing 0.17 M *HF* and 0.23 M *NaF*? The K_a value for hydrofluoric acid is 3.5×10^{-4}.

$$HF\,(aq) \rightleftharpoons H^+\,(aq) + F^-\,(aq)$$

Concentration	$HF\,(aq) \rightleftharpoons H^+\,(aq) + F^-\,(aq)$		
Initial	0.17	0.00	0.23
Change	$-x$	$+x$	$+x$
Equilibrium	$0.17 - x$	x	$0.23 + x$

$$K_a = \frac{[H^+][F^-]}{[HF]}$$

$$3.5 \times 10^{-4} = \frac{[x][0.23 + x]}{[0.17 - x]}$$

$$3.5 \times 10^{-4} = \frac{[x][0.23 + \cancel{x}]}{[0.17 - \cancel{x}]}$$

$$3.5 \times 10^{-4} = \frac{x \, (0.23)}{0.17}$$

$$x = \frac{\left(3.5 \times 10^{-4}\right) \times (0.17)}{0.23} = 2.6 \times 10^{-4} \, M$$

Percent ionization $= \dfrac{x}{0.17 \, M} \times 100 = \dfrac{2.6 \times 10^{-4} \, M}{0.17 \, M} \times 100\% = 0.15\%$

Our assumption (simplification) is valid, thus we can now calculate the pH:

$$pH = -\log \left(2.6 \times 10^{-4}\right) = \mathbf{3.59}$$

111. What is the pH of a buffer system containing 0.10 M $HCHO_2$ and 0.10 M $NaCHO_2$? The K_a value for formic acid is 1.8×10^{-4}.

$$HCHO_2 \, (aq) \rightleftharpoons H^+ \, (aq) + CHO_2^- \, (aq)$$

Concentration	$HCHO_2 \, (aq) \rightleftharpoons$	$H^+ \, (aq) +$	$CHO_2^- \, (aq)$
Initial	0.10	0.00	0.10
Change	$-x$	$+x$	$+x$
Equilibrium	$0.10 - x$	x	$0.10 + x$

$$K_a = \frac{[H^+][CHO_2^-]}{[HCHO_2]}$$

$$1.8 \times 10^{-4} = \frac{[x][0.10 + x]}{[0.10 - x]}$$

$$1.8 \times 10^{-4} = \frac{[x][0.10 + \cancel{x}]}{[0.10 - \cancel{x}]}$$

$$1.8 \times 10^{-4} = \frac{x \, (0.10)}{0.10}$$

$$x = \frac{\left(1.8 \times 10^{-4}\right) \times (0.10)}{0.10} = 1.8 \times 10^{-4} \, M$$

Percent ionization $= \dfrac{x}{0.10 \, M} \times 100 = \dfrac{1.8 \times 10^{-4} \, M}{0.10 \, M} \times 100\% = 0.18\%$

Our assumption (simplification) is valid, thus we can now calculate the pH:

$$pH = -\log \left(1.8 \times 10^{-4}\right) = \mathbf{3.74}$$

112. What is the pH of a buffer system containing 0.18 M NH_3 and 0.26 M NH_4Cl ? The K_b value for ammonia is 1.8×10^{-5}.

$$NH_3\ (aq) + H_2O\ (l) \rightleftharpoons NH_4^+\ (aq) + OH^-\ (aq)$$

Concentration	$NH_3\ (aq) + H_2O\ (l) \rightleftharpoons$	$NH_4^+\ (aq) +$	$OH^-\ (aq)$
Initial	0.18	0.26	0.00
Change	$-x$	$+x$	$+x$
Equilibrium	$0.18 - x$	$0.26 + x$	x

$$K_b = \frac{[OH^-][NH_4^+]}{[NH_3]}$$

$$1.8 \times 10^{-5} = \frac{[x][0.26 + x]}{[0.18 - x]}$$

$$1.8 \times 10^{-5} = \frac{[x][0.26 + \cancel{x}]}{[0.18 - \cancel{x}]}$$

$$1.8 \times 10^{-5} = \frac{x(0.26)}{0.18}$$

$$x = \frac{\left(1.8 \times 10^{-5}\right) \times (0.18)}{0.26} = 1.2 \times 10^{-5}\ M$$

Percent ionization $= \dfrac{x}{0.18\ M} \times 100 = \dfrac{1.2 \times 10^{-5}\ M}{0.18\ M} \times 100\% = 0.0067\%$

Our assumption (simplification) is valid, thus we can now calculate the pOH and then the pH:

$$pOH = -\log\left(1.2 \times 10^{-5}\right) = 4.92$$

$$pH = 14.00 - pOH = \mathbf{9.08}$$

113. What is the pH of a buffer system containing 0.24 M CH_3NH_2 and 0.13 M CH_3NH_3Br? The K_b value for methylamine is 4.4×10^{-4}.

$$CH_3NH_2\ (aq) + H_2O\ (l) \rightleftharpoons CH_3NH_3^+\ (aq) + OH^-\ (aq)$$

Concentration	$CH_3NH_2\ (aq) + H_2O\ (l) \rightleftharpoons$	$CH_3NH_3^+\ (aq) +$	$OH^-\ (aq)$
Initial	0.24	0.13	0.00
Change	$-x$	$+x$	$+x$
Equilibrium	$0.24 - x$	$0.13 + x$	x

$$K_b = \frac{[OH^-][CH_3NH_3^+]}{[CH_3NH_2]}$$

$$4.4 \times 10^{-4} = \frac{[x][0.13 + x]}{[0.24 - x]}$$

$$4.4 \times 10^{-4} = \frac{[x][0.13 + \cancel{x}]}{[0.24 - \cancel{x}]}$$

$$4.4 \times 10^{-4} = \frac{x(0.13)}{0.24}$$

$$x = \frac{\left(4.4 \times 10^{-4}\right) \times (0.24)}{0.13} = 8.1 \times 10^{-4} \ M$$

$$\text{Percent ionization} = \frac{x}{0.24 \ M} \times 100 = \frac{8.1 \times 10^{-4} \ M}{0.24 \ M} \times 100\% = 0.34\%$$

Our assumption (simplification) is valid, thus we can now calculate the pOH and then the pH:

$$pOH = -\log\left(8.1 \times 10^{-4}\right) = 3.09$$

$$pH = 14.00 - pOH = \mathbf{10.91}$$

114. What is the pH of a buffer system containing 0.28 M $C_2H_5NH_2$ and 0.37 M $C_2H_5NH_3Br$? The K_b value for ethylamine is 5.6×10^{-4}.

$$C_2H_5NH_2 \ (aq) + H_2O \ (l) \rightleftharpoons C_2H_5NH_3^+ \ (aq) + OH^- \ (aq)$$

Concentration	$C_2H_5NH_2 \ (aq) + H_2O \ (l) \rightleftharpoons C_2H_5NH_3^+ \ (aq) + OH^- \ (aq)$		
Initial	0.28	0.37	0.00
Change	$-x$	$+x$	$+x$
Equilibrium	$0.28 - x$	$0.37 + x$	x

$$K_b = \frac{[OH^-][C_2H_5NH_3^+]}{[C_2H_5NH_2]}$$

$$5.6 \times 10^{-4} = \frac{[x][0.37 + x]}{[0.28 - x]}$$

$$5.6 \times 10^{-4} = \frac{[x][0.37 + \cancel{x}]}{[0.28 - \cancel{x}]}$$

$$5.6 \times 10^{-4} = \frac{x(0.37)}{0.28}$$

$$x = \frac{\left(5.6 \times 10^{-4}\right) \times (0.28)}{0.37} = 4.2 \times 10^{-4} \ M$$

Percent ionization $= \dfrac{x}{0.28 \ M} \times 100 = \dfrac{4.2 \times 10^{-4} \ M}{0.28 \ M} \times 100\% = 0.15\%$

Our assumption (simplification) is valid, thus we can now calculate the pOH and then the pH:

$$pOH = -\log\left(4.2 \times 10^{-4}\right) = 3.38$$

$$pH = 14.00 - pOH = \mathbf{10.62}$$

115. What is the pH of a buffer system containing 0.10 M NH_3 and 0.10 M NH_4Cl? The K_b value for ammonia is 1.8×10^{-5}.

$$NH_3 \ (aq) + H_2O \ (l) \rightleftharpoons NH_4^+ \ (aq) + OH^- \ (aq)$$

Concentration	$NH_3 \ (aq) + H_2O \ (l) \rightleftharpoons$	$NH_4^+ \ (aq) +$	$OH^- \ (aq)$
Initial	0.10	0.10	0.00
Change	$-x$	$+x$	$+x$
Equilibrium	$0.10 - x$	$0.10 + x$	x

$$K_b = \frac{[OH^-][NH_4^+]}{[NH_3]}$$

$$1.8 \times 10^{-5} = \frac{[x][0.10 + x]}{[0.10 - x]}$$

$$1.8 \times 10^{-5} = \frac{[x][0.10 + \cancel{x}]}{[0.10 - \cancel{x}]}$$

$$1.8 \times 10^{-5} = \frac{x(0.10)}{0.10}$$

$$x = \frac{\left(1.8 \times 10^{-5}\right) \times (0.10)}{0.10} = 1.8 \times 10^{-5} \ M$$

Percent ionization $= \dfrac{x}{0.10 \ M} \times 100 = \dfrac{1.8 \times 10^{-5} \ M}{0.10 \ M} \times 100\% = 0.018\%$

Our assumption (simplification) is valid, thus we can now calculate the pOH and then the pH:

$$pOH = -\log\left(1.8 \times 10^{-5}\right) = 4.74$$

$$pH = 14.00 - pOH = \mathbf{9.26}$$

116. What is the Henderson-Hasselbalch equation? Show how it is derived.

The Henderson-Hasselbalch equation allows for the pH calculation of a buffer system. It is derived as follows:

$$HA\,(aq) \rightleftharpoons H^+\,(aq) + A^-\,(aq)$$

$$K_a = \frac{[H^+][A^-]}{[HA]}$$

$$[H^+] = \frac{K_a\,[HA]}{[A^-]}$$

$$-\log\,[H^+] = -\log\left(\frac{K_a\,[HA]}{[A^-]}\right)$$

$$-\log\,[H^+] = -\log K_a - \log\frac{[HA]}{[A^-]}$$

$$-\log\,[H^+] = -\log K_a + \log\frac{[A^-]}{[HA]}$$

$$pH = pK_a + \log\frac{[A^-]}{[HA]}$$

117. According to the Henderson-Hasselbalch equation, the pH = pK_a when which of the following is true?

$$HA\,(aq) \rightleftharpoons H^+\,(aq) + A^-\,(aq)$$

a. $[A^-]/[HA] = 0$
b. $\log\,([A-]/[HA]) = 1$
c. $[A^-] \gg [HA] = 0$
d. $\mathbf{[A^-] = [HA]}$

118. Calculate the pH of the solution in question 108 using the Henderson-Hasselbalch equation and compare your answers.

$$HCHO_2\,(aq) \rightleftharpoons H^+\,(aq) + CHO_2^-\,(aq)$$

$$pH = pK_a + \log\frac{[CHO_2^-]}{[HCHO_2]}$$

$$pH = 3.74 + \log\frac{[0.20]}{[0.25]}$$

$$pH = 3.64$$

119. Calculate the pH of the solution in question 109 using the Henderson-Hasselbalch equation and compare your answers.

$$HC_2H_3O_2 (aq) \rightleftharpoons H^+ (aq) + C_2H_3O_2^- (aq)$$

$$pH = pK_a + \log \frac{[C_2H_3O_2^-]}{[HC_2H_3O_2]}$$

$$pH = 4.74 + \log \frac{[0.15]}{[0.10]}$$

$$pH = 4.92$$

120. Calculate the pH of the solution in question 110 using the Henderson-Hasselbalch equation and compare your answers.

$$HF (aq) \rightleftharpoons H^+ (aq) + F^- (aq)$$

$$pH = pK_a + \log \frac{[F^-]}{[HF]}$$

$$pH = 3.46 + \log \frac{[0.23]}{[0.17]}$$

$$pH = 3.59$$

121. Calculate the pH of the solution in question 111 using the Henderson-Hasselbalch equation and compare your answers.

$$HCHO_2 (aq) \rightleftharpoons H^+ (aq) + CHO_2^- (aq)$$

$$pH = pK_a + \log \frac{[CHO_2^-]}{[HCHO_2]}$$

$$pH = 3.74 + \log \frac{[0.10]}{[0.10]}$$

$$pH = 3.74$$

*Notice that the pH = pK_a when the acid and conjugate base concentrations are equal.

122. How can the Henderson-Hasselbalch equation be modified when working with basic buffers?

The Henderson-Hasselbalch equation can be modified as follows when working with basic buffers:

$$B (aq) + H_2O (l) \rightarrow BH^+ (aq) + OH^- (aq)$$

$$pOH = pK_b + \log \frac{[BH^+]}{[B]}$$

123. Calculate the pH of the solution in question 112 using the modified Henderson-Hasselbalch equation for basic buffers and compare your answers.

$$NH_3\ (aq) + H_2O\ (l) \rightleftharpoons NH_4^+\ (aq) + OH^-\ (aq)$$

$$pOH = pK_b + \log\frac{[NH_4^+]}{[NH_3]}$$

$$pOH = 4.74 + \log\frac{[0.26]}{[0.18]}$$

$$pOH = 4.90$$

$$pH = 9.10$$

124. Calculate the pH of the solution in question 113 using the modified Henderson-Hasselbalch equation for basic buffers and compare your answers.

$$CH_3NH_2\ (aq) + H_2O\ (l) \rightleftharpoons CH_3NH_3^+\ (aq) + OH^-\ (aq)$$

$$pOH = pK_b + \log\frac{[CH_3NH_3^+]}{[CH_3NH_2]}$$

$$pOH = 3.36 + \log\frac{[0.13]}{[0.24]}$$

$$pOH = 3.09$$

$$pH = 10.91$$

125. Calculate the pH of the solution in question 114 using the modified Henderson-Hasselbalch equation for basic buffers and compare your answers.

$$C_2H_5NH_2\ (aq) + H_2O\ (l) \rightleftharpoons C_2H_5NH_3^+\ (aq) + OH^-\ (aq)$$

$$pOH = pK_b + \log\frac{[C_2H_5NH_3^+]}{[C_2H_5NH_2]}$$

$$pOH = 3.25 + \log\frac{[0.37]}{[0.28]}$$

$$pOH = 3.37$$

$$pH = 10.63$$

126. Calculate the pH of the solution in question 115 using the modified Henderson-Hasselbalch equation for basic buffers and compare your answers.

$$NH_3\ (aq) + H_2O\ (l) \rightleftharpoons NH_4^+\ (aq) + OH^-\ (aq)$$

$$pOH = pK_b + \log\frac{[NH_4^+]}{[NH_3]}$$

$$pOH = 4.74 + \log\frac{[0.10]}{[0.10]}$$

$$pOH = 4.74$$

$$pH = 9.26$$

*Notice that the $pOH = pK_b$ when the base and conjugate acid concentrations are equal.

127. Calculate the pH of a solution that is composed of 305 ml of 0.50 M *HF* and 445 ml of 0.60 M *NaF*. The K_a value for hydrofluoric acid is 3.5×10^{-4}.

Total solution volume = 305 ml *HF* + 445 ml *NaF* = 750 ml total volume (0.750 L).

$$305\ ml \times \frac{1\ L}{1{,}000\ ml} \times \frac{0.50\ mols\ HF}{1\ L\ Sol'n} \times \frac{1}{0.750\ L} = 0.20\ M\ HF$$

$$445\ ml \times \frac{1\ L}{1{,}000\ ml} \times \frac{0.60\ mols\ NaF}{1\ L\ Sol'n} \times \frac{1}{0.750\ L} = 0.36\ M\ NaF$$

$$HF(aq) \rightleftharpoons H^+(aq) + F^-(aq)$$

$$pH = pK_a + \log\frac{[F^-]}{[HF]}$$

$$pH = 3.46 + \log\frac{[0.36]}{[0.20]}$$

$$pH = 3.72$$

128. Calculate the pH of a solution that is composed of 225 ml of 0.10 M CH_3NH_2 and 175 ml of 0.25 M CH_3NH_3Br. The K_b value for methylamine is 4.4×10^{-4}.

Total solution volume = 225 ml CH_3NH_2 + 175 ml CH_3NH_3Br = 400 ml total volume (0.400 L).

$$225\ ml \times \frac{1\ L}{1{,}000\ ml} \times \frac{0.10\ mols\ CH_3NH_2}{1\ L\ Sol'n} \times \frac{1}{0.400\ L} = 0.056\ M\ CH_3NH_2$$

$$175\ ml \times \frac{1\ L}{1{,}000\ ml} \times \frac{0.25\ mols\ CH_3NH_3Br}{1\ L\ Sol'n} \times \frac{1}{0.400\ L} = 0.11\ M\ CH_3NH_3Br$$

$$CH_3NH_2(aq) + H_2O(l) \rightleftharpoons CH_3NH_3^+(aq) + OH^-(aq)$$

$$pOH = pK_b + \log\frac{[CH_3NH_3^+]}{[CH_3NH_2]}$$

$$pOH = 3.36 + \log\frac{[0.11]}{[0.056]}$$

$$pOH = 3.65$$

$$pH = 14.00 - pOH = 10.35$$

129. Calculate the ratio of $NaC_2H_3O_2$ to $HC_2H_3O_2$ needed in order to generate a buffer system with a pH = 4.25. The K_a value for acetic acid is 1.8×10^{-5}.

$$HC_2H_3O_2\,(aq) \rightleftharpoons H^+\,(aq) + C_2H_3O_2^-\,(aq)$$

$$pH = pK_a + \log\frac{[C_2H_3O_2^-]}{[HC_2H_3O_2]}$$

$$4.25 = 4.74 + \log x$$

Where x = the ratio of $NaC_2H_3O_2$ to $HC_2H_3O_2$:

$$x = antilog\,(4.25 - 4.74) = 0.32$$

130. Calculate the ratio of NaF to HF needed in order to generate a buffer system with a pH = 3.74. The K_a value for hydrofluoric acid is 3.5×10^{-4}.

$$HF\,(aq) \rightleftharpoons H^+\,(aq) + F^-\,(aq)$$

$$pH = pK_a + \log\frac{[F^-]}{[HF]}$$

$$3.74 = 3.46 + \log x$$

Where x = the ratio of NaF to HF:

$$x = antilog\,(3.74 - 3.46) = 1.9$$

131. Calculate the ratio of NH_4Cl to NH_3 needed in order to generate a buffer system with a pH = 9.75. The K_b value for ammonia is 1.8×10^{-5}.

$$NH_3\,(aq) + H_2O\,(l) \rightleftharpoons NH_4^+\,(aq) + OH^-\,(aq)$$

$$pOH = 14.00 - pH = 4.25$$

$$pOH = pK_b + \log\frac{[NH_4^+]}{[NH_3]}$$

$$4.25 = 4.74 + \log x$$

Where x = the ratio of NH_4Cl to NH_3:

$$x = antilog\,(4.25 - 4.74) = 0.32$$

132. Calculate the ratio of CH_3NH_3Br to CH_3NH_2 needed in order to generate a buffer system with a pH = 10.25. The K_b value for methylamine is 4.4×10^{-4}.

$$CH_3NH_2\,(aq) + H_2O\,(l) \rightleftharpoons CH_3NH_3^+\,(aq) + OH^-\,(aq)$$

$$pOH = 14.00 - pH = 3.75$$

$$pOH = pK_b + \log\frac{[CH_3NH_3^+]}{[CH_3NH_2]}$$

$$3.75 = 3.36 + \log x$$

Where x = the ratio of CH_3NH_3Br to CH_3NH_2:

$$x = antilog\ (3.75 - 3.36) = 2.5$$

133. Calculate the pH of a buffer solution containing 0.20 M acetic acid and 0.15 M sodi-
      um acetate if 0.010 mols of **HCl** were added to the buffer system. Assume a 1.0 liter
      total solution and ignore any small changes in volume that might occur upon **acid**
      addition. The K_a value for acetic acid is 1.8×10^{-5}.

      pH before addition of acid:

      $$HC_2H_3O_2\,(aq) \rightleftharpoons H^+\,(aq) + C_2H_3O_2^-\,(aq)$$

      $$pH = pK_a + \log\frac{[C_2H_3O_2^-]}{[HC_2H_3O_2]}$$

      $$pH = 4.74 + \log\frac{[0.15]}{[0.20]}$$

      $$pH = 4.62$$

      pH after addition of acid:

      $$HC_2H_3O_2\,(aq) \rightleftharpoons H^+\,(aq) + C_2H_3O_2^-\,(aq)$$

      $$pH = pK_a + \log\frac{[C_2H_3O_2^-]}{[HC_2H_3O_2]}$$

      $$pH = 4.74 + \log\frac{[0.15 - 0.01]}{[0.20 + 0.01]}$$

      $$pH = 4.56$$

134. Calculate the pH of a buffer solution containing 0.20 M acetic acid and 0.15 M sodium
      acetate if 0.010 mols of **NaOH** were added to the buffer system. Assume a 1.0 liter
      total solution and ignore any small changes in volume that might occur upon **base**
      addition. The K_a value for acetic acid is 1.8×10^{-5}.

      pH before addition of base:

      $$HC_2H_3O_2\,(aq) \rightleftharpoons H^+\,(aq) + C_2H_3O_2^-\,(aq)$$

      $$pH = pK_a + \log\frac{[C_2H_3O_2^-]}{[HC_2H_3O_2]}$$

$$pH = 4.74 + \log\frac{[0.15]}{[0.20]}$$

$$pH = 4.62$$

pH after addition of base:

$$HC_2H_3O_2(aq) \rightleftharpoons H^+(aq) + C_2H_3O_2^-(aq)$$

$$pH = pK_a + \log\frac{[C_2H_3O_2^-]}{[HC_2H_3O_2]}$$

$$pH = 4.74 + \log\frac{[0.15 + 0.01]}{[0.20 - 0.01]}$$

$$pH = 4.67$$

135. Calculate the pH change of 1.0 L of neutral water when 0.010 mols of **HCl** is added. Ignore any small changes in volume that might occur upon **acid** addition. Compare your answer to question 133 where the same amount of acid is added to an acidic buffer system.

pH of neutral water before acid addition = 7.00

pH after acid addition:

$$pH = -\log[H^+] = -\log[0.01] = 2.00$$

If we compare this answer to question 133, we see that the pH drops dramatically here (from 7.00 to 2.00) while a very subtle drop occurs with the buffer system (from 4.62 to 4.56).

136. Calculate the pH change of 1.0 L of neutral water when 0.010 mols of **NaOH** is added. Ignore any small changes in volume that might occur upon **base** addition. Compare your answer to question 134 where the same amount of base is added to an acidic buffer system.

pH of neutral water before base addition = 7.00

pH after base addition:

$$pOH = -\log[OH^-] = -\log[0.01] = 2.00$$

$$pH = 14.00 - pOH = 12.00$$

If we compare this answer to question 134, we see that the pH increases quite dramatically here (from 7.00 to 12.00) while a very subtle increase occurs with the buffer system (from 4.62 to 4.67).

137. Calculate the pH of a buffer solution containing 0.20 M methylamine and 0.15 M methylammonium chloride if 0.010 mols of **HCl** were added to the buffer system. Assume a 1.0 liter total solution, and ignore any small changes in volume that might occur upon **acid** addition. The K_b value for methylamine 4.4 × 10^{-4}. Compare your answer to question 135 where the same amount of acid is added to pure neutral water.

pH before addition of acid:

$$CH_3NH_2\ (aq) + H_2O\ (l) \rightleftharpoons CH_3NH_3^+\ (aq) + OH^-\ (aq)$$

$$pOH = pK_b + \log\frac{[CH_3NH_3^+]}{[CH_3NH_2]}$$

$$pOH = 3.36 + \log\frac{[0.15]}{[0.20]}$$

$$pOH = 3.24$$

$$pH = 14.00 - pOH = 10.76$$

pH after addition of acid:

$$CH_3NH_2\ (aq) + H_2O\ (l) \rightleftharpoons CH_3NH_3^+\ (aq) + OH^-\ (aq)$$

$$pOH = pK_b + \log\frac{[CH_3NH_3^+]}{[CH_3NH_2]}$$

$$pOH = 3.36 + \log\frac{[0.15 + 0.01]}{[0.20 - 0.01]}$$

$$pOH = 3.29$$

$$pH = 14.00 - pOH = 10.71$$

If we compare this answer to question 135, we see that the pH decreases very subtly here (from 10.76 to 10.71) while a dramatic decrease is observed when the same amount of acid is added to pure neutral water (from 7.00 to 2.00).

138. Calculate the pH of a buffer solution containing 0.20 M methylamine and 0.15 M methylammonium chloride if 0.010 mols of **NaOH** were added to the buffer system. Assume a 1.0 liter total solution, and ignore any small changes in volume that might occur upon **base** addition. The K_b value for methylamine 4.4 × 10^{-4}. Compare your answer to question 136 where the same amount of base is added to pure neutral water.

pH before addition of base:

$$CH_3NH_2\ (aq) + H_2O\ (l) \rightleftharpoons CH_3NH_3^+\ (aq) + OH^-\ (aq)$$

$$pOH = pK_b + \log\frac{[CH_3NH_3^+]}{[CH_3NH_2]}$$

$$pOH = 3.36 + \log\frac{[0.15]}{[0.20]}$$

$$pOH = 3.24$$

$$pH = 14.00 - pOH = 10.76$$

pH after addition of base:

$$CH_3NH_2\ (aq) + H_2O\ (l) \rightleftharpoons CH_3NH_3^+\ (aq) + OH^-\ (aq)$$

$$pOH = pK_b + \log\frac{[CH_3NH_3^+]}{[CH_3NH_2]}$$

$$pOH = 3.36 + \log\frac{[0.15 - .01]}{[0.20 + 0.01]}$$

$$pOH = 3.18$$

$$pH = 14.00 - pOH = 10.82$$

If we compare this answer to question 136, we see that the pH increases very subtly here (from 10.76 to 10.82) while a dramatic increase is observed when the same amount of base is added to pure neutral water (from 7.00 to 12.00).

139. What two major factors are important to consider when determining how effective a particular buffer is at neutralizing either added acid or base?

The two major factors that influence buffer effectiveness include the relative concentrations of the weak acid and conjugate base (or weak base and conjugate acid), as well as the absolute concentrations of both components. Buffers tend to be more effective when the relative concentrations of weak acid and conjugate base (or weak base and conjugate acid) are equal, or in a 1:1 ratio, and with higher concentrations of both.

140. What is the buffer range of a particular buffer system?

The buffer range of a particular buffer system is the pH range in which a particular acid and its conjugate base (or weak base and its conjugate acid) are effective. Generally speaking, the effective range for a given buffer is within one pH unit on either side (one unit lower and one unit higher) than its pK_a or pK_b value.

141. Would formic acid ($K_a = 1.8 \times 10^{-4}$) or hypochlorus acid ($K_a = 2.9 \times 10^{-8}$) be a better choice for a buffer solution with a pH of 7.20? Why?

Hypochlorus acid would be a better choice for a buffer solution with a pH of 7.20 because its pK_a value is much closer to this pH (7.54).

142. Would formic acid ($K_a = 1.8 \times 10^{-4}$) or hypochlorus acid ($K_a = 2.9 \times 10^{-8}$) be a better choice for a buffer solution with a pH of 4.00? Why?

Formic acid would be a better choice for a buffer solution with a pH of 4.00 because its pK_a value is much closer to this pH (3.74).

KEY TERMS

Acid   A molecular compound that undergoes ionization when dissolved in water to form H^+ ions.

Acid-base reactions   (also known as a neutralization reaction) When acids and bases are mixed, OH^- anions from the base combine with the H^+ cations from the acid to form water, H_2O. Hence, the reaction of an acid with a base produces a salt (ionic compound) and water.

Acidic buffer   A solution which resists changes in pH due to addition of small amounts of acid or base. An acidic buffer is composed of a weak acid and its conjugate base in solution.

Acid ionization constant (K_a)   The equilibrium constant for the ionization reaction of acids, which is very useful for calculations involving weak acids.

Amphoteric   A term which refers to a compound that can act as both an acid and a base.

Analyte   A solution of unknown concentration which is the object of a titration experiment.

Arrhenius acid   According to the Arrhenius definition of acids and bases, an Arrhenius acid produces H^+ ions in aqueous solution.

Arrhenius base   According to the Arrhenius definition of acids and bases, an Arrhenius base produces OH^- ions in aqueous solution.

Arrhenius definition of acids and bases   An **acid** is a molecular compound that undergoes ionization when dissolved in water to form H^+ ions, and a **base** is any substance that increases the concentration of OH^- ions when dissolved in water.

Autoionization   The process wherein water acts as an acid and a base simultaneously.

Base   A base is any substance that increases the concentration of OH^- ions when dissolved in water.

Base ionization constant (K_b)   The equilibrium constant for the ionization reaction of bases, which is very useful for weak bases.

Basic buffer   A solution which resists changes in pH due to addition of small amounts of acid or base. A basic buffer is composed of a weak base and its conjugate acid in solution.

Binary acid   An acid which is composed of only two elements, hydrogen and a nonmetal.

Brønsted-Lowry acid   A proton donor.

Brønsted-Lowry base   A proton acceptor.

Brønsted-Lowry definition of acids and bases   This definition focuses on the proton (H^+) ion. H^+ cations are essentially protons and are therefore often referred to as such. Using this definition, we can say that a Brønsted-Lowry acid is a proton donor, while a Brønsted-Lowry base is a proton acceptor.

Buffer range   The pH range over which a particular buffer is effective.

Buffers   Solutions that resist changes in pH due to addition of small amounts of strong acids or bases.

Burette   A device which consists of a long glass, graduated cylinder used in chemistry to dispense precise volumes of chemical solutions.

Common ion effect   The effect on proton equilibria arising from a solution containing two compounds which share a common ion. In other words, the common ion effect is the inhibition of the dissociation of a weak electrolyte due to the presence of a common ion.

Conjugate acid-base pairs   Two substances that are related to one another by the transfer of a proton.

Diprotic acids   Acids which contain two ionizable, acidic protons.

Endpoint   The point at which an indicator in a titration experiment exhibits a color change.

Equivalence point   The volume in a titration at which the number of moles of added OH^- ions from the $NaOH$ solution equals the number of H^+ ions present in the HCl solution.

Henderson-Hasselbalch equation   A mathematical expression which gives the pH of a solution as a function of pK_a and the concentrations of an acid and its conjugate base.

Hydronium ion   The H_3O^+ ion present in all aqueous acidic solutions.

Indicator   A dye that changes color based on the acidity/basicity of the solution.

Ion product of water (K_w)   The product of the concentration of hydronium and hydroxide in an aqueous solution.

Lewis acid   According to the Lewis definition of acids and bases, a Lewis acid is an electron pair acceptor.

Lewis bases   According to the Lewis definition of acids and bases, a Lewis base is an electron pair donor.

Monoprotic acids   Acids which contain only one ionizable, acidic proton.

Neutral   When referring to acids and bases, $pH = 7$.

Neutralization reaction   When acids and bases are mixed, OH^- anions from the base combine with the H^+ cations from the acid to form water, H_2O. Hence, the reaction of an acid with a base produces a salt (ionic compound) and water.

Oxyacid   An acid composed of hydrogen and an oxyanion, or an anion containing a nonmetal and oxygen.

Percent ionization   The ratio of the ionized acid concentration to the initial acid concentration multiplied by 100%.

pH   The negative logarithm of the hydronium concentration in a solution.

pH **curve**   A plot of the evolution of the pH of an analyte solution with added volume of acid or base in a titration experiment.

pOH   The negative logarithm of the hydroxide concentration.

Polyprotic acids   Acids which contain two or more ionizable, acidic protons.

Strong acids   Acids which completely dissociate into ions when dissolved in water and are therefore strong electrolytes.

Strong bases   Bases which completely ionize when dissolved in water.

Titrant   A solution of known concentration in a titration experiment, added to the analyte solution using a burette.

Titration curve A plot of the evolution of the pH of an analyte solution with added volume of acid or base in a titration experiment.

Titration A common laboratory technique involving acids and bases wherein a solution of known concentration called the titrant is reacted with another substance of unknown concentration, known as the analyte.

Weak acids Acids which only partially ionize when dissolved in water and are therefore weak electrolytes.

Weak bases Bases which undergo only partial ionization when dissolved in water.

Thermodynamics & Thermochemistry

CHAPTER 12

KEY CONCEPTS

- Kinetic and Potential Energy
- The First Law of Thermodynamics
- Internal Energy and Changes in Internal Energy
- Heat, Work, and Internal Energy
- Exothermic and Endothermic Reactions
- Reaction Enthalpy and Stoichiometry
- Constant Volume Calorimetry
- Constant Pressure Calorimetry
- Hess's Law and Estimating Reaction Enthalpies
- Writing Standard Formation Reaction Equations
- Estimating Reaction Enthalpies from Standard Heats of Formation
- Estimating Reaction Enthalpies from Bond Energies
- The Born-Haber Cycle and Lattice Energies of Ionic Solids
- Entropy and the Second Law of Thermodynamics
- Gibbs Free Energy and Reaction Spontaneity
- Gibbs Free Energy and Nonstandard Conditions
- Gibbs Free Energy and the Equilibrium Constant

THE FIRST LAW OF THERMODYNAMICS AND THE NATURE OF ENERGY

1. Define thermodynamics and thermochemistry.

   Thermodynamics is defined as the scientific discipline that is concerned with the transfer of energy from one system to another, and its transformation from one form to another. Thermochemistry is the field of thermodynamics which deals with the energy changes associated with chemical change.

2. Define the first law of thermodynamics (also known as the law of conservation of energy).

   The first law of thermodynamics explains that the total energy in the universe is a constant and cannot be altered due to any process. This can be shown in the following expression: $\Delta E_{universe} = 0$.

3. Define potential and kinetic energy.

   Potential energy is the energy associated with, or due to, composition or position (i.e. stored energy). Kinetic energy is the energy associated with, or due to, motion. The kinetic energy of an object with a mass, m, is given as:

   $$KE = \frac{1}{2}mv^2 ,$$

   where v is the velocity of the mass (or object) in question.

4. A ball with a mass of 2 kg is thrown straight up in the air with an initial velocity of 2 m/s. At the ball's highest point, what is the kinetic energy of the ball?

   Because the velocity is 0 m/s at the ball's highest point, the kinetic energy will be 0 J.

   $$KE = \frac{1}{2}mv^2 = \frac{1}{2}(2 \; kg)\left(0\frac{m}{s}\right)^2 = 0 \; J$$

5. An object is in motion with a velocity of 3.24 m/s. If the object has a mass of 5.31 kg, what is its kinetic energy?

   $$KE = \frac{1}{2}mv^2 = \frac{1}{2}(5.31 \; kg)\left(3.24\frac{m}{s}\right)^2 = 27.9 \; J$$

6. If a particular system gains energy, the _____ must lose an equal amount of energy (to the system). Likewise, if the _____ loses energy, the surroundings must gain an equal amount of energy (from the system).

   surroundings

   system

7. Define internal energy.

   The internal energy of a system is defined as the sum of all of the potential and kinetic energies of all the particles which constitute the system.

8. The internal energy of a system has a net gain/loss of energy if $\Delta E > 0$.

   gain

9. The internal energy of a system has a net gain/loss of energy if $\Delta E < 0$.

   loss

10. What are the two mechanisms by which energy can be transferred between the system and the surroundings?

    Heat (q) and work (w); this can be described mathematically through the expression: $\Delta E_{sys} = q + w$.

11. What is heat? What is the difference between heat and temperature?

    Heat (q) is the transfer of thermal energy (measured in joules) between the system and surroundings. It is not to be confused with temperature which is a measure of the average kinetic energy of the particles which make up the system.

12. Is q_{sys} positive or negative if the temperature of the system increases due to an event or process?

$$q_{sys} > 0$$

13. Is q_{sys} positive or negative if the temperature of the system decreases due to an event or process?

$$q_{sys} < 0$$

14. If work is done on the system by the surroundings due to an event or process, will the work term be a positive or negative contribution to the internal energy change?

$$w > 0$$

15. What is a state function?

    A state function is a property that depends only on the current state of the system in question.

16. Define chemical energy.

    Chemical energy is the potential energy associated with chemical composition, the relative distributions of electrons and nuclei in atoms and molecules.

17. If the $E_{react} > E_{prod}$, then the ΔE for the reaction (ΔE_{rxn}) is _____ zero and the reaction _____ to/from the surroundings.
    a. less than/releases energy
    b. greater than/releases energy
    c. less than/absorbs energy
    d. greater than/absorbs energy

    less than/releases energy

18. If the $E_{react} < E_{prod}$, then the ΔE for the reaction (ΔE_{rxn}) is _____ zero and the reaction _____ to/from the surroundings.
    a. less than/releases energy
    b. greater than/releases energy
    c. less than/absorbs energy
    d. greater than/absorbs energy

    greater than/absorbs energy

19. A chemical system produces 155.0 kJ of heat and does 140.5 kJ of work. What is its internal energy change?

$$q_{sys} = -155.0 \; kJ$$

$$w = -140.5 \; kJ$$

$$\Delta E_{sys} = q_{sys} + w = (-155 \; kJ) + (-140.5 \; kJ) = \boldsymbol{-295.5 \; kJ}$$

20. A chemical system absorbs 155 kJ of heat and does 140.5 kJ of work. What is its internal energy change?

$$q_{sys} = +155.0 \; kJ$$

$$w = -140.5 \; kJ$$

$$\Delta E_{sys} = q_{sys} + w = (+155 \; kJ) + (-140.5 \; kJ) = \boldsymbol{+14.5 \; kJ}$$

21. A chemical system produces 155 kJ of heat and has 140.5 kJ of work done on it by the surroundings. What is its internal energy change?

$$q_{sys} = -155.0 \; kJ$$

$$w = +140.5 \; kJ$$

$$\Delta E_{sys} = q_{sys} + w = (-155 \; kJ) + (140.5 \; kJ) = \boldsymbol{-14.5 \; kJ}$$

22. A chemical system absorbs 155 kJ of heat and has 140.5 kJ of work done on it by the surroundings. What is its internal energy change?

$$q_{sys} = +155.0 \; kJ$$

$$w = +140.5 \; kJ$$

$$\Delta E_{sys} = q_{sys} + w = (155 \; kJ) + (140.5 \; kJ) = \boldsymbol{+295.5 \; kJ}$$

QUANTIFYING HEAT

23. Define the heat capacity of a substance.

The heat capacity of a substance represents the amount of energy required to raise the temperature of the substance by 1°C. Therefore, the higher the heat capacity the more energy required to increase the temperature of the system.

24. Define the specific heat capacity of a substance.

The specific heat capacity is the amount of heat (in joules) required to raise the temperature of 1 gram of a substance by 1°C.

25. Suppose an object is allowed to cool to room temperature (23.2°C). How much heat (in joules) is lost if the object had an initial temperature of 56.5°C? The sample weighs 5.45 g and has a specific heat capacity of 0.790 $\frac{J}{g \cdot °C}$.

$$\Delta T = T_f - T_i = 23.2°C - 56.5°C = -33.3°C$$

$$q = m \cdot C_s \cdot \Delta T = (5.45\ g)\left(0.790\ \frac{J}{g \cdot °C}\right)(-33.3°C) = \textbf{\textit{-143 J}}$$

26. Ethanol is heated to 40.1°C and is allowed to cool to 23.2°C. The sample has a mass of 9.87 g and a specific heat capacity of 2.42 $\frac{J}{g \cdot °C}$. How much heat is lost?

$$\Delta T = T_f - T_i = 23.2°C - 40.1°C = -16.9°C$$

$$q = m \cdot C_s \cdot \Delta T = (9.87\ g)\left(2.42\ \frac{J}{g \cdot °C}\right)(-16.9°C) = \textbf{\textit{-404 J}}$$

27. What is the identity of a substance that weighs 2.81 g if it takes 34.7 J of energy to heat it from 5.00°C to 37.1°C (hint-see Table 12.2)?

We can use this information to solve for the specific heat capacity, and then identify the unknown object based on the heat capacities reported in Table 12.2.

$$\Delta T = T_f - T_i = 37.1°C - 5.00°C = 32.1°C$$

$$q = m \cdot C_s \cdot \Delta T$$

$$C_s = \frac{q}{m \cdot \Delta T} = \frac{34.7\ J}{(2.81\ g \times 32.1°C)} = \textbf{0.385}\ \frac{\textbf{\textit{J}}}{\textbf{\textit{g}} \cdot °\textbf{C}}$$

Based on this specific heat capacity, we can determine that this object is very likely copper, assuming it is a pure substance.

28. What is the identity of a substance that weighs 15.2 g if it takes 86.5 J of energy to heat it from 24.8°C to 32.0°C (hint-see Table 12.2)?

We can use this information to solve for the specific heat capacity, and then identify the unknown object based on this number using Table 12.2 after we determine ΔT.

$$\Delta T = T_f - T_i = 32.0°C - 24.8°C = 7.20°C$$

$$q = m \cdot C_s \cdot \Delta T$$

$$C_s = \frac{q}{m \cdot \Delta T} = \frac{86.5\ J}{(15.2\ g \times 7.20°C)} = \textbf{0.790}\ \frac{\textbf{\textit{J}}}{\textbf{\textit{g}} \cdot °\textbf{C}}$$

Based on this specific heat capacity, we can determine that this object is likely granite.

29. If 49.4 J of energy is required to heat a certain volume of liquid bromine from 25.0°C to 28.5°C, what volume (ml) of liquid bromine is present? The specific heat capacity and density of liquid bromine are 0.226 $\frac{J}{g \cdot °C}$ and 3.12 g/ml respectively.

First, we find ΔT and the mass of the liquid bromine:

$$\Delta T = T_f - T_i = 28.5°C - 25.0°C = 3.5°C$$

$$q = m \cdot C_s \cdot \Delta T$$

$$m = \frac{q}{C_s \cdot \Delta T}°C$$

$$m = \frac{49.4 \; J}{0.226 \; \frac{J}{g \cdot °C} \cdot 3.5°C} = 62.5 \; g$$

Now we can find the volume from the density:

$$62.5 \; g \times \frac{1 \; ml}{3.12 \; g} = \textbf{20.0 \textit{ml}}$$

30. With a 45.8 g sample of water, how much heat is required to heat the water from 22.3°C to 35.8°C?

$$\Delta T = T_f - T_i = 35.8°C - 22.3°C = 13.5°C$$

$$q = m \cdot C_s \cdot \Delta T$$

$$q = 45.8 \; g \cdot 4.184 \; \frac{J}{g \cdot °C} \cdot 13.5°C = \textbf{2587.0 \textit{J}}$$

31. Given that mercury has a specific heat of 0.140 $\frac{J}{g \cdot °C}$, what is the mass of a sample of pure mercury if 550.0 J of energy was required to heat the sample from 22.3°C to 78.5°C?

$$\Delta T = T_f - T_i = 78.5°C - 22.3°C = 56.2°C$$

$$q = m \cdot C_s \cdot \Delta T$$

$$550.0 \; J = m_{mercury} \cdot 0.140 \; \frac{J}{g \cdot °C} \cdot 56.2°C$$

$$m_{mercury} = \frac{550.0 \; J}{0.140 \; \frac{J}{g \cdot °C} \cdot 56.2°C} = \textbf{69.9 \textit{g}}$$

32. Calculate the specific heat of gold if a 56.8-g sample of gold underwent an elevation in temperature of 36.0 °C, and absorbed 593.0 J of energy.

$$q = m \cdot C_s \cdot \Delta T$$

$$\Delta T = 36.0 \; ^\circ C$$

$$593.0 \; J = 56.8 \; g \cdot C_s \cdot 36.0 ^\circ C$$

$$C_s = \frac{593.0 \; J}{56.8 \; g \cdot 36.0 ^\circ C} = 0.290 \; \frac{J}{g \cdot ^\circ C}$$

33. If 1.65 L of pure water with an initial temperature of 22.00°C is heated and absorbs 219.4 kJ of heat. Assuming the density of water is 1.00 g/ml, what is the final temperature of the water?

$$q = 219.4 \; kJ \times \frac{1000 \; J}{1 \; kJ} = 2.194 \times 10^5 \; J$$

$$m = 1.65 \; L \times \frac{1000 \; ml}{L} \times \frac{1.00 \; g}{ml} = 1650 \; g$$

$$\Delta T = T_f - 22.00 ^\circ C$$

We find the specific heat of water in Table 12.2:

$$C_{s, \, water} = 4.184 \frac{J}{g \cdot ^\circ C}$$

First, we solve for ΔT:

$$q = m \cdot C_s \cdot \Delta T$$

$$\Delta T = \frac{q}{m \cdot C_s} = \frac{2.194 \times 10^5 \; J}{(1650 \; g)\left(4.184 \frac{J}{g \cdot ^\circ C}\right)} = 31.78 ^\circ C$$

Next, we solve for T_f:

$$\Delta T = T_f - 22.00 ^\circ C = 31.78 ^\circ C$$

$$T_f = 31.78 ^\circ C + 22.00 ^\circ C = \mathbf{53.78 ^\circ C}$$

34. Suppose a metal sample with an unknown specific heat capacity has a mass of 34.3 g. The metal is heated to 72.3°C and then submerged in 100.0 g of water (with an initial temperature of 23.2°C) in an insulated container. The transfer of heat between the metal and water causes the temperature of the water to increase to 24.7°C. What is the heat capacity of the metal?

$$q_{metal} = -q_{water}$$

Thus:

$$m_{metal} \cdot C_{s,\ metal} \cdot \Delta T_{metal} = -\left(m_{water} \cdot C_{s,\ water} \cdot \Delta T_{water} \right)$$

$$C_{s,\ metal} = \frac{-\left(m_{water} \cdot C_{s,\ water} \cdot \Delta T_{water} \right)}{m_{metal} \cdot \Delta T_{metal}}$$

The specific heat capacity of water is $4.184\ \dfrac{J}{g \cdot °C}$, so we now just solve for $C_{s,\ metal}$.

$$C_{s,\ metal} = \frac{-(100.0\ g)\left(4.184\dfrac{J}{g \cdot °C} \right)(1.50°C)}{(34.3\ g)(-47.6°C)} = 0.384\ \frac{J}{g \cdot °C}$$

35. Suppose you have a metal sample of unknown mass with a specific heat capacity of $0.329\ \dfrac{J}{g \cdot °C}$. The metal is heated to 47.4°C and then submerged in 5.00 g of water (with an initial temperature of 23.2°C) in an insulated container. The transfer of heat between the metal and water causes the temperature of the water to increase to 28.9°C. What is the mass of the metal?

$$q_{metal} = -q_{water}$$

Thus:

$$m_{metal} \cdot C_{s,\ metal} \cdot \Delta T_{metal} = -\left(m_{water} \cdot C_{s,\ water} \cdot \Delta T_{water} \right)$$

$$m_{metal} = \frac{-\left(m_{water} \cdot C_{s,\ water} \cdot \Delta T_{water} \right)}{C_{s,\ metal} \cdot \Delta T_{metal}}$$

The specific heat capacity of water is $4.184\ \dfrac{J}{g \cdot °C}$, so we now just solve for m_{metal}.

$$m_{metal} = \frac{-(5.00\ g)\left(4.184\dfrac{J}{g \cdot °C} \right)(5.70°C)}{\left(0.329\ \dfrac{J}{g \cdot °C} \right)(-18.5°C)} = \textbf{19.6\ g}$$

36. A 35.7 g sample of iron is heated to 123.70°C and is then placed into a coffee cup calorimeter with 100.0 g of water at 22.30°C. After the metal has cooled, the temperature of the water changed to 26.04°C.

    a. What released heat?

    The sample of iron.

    b. What absorbed heat?

    The water.

c. Calculate the heat absorbed by the water.

$$q_w = m_w \cdot C_{s,w} \cdot \Delta T_w$$

$$q_w = (100.0 \ g) \cdot \left(4.184 \ \frac{J}{g \cdot {}^\circ C}\right) \cdot (26.04{}^\circ C - 22.30{}^\circ C) = \textbf{1565 } \textbf{\textit{J}}$$

d. Calculate the specific heat of the iron.

$$q_w = -q_{Fe} = -\left(m_{Fe} \cdot C_{s,Fe} \cdot \Delta T_{Fe}\right)$$

$$m_w \cdot C_{s,w} \cdot \Delta T_w = -\left(m_{Fe} \cdot C_{s,Fe} \cdot \Delta T_{Fe}\right)$$

$$C_{s,Fe} = \frac{m_w \cdot C_{s,w} \cdot \Delta T_w}{-\left(m_{Fe} \cdot \Delta T_{Fe}\right)} = \frac{(100.0 \ g)\left(4.184 \ \frac{J}{g \cdot {}^\circ C}\right)(26.04{}^\circ C - 22.3{}^\circ C)}{-(35.7 \ g)(26.04{}^\circ C - 123.7{}^\circ C)}$$

$$C_{s,Fe} = \textbf{0.449} \ \frac{\textbf{\textit{J}}}{\textbf{\textit{g}} \cdot {}^\circ\textbf{\textit{C}}}$$

37. A 50.0 g sample of aluminum is heated to 350.0°C and is then placed into a coffee cup calorimeter with 400.0 g of water at 22.3°C. After the metal has cooled, the temperature of the water changed to 30.85°C.

   a. What released heat?

   The aluminum.

   b. What absorbed heat?

   The water.

   c. Calculate the specific heat of the metal.

$$q_w = -q_{Al} = -\left(m_{Al} \cdot C_{s,Al} \cdot \Delta T_{Al}\right)$$

$$m_w \cdot C_{s,w} \cdot \Delta T_w = -\left(m_{Al} \cdot C_{s,Al} \cdot \Delta T_{Al}\right)$$

$$C_{s,Al} = \frac{m_w \cdot C_{s,w} \cdot \Delta T_w}{-\left(m_{Al} \cdot \Delta T_{Al}\right)} = \frac{(400.0 \ g)\left(4.184 \ \frac{J}{g \cdot {}^\circ C}\right)(30.85{}^\circ C - 22.3{}^\circ C)}{-(50.0 \ g)(30.85{}^\circ C - 350.0{}^\circ C)}$$

$$C_{s,Al} = \textbf{0.897} \ \frac{\textbf{\textit{J}}}{\textbf{\textit{g}} \cdot {}^\circ\textbf{\textit{C}}}$$

QUANTIFYING WORK

38. What is the type of work done through the expansion or compression of gases?

   Pressure-Volume Work

39. Is work positive or negative when the system expands against an external pressure?

   When work is done on the surroundings by the system, $\Delta V > 0$ and $w < 0$.

40. Is work positive or negative when the system is compressed by an external pressure?

   When work is done on the system by the surroundings, $\Delta V < 0$ and $w > 0$.

41. A balloon expands by 0.55 L against an external pressure of 1.05 atm. Calculate the work done by this expansion in joules.

$$\Delta V = +0.55 \ L$$

$$w = -P\Delta V = -(1.05 \ atm)(0.55 \ L)\left(\frac{101.3 \ J}{1 \ atm \cdot L}\right) = \mathbf{-58.5 \ J}$$

42. If a chemical system absorbs 25.3 kJ of heat and expands from an initial volume of 0.750 L to a final volume of 2.750 L against an external pressure of 3.10 atm, calculate the internal energy change due to this process.

$$\Delta E = q + w$$

$$q = +25.3 \ kJ$$

$$\Delta V = V_f - V_i = 2.750 \ L - 0.750 \ L = 2.000 \ L$$

$$w = -P\Delta V = -(3.10 \ atm)(2.000 \ L)\left(\frac{101.3 \ J}{1 \ atm \cdot L}\right)\left(\frac{1 \ kJ}{1000 \ J}\right) = -0.628 \ kJ$$

$$\Delta E = q + w = 25.3 \ kJ + (-0.628 \ kJ) = \mathbf{24.7 \ kJ}$$

43. A chemical system is compressed by an external pressure of 1.75 atm from an initial volume of 3.27 L to a final volume of 1.75 L. If the system absorbed 225 J of heat, what is the internal energy change for this process?

$$\Delta E = q + w$$

$$q = +225 \ J$$

$$\Delta V = V_f - V_i = 1.75 \ L - 3.27 \ L = -1.52 \ L$$

$$w = -P\Delta V = -(1.75 \ atm)(-1.52 \ L)\left(\frac{101.3 \ J}{1 \ atm \cdot L}\right) = +269.5 \ J$$

$$\Delta E = q + w = 225 \ J + 269.5 \ J = \mathbf{495 \ J}$$

ENTHALPY

44. Define enthalpy.

    Enthalpy is a quantity defined as the sum of the internal energy of a system plus the product of its pressure and volume under conditions of constant pressure.

45. Is enthalpy an extensive or intensive property?

    Enthalpy is an extensive property.

46. Define the terms exothermic in the context of chemical reactions.

    Reactions which give off heat ($\Delta H_{rxn} < 0$) are referred to as exothermic reactions.

47. Define the term endothermic in the context of chemical reactions.

    Reactions which absorb heat ($\Delta H_{rxn} > 0$) are referred to as endothermic reactions.

48. If the ΔH_{rxn} for a thermochemical reaction is less than zero, then is the reaction an endothermic or exothermic process?

    Exothermic

49. If the ΔH_{rxn} for a thermochemical reaction is greater than zero, then is the reaction an endothermic or exothermic process?

    Endothermic

50. Indicate whether each of the following processes is endothermic or exothermic:

    a. Propane burning in a gas barbeque grill.

        Exothermic ($\Delta H < 0$)

    b. Water boiling on a stove top.

        Endothermic ($\Delta H > 0$)

    c. Condensation of water vapor from the air onto an ice-cold soda can.

        Exothermic ($\Delta H < 0$)

51. Indicate whether each of the following processes is endothermic or exothermic:

    a. Wood burning.

        Exothermic ($\Delta H < 0$)

    b. A liquid freezing.

        Exothermic ($\Delta H < 0$)

    c. Acetone (nail polish remover) evaporating.

        Endothermic ($\Delta H > 0$)

52. If a chemical reaction takes place wherein 1 mole of a compound is consumed and the reaction gives off 2786 kJ of heat and does 17 kJ of work, what are ΔE and ΔH for the reaction?

$$\Delta H = -2786 \frac{kJ}{mol}$$

$$\Delta E = q + w = \Delta H + w = -2786 \frac{kJ}{mol} - 17 \frac{kJ}{mol} = \boldsymbol{-2803 \ kJ}$$

53. If 1 mole of propane (C_3H_8) undergoes a combustion reaction at a pressure of 1 atm and has an internal energy change of -2049 kJ, how much work is done if the enthalpy of the reaction is $\Delta H = \boldsymbol{-2044 \ kJ}$?

$$\Delta E = q + w = \Delta H + w$$

$$w = \Delta E - \Delta H = (-2049 \ kJ) - (-2044 \ kJ) = \boldsymbol{-5 \ kJ}$$

54. According to the following reaction, determine the amount of heat (kJ) that will be generated from the complete consumption of the following amounts of each reactant:

$$CH_4(g) + 2O_2(g) \rightarrow CO_2(g) + 2H_2O(l) \quad \Delta H_{rxn} = -882.0 \ kJ \ / \ mol$$

a. 17.0 g $CH_4(g)$

$$17.0 \ g \ CH_4 \times \frac{1 \ mol \ CH_4}{16.05 \ g} \times \frac{-882.0 \ kJ}{1 \ mol \ CH_4} = \boldsymbol{-934 \ kJ}$$

b. 16.9 g $O_2(g)$

$$16.9 \ g \ O_2 \times \frac{1 \ mol \ O_2}{32.00 \ g} \times \frac{-882.0 \ kJ}{2 \ mol \ O_2} = \boldsymbol{-233 \ kJ}$$

55. According to the following reaction, determine the amount of heat (kJ) that will be generated from the production of the following amounts of each product:

$$CH_4(g) + 2O_2(g) \rightarrow CO_2(g) + 2H_2O(l) \quad \Delta H_{rxn} = -882.0 \ kJ \ / \ mol$$

a. 46.7 g $CO_2(g)$

$$46.7 \ g \ CO_2 \times \frac{1 \ mol \ CO_2}{44.01 \ g} \times \frac{-882.0 \ kJ}{1 \ mol \ CO_2} = \boldsymbol{-936 \ kJ}$$

b. 9.50 g $H_2O(l)$

$$9.50 \ g \ H_2O \times \frac{1 \ mol \ H_2O}{18.02 \ g} \times \frac{-882.0 \ kJ}{2 \ mol \ H_2O} = \boldsymbol{-232 \ kJ}$$

56. According to the following reaction, determine the amount of heat (kJ) that will be generated from the complete consumption of the following amounts of each reactant:

$$2C_2H_6(g) + 7O_2(g) \rightarrow 4CO_2(g) + 6H_2O(g) \quad \Delta H_{rxn} = -2856.6 \ kJ \ / \ mol$$

a. 5.00 g C_2H_6 (g)

$$5.00 \; g \; C_2H_6 \times \frac{1 \; mol \; C_2H_6}{30.08 \; g} \times \frac{-2856.6 \; kJ}{2 \; mol \; CH_4} = \textbf{-237 kJ}$$

b. 9.30 g O_2 (g)

$$9.30 \; g \; O_2 \times \frac{1 \; mol \; O_2}{32.00 \; g} \times \frac{-2856.6 \; kJ}{7 \; mol \; O_2} = \textbf{-119 kJ}$$

57. According to the following reaction, determine the amount of heat (kJ) that will be generated from the production of the following amounts of each product:

$$2C_2H_6(g) + 7O_2(g) \rightarrow 4CO_2(g) + 6H_2O(g) \quad \Delta H_{rxn} = \text{-2856.6 kJ / mol}$$

a. 14.6 g CO_2 (g)

$$14.6 \; g \; CO_2 \times \frac{1 \; mol \; CO_2}{44.01 \; g} \times \frac{-2856.6 \; kJ}{4 \; mol \; CO_2} = \textbf{-237 kJ}$$

b. 9.00 g H_2O (l)

$$9.00 \; g \; H_2O \times \frac{1 \; mol \; H_2O}{18.02 \; g} \times \frac{-2856.6 \; kJ}{6 \; mol \; H_2O} = \textbf{-238 kJ}$$

58. What mass of octane (C_8H_{18}) must be burned to generate 2375 kJ of heat according to the following thermochemical reaction?

$$2 \; C_8H_{18}(l) + 25 \; O_2(g) \rightarrow 16 \; CO_2(g) + 18 \; H_2O(g) \quad \Delta H_{rxn} = -10{,}148.2 \; kJ \cdot mol^{-1}$$

We begin with the given heat and convert this quantity to the equivalent quantity in moles of octane, which is then converted to mass using the molar mass of octane as a conversion factor:

$$-2375 \; kJ \times \frac{2 \; mol \; C_8H_{18}}{-10148.2 \; kJ} \times \frac{114.23 \; g \; C_8H_{18}}{1 \; mol \; C_8H_{18}} = \textbf{53.47 g } \boldsymbol{C_8H_{18}}.$$

59. Consider the following thermochemical reaction. If this reaction is carried out with 45.00 ml of a 0.475 M HCl (aq) solution, and the resulting reaction produces 3.87 kJ of heat, is HCl the limiting reagent?

$$Mg(s) + 2 \; HCl(aq) \rightarrow MgCl_2(aq) + H_2(g) \quad \Delta H_{rxn}^o = -467 \; kJ$$

We begin by determining the amount of energy that is produced by complete consumption of the HCl present in the reaction mixture. This is accomplished by converting the volume and concentration of the HCl solution to moles and then converting that quantity to heat.

$$45.00 \; ml \; HCl \times \frac{1 \; L \; HCl}{1000 \; ml \; HCl} \times \frac{0.475 \; mol \; HCl}{1 \; L \; HCl} \times \frac{-467 \; kJ}{2 \; mol \; HCl} = -4.99 \; kJ$$

Since this is a greater quantity of heat than the reaction ultimately produced (3.87 kJ), we conclude that HCl is not the limiting reagent.

CALORIMETRY

60. Define calorimetry.

Calorimetry is defined as a scientific discipline directed toward the measurement of heat.

61. What is a calorimeter?

A calorimeter is an apparatus which is used to perform chemical reactions under controlled conditions such that temperature changes can be carefully measured.

62. Suppose 5.0 g of octane is placed in a bomb calorimeter with a known heat capacity of 12.71 $\frac{kJ}{°C}$. The reaction is ignited, and the temperature of the calorimeter rises from 22.3°C to 27.8°C. Determine the internal energy change of this combustion reaction.

First, calculate the change in temperature:

$$\Delta T = T_f - T_i = 27.8°C - 22.3°C = 5.5°C$$

Next, calculate the moles of octane consumed in the reaction:

$$5.0 \ g \ C_8H_{18} \times \frac{1 \ mol \ C_8H_{18}}{114.23 \ g \ C_8H_{18}} = 0.044 \ mol \ C_8H_{18}$$

Finally, calculate the ΔE_{rxn}:

$$\Delta E_{rxn} = \frac{-(C_{cal} \times \Delta T)}{n_{octane}} = \frac{-\left(12.71\frac{kJ}{°C}\right)(5.5°C)}{0.044 \ mol} = -1.6 \times 10^2 \ \frac{kJ}{mol}$$

63. Suppose 1.013 g of naphthalene ($C_{10}H_8$) is placed in a bomb calorimeter with a known heat capacity of 11.67 kJ/°C. The naphthalene is ignited, and the temperature of the calorimeter rises from 25.00°C to 28.50°C. Determine the internal energy change of this combustion reaction.

First, calculate the change in temperature:

$$\Delta T = T_f - T_i = 28.50°C - 25.00°C = 3.50°C$$

Next, calculate the moles of aluminum consumed in the reaction:

$$1.013 \ g \ C_{10}H_8 \times \frac{1 \ mol \ C_{10}H_8}{128.17 \ g \ C_{10}H_8} = 0.00790357 \ mol \ C_{10}H_8$$

Finally, calculate the ΔE_{rxn}:

$$\Delta E_{rxn} = \frac{-(C_{cal} \times \Delta T)}{n} = \frac{-\left(11.67\frac{kJ}{°C}\right)(3.50°C)}{0.00790357 \ mol} = -5.17 \times 10^3 \ kJ \cdot mol^{-1}$$

64. 0.1573 g of Zn is delivered to a coffee cup calorimeter containing 50.00 ml of an aqueous *HCl* solution. Write the balanced thermochemical equation for the reaction which ensues if the temperature of the solution rises from 21.31°C to 23.06°C, assuming the zinc is completely consumed. (Assume the density of the solution is 1.00 g/ml and the specific heat of the solution is that of water 4.184 $\dfrac{J}{g \cdot °C}$.)

$$Zn(s) + 2\ HCl(aq) \rightarrow ZnCl_2(aq) + H_2(g) \quad \Delta H_{rxn} = ?$$

In constant-pressure calorimetry, we assume the solution is the surroundings:

$$\Delta H_{rxn} = \dfrac{q_{rxn}}{n} = \dfrac{-(m_{soln} \cdot C_{s,water} \cdot \Delta T_{soln})}{n_{Zn}} =$$

$$\Delta H_{rxn} = \dfrac{-\left(50.00\ ml \times \dfrac{1.00\ g}{ml}\right)\left(4.184\ \dfrac{J}{g \cdot °C}\right)(23.06°C - 21.31°C)}{\left(0.1573\ g\ Zn \times \dfrac{1\ mol\ Zn}{65.38\ g\ Zn}\right)}$$

$$\Delta H_{rxn} = -152165.4\ J \cdot mol^{-1} = -152.2\ kJ \cdot mol^{-1}$$

Since the coefficient for Zn is 1 in the balanced equation:

$$\boldsymbol{Zn(s) + 2\ HCl(aq) \rightarrow ZnCl_2(aq) + H_2(g) \quad \Delta H_{rxn} = -152.2\ kJ \cdot mol^{-1}}$$

HESS'S LAW

65. What is Hess's Law?

Hess's Law states that the enthalpy change of an overall chemical process is equal to the sum of the enthalpy changes for individual steps in that process.

66. How does multiplying an equation by a certain factor affect ΔH?

When a particular reaction is multiplied by a certain factor, then ΔH is multiplied by the same factor (enthalpy is an extensive property).

67. How does dividing an equation by a certain factor affect ΔH?

When a particular reaction is divided by a certain factor, then ΔH is divided by the same factor (enthalpy is an extensive property).

68. How does reversing a reaction equation affect ΔH?

When a particular reaction is reversed, then the sign of ΔH is also reversed (if a reaction is exothermic in the forward direction, then it is endothermic in the reverse direction by the same amount and vice versa).

69. Given the following equation:

$$3\,O_2(g) \rightarrow 2\,O_3(g) \quad \Delta H = +285.4\ kJ$$

What is the value of ΔH for the following reaction:

$$\frac{3}{2}O_2(g) \rightarrow O_3(g)$$

Since $\frac{3}{2}O_2(g) \rightarrow O_3(g)$ is half of $3\,O_2(g) \rightarrow 2O_3(g)$, the new enthalpy will also be ½ of the original enthalpy.

Thus we get,

$$\frac{1}{2}\,(+285.4\ kJ) = \textbf{+142.7 kJ}$$

70. Given the following equation:

$$2Ag_2S(s) + 2H_2O(l) \rightarrow 4Ag(s) + 2H_2S(g) + O_2(g) \quad \Delta H = +595.5\ kJ$$

Calculate ΔH for the following reaction:

$$Ag(s) + \frac{1}{2}H_2S(g) + \frac{1}{4}O_2(g) \rightarrow \frac{1}{2}Ag_2S(s) + \frac{1}{2}H_2O(l)$$

Since $Ag(s) + \frac{1}{2}H_2S(g) + \frac{1}{4}O_2(g) \rightarrow \frac{1}{2}Ag_2S(s) + \frac{1}{2}H_2O(l)$ is a fourth of

$2Ag_2S(s) + 2H_2O(l) \rightarrow 4Ag(s) + 2H_2S(g) + O_2(g)$, the new enthalpy will also be ¼ of the original

enthalpy. Thus we get,

$$\frac{1}{4}\,(+595.5\ kJ) = \textbf{-148.9 kJ}$$

71. Given the following reactions and their associated enthalpies:

1. $2NO\,(g) + O_2\,(g) \rightarrow 2NO_2\,(g) \quad \Delta H = -116.2\ kJ$

2. $2NO\,(g) \rightarrow N_2(g) + O_2\,(g) \quad\quad \Delta H = -182.6\ kJ$

Calculate the enthalpy of the following reaction:

$$N_2(g) + 2O_2\,(g) \rightarrow 2NO_2(g)$$

Since we have $2NO_2$ on the product side in reaction #1, and that is where we want it in the desired reaction, we are going to leave this reaction alone with $\Delta H = -116.2\ kJ$. In reaction #2 however, we have N_2 on the product side and we want it in the reactants. Thus, we will flip this reaction and change the sign of ΔH. We now add the ΔH values for reaction #1 ($\Delta H = -116.2\ kJ$) and this new ΔH value for reaction #2 ($\Delta H = +182.6\ kJ$).

$$2NO\,(g) + O_2\,(g) \rightarrow 2NO_2\,(g) \qquad \Delta H = -116.2\ kJ$$

$$\underline{N_2(g) + O_2\,(g) \rightarrow 2NO\,(g) \qquad \Delta H = +182.6\ kJ}$$

$$N_2(g) + 2O_2\,(g) \rightarrow 2NO_2(g) \qquad \textbf{\Delta H = 66.4 kJ}$$

72. Given the following reactions and their associated enthalpies:

   1. $2CaCO_3 \ (s) \rightarrow 2Ca \ (s) + 2CO_2 \ (g) + O_2 \ (g)$ $\Delta H = +1628.2 \ kJ$

   2. $2CaO \ (s) \rightarrow 2Ca \ (s) + O_2 \ (g)$ $\Delta H = +1269.8 \ kJ$

Calculate the enthalpy of the following reaction:

$$CaCO_3(s) \rightarrow \ CaO \ (s) + CO_2 \ (g)$$

Since we have 2 $CaCO_3$ on the reactant side in reaction #1, and we want 1 $CaCO_3$ on the reactant side of the equation of interest, we will divide everything including ΔH by 2 ($\Delta H = \frac{+1628.2}{2} = +814.1 \ kJ$). In reaction #2, we have 2 CaO on the reactant side and we want 1 CaO on the product side. Thus, we will reverse this reaction equation (change the sign of ΔH) and divide everything by 2 including ΔH ($\Delta H = \frac{-1269.8}{2} = -634.9 \ kJ$). We now add the new ΔH values for reactions #1 ($\Delta H = +814.1 \ kJ$) and reaction #2 ($\Delta H = -634.9 \ kJ$).

$$CaCO_3 \ (s) \rightarrow \cancel{Ca \ (s)} + CO_2 \ (g) + \cancel{1/2 \ O_2} \ (g) \quad \Delta H = +814.1 \ kJ$$

$$\underline{\cancel{Ca \ (s)} + \cancel{1/2 \ O_2} \ (g) \rightarrow CaO \ (s) \qquad\qquad\qquad \Delta H = -634.9 \ kJ}$$

$$CaCO_3(s) \rightarrow \ CaO \ (s) + CO_2 \ (g) \qquad\qquad\qquad \boldsymbol{\Delta H = +179.2 \ kJ}$$

73. Given the following reactions and their associated enthalpies:

   1. $S \ (s) + O_2 \ (g) \rightarrow SO_2 \ (g)$ $\Delta H = -296.8 \ kJ$

   2. $2S \ (s) + 3O_2 \ (g) \rightarrow 2SO_3 \ (g)$ $\Delta H = -792.0 \ kJ$

Calculate the enthalpy of the following reaction:

$$2SO_2 \ (g) + O_2 \ (g) \rightarrow \ 2SO_3 \ (g)$$

Since we have SO_2 on the product side in reaction #1, and we want $2SO_2$ on the reactant side in the desired reaction, we are going to reverse this reaction (change the sign of ΔH) and multiply everything by 2 including ΔH ($\Delta H = 2 \times (+296.8) = +593.6 \ kJ$). In reaction #2, we already have $2SO_3$ on the product side, which is where we want it so we are going to leave this reaction alone with $\Delta H = -792.0 \ kJ$. We now add the new ΔH value for reaction #1 ($\Delta H = +593.6 \ kJ$) and the original ΔH value for reaction #2 ($\Delta H = -792.0 \ kJ$).

$$2SO_2 \ (g) \rightarrow \cancel{2S} \ (s) + \cancel{2O_2} \ (g) \qquad\qquad \Delta H = +593.6 \ kJ$$

$$\underline{\cancel{2S} \ (s) + \cancel{3O_2} \ (g) + O_2(g) \rightarrow 2SO_3 \ (g) \qquad \Delta H = -792.0 \ kJ}$$

$$2SO_2 \ (g) + O_2 \ (g) \rightarrow \ 2SO_3 \ (g) \qquad\qquad \boldsymbol{\Delta H = -198.4 \ kJ}$$

74. Given the following reactions and their associated enthalpies:

    1. $2CO\,(g) + O_2\,(g) \rightarrow 2CO_2\,(g)$ $\Delta H = -566.0\ kJ$

    2. $2Fe\,(s) + O_2\,(g) \rightarrow 2FeO\,(s)$ $\Delta H = -544.0\ kJ$

Calculate the enthalpy of the following reaction:

$$FeO\,(s) + CO\,(g) \rightarrow Fe\,(s) + CO_2\,(g)$$

Since we have $2CO$ on the reactant side in reaction #1, and we want CO on the reactant side in the desired reaction, we are going to divide everything by 2 including ΔH ($\Delta H = \dfrac{-566.0}{2} = -283\ kJ$). In reaction #2, we have $2\ FeO$ on the product side, and we want FeO on the reactant side, so we are going to flip this reaction (change the sign of ΔH) and divide everything by 2 including ΔH ($\Delta H = \dfrac{+544.0}{2} = +272.0\ kJ$). We now add the new ΔH values for reaction #1 ($\Delta H = -283.0\ kJ$) and reaction #2 ($\Delta H = +272.0\ kJ$).

$CO\,(g) + \cancel{1/2\,O_2}\,(g) \rightarrow CO_2\,(g)$ $\Delta H = -283.0\ kJ$

$FeO\,(s) \rightarrow Fe\,(s) + \cancel{1/2\,O_2}\,(g)$ $\Delta H = +272.0\ kJ$

$\overline{FeO\,(s) + CO\,(g) \rightarrow Fe\,(s) + CO_2\,(g)}$ $\overline{\Delta H = -11.0\ \textbf{kJ}}$

75. Given the following reactions and their associated enthalpies:

    1. $2NO\,(g) \rightarrow N_2\,(g) + O_2\,(g)$ $\Delta H = -182.6\ kJ$

    2. $2H_2\,(g) + O_2\,(g) \rightarrow 2H_2O\,(g)$ $\Delta H = -483.6\ kJ$

    3. $C\,(s) + O_2\,(g) \rightarrow CO_2\,(g)$ $\Delta H = -393.5\ kJ$

Calculate the enthalpy of the following reaction:

$$3N_2\,(g) + 4H_2\,(g) + C\,(s) + 6O_2\,(g) \rightarrow 6NO\,(g) + 4H_2O\,(g) + CO_2\,(g)$$

Since we have N_2 on the product side in reaction #1, and we want $3N_2$ on the reactant side in the desired reaction, we are going to flip this reaction (change the sign of ΔH) and multiply everything by 3 including ΔH ($\Delta H = 3 \times (+182.6) = +547.8\ kJ$). In reaction #2, we have $2H_2$ on the reactant side, and we want $4H_2$ on the reactant side, so we are going to multiply everything by 2 including ΔH ($\Delta H = 2 \times (-483.6) = -967.2\ kJ$). We will keep reaction #3 as is because we have C on the reactant side, and that is where we want it. We now add the new ΔH values for reaction #1 ($\Delta H = +547.8\ kJ$), reaction #2 ($\Delta H = -967.2\ kJ$), and reaction #3 ($\Delta H = -393.5\ kJ$).

$3N_2\,(g) + 3O_2\,(g) \rightarrow 6NO\,(g)$ $\Delta H = +547.8\ kJ$

$4H_2\,(g) + 2O_2\,(g) \rightarrow 4H_2O\,(g)$ $\Delta H = -967.2\ kJ$

$C\,(s) + O_2\,(g) \rightarrow CO_2\,(g)$ $\Delta H = -393.5\ kJ$

$\overline{3N_2\,(g) + 4H_2\,(g) + C\,(s) + 6O_2\,(g) \rightarrow 6NO\,(g) + 4H_2O\,(g) + CO_2\,(g)}$ $\overline{\Delta H = -812.9\ \textbf{kJ}}$

STANDARD CONDITIONS AND ENTHALPIES OF FORMATION

76. Define the standard enthalpy of reaction.

   Standard enthalpy of reaction is defined as the enthalpy change corresponding to a reaction at constant pressure wherein all reactants and products are in their respective standard states.

77. Define the standard enthalpy of formation.

   The standard enthalpy of formation is defined as the enthalpy change associated with the standard formation reaction of a substance.

78. Use standard enthalpies of formation (Appendix II) to calculate ΔH^{o}_{rxn} for each of the following reactions:

   a. $CH_4(g) + 2\ O_2\ (g) \rightarrow CO_2(g) + 2\ H_2O(g)$

   $\Delta H^{\circ}_f(products) = \Delta H^{\circ}_f\left(CO_2\right) + 2\Delta H^{\circ}_f(H_2O)$

   $= (1)(-393.5) + (2)(-241.8) = -877.1\ kJ/mol$

   $\Delta H^{\circ}_f(reactants) = \Delta H^{\circ}_f\left(CH_4\right) + 2\Delta H^{\circ}_f\ O_2$

   $= (1)(-74.4) + (2)(0) = -74.4\ kJ/mol$

   $\Delta H^{\circ}_{rxn} = \Delta H^{\circ}_f(products) - \Delta H^{\circ}_f(reactants)$

   $\Delta H^{\circ}_{rxn} = (-877.1) - (-74.4) = \textbf{-802.7 kJ/mol}$

   b. $2\ CH_3OH(l) + 3\ O_2(g) \rightarrow 2\ CO_2(g) + 4\ H_2O(l)$

   $\Delta H^{\circ}_f(products) = 2\Delta H^{\circ}_f\left(CO_2\right) + 4\Delta H^{\circ}_f(H_2O)$

   $= (2)(-393.5) + (4)(-241.8) = -1754.2\ kJ/mol$

   $\Delta H^{\circ}_f(reactants) = 2\Delta H^{\circ}_f\left(CH_3OH\right) + 3\Delta H^{\circ}_f\ O_2$

   $= (2)(-239.1) + (3)(0) = -478.2\ kJ/mol$

   $\Delta H^{\circ}_{rxn} = \Delta H^{\circ}_f(products) - \Delta H^{\circ}_f(reactants)$

   $\Delta H^{\circ}_{rxn} = (-1754.2) - (-478.2) = \textbf{-1276 kJ/mol}$

79. Calculate the ΔH^{o}_{rxn} for the following reaction using the data presented in Appendix II:

$$C(s) + H_2O(g) \rightarrow CO(g) + H_2(g)$$

From Appendix II, we get the following ΔH^{o} values:

$$C(s) = 0.0 \frac{kJ}{mol}$$

$$H_2O(g) = -241.8 \frac{kJ}{mol}$$

$$CO(g) = -110.5 \frac{kJ}{mol}$$

$$H_2(g) = 0.0 \frac{kJ}{mol}.$$

$$\Delta H^{o}_{rxn} = \sum (n \Delta H^{o}_{f})_{prod} - \sum (n \Delta H^{o}_{f})_{react}$$

$$\Delta H^{o}_{rxn} = \left[\left(-110.5 \frac{kJ}{mol} \right) + \left(0.0 \frac{kJ}{mol} \right) \right] - \left[\left(0.0 \frac{kJ}{mol} \right) + \left(-241.8 \frac{kJ}{mol} \right) \right] = \mathbf{131.3 \frac{kJ}{mol}}$$

80. Calculate the ΔH^{o}_{rxn} for the following reaction using the data presented in Appendix II:

$$N_2(g) + O_2(g) \rightarrow 2NO(g)$$

From Appendix II, we get the following ΔH^{o} values:

$$N_2(g) = 0.0 \frac{kJ}{mol}$$

$$O_2(g) = 0.0 \frac{kJ}{mol}$$

$$NO(g) = 91.3 \frac{kJ}{mol}$$

$$\Delta H^{o}_{rxn} = \sum (n \Delta H^{o}_{f})_{prod} - \sum (n \Delta H^{o}_{f})_{react}$$

$$\Delta H^{o}_{rxn} = \left[2 \times \left(91.3 \frac{kJ}{mol} \right) \right] - \left[\left(0.0 \frac{kJ}{mol} \right) + \left(0.0 \frac{kJ}{mol} \right) \right] = \mathbf{182.6 \frac{kJ}{mol}}$$

81. Calculate the ΔH^{o}_{rxn} for the following reaction using the data presented in Appendix II:

$$CaCO_3(s) \rightarrow CaO(s) + CO_2(g)$$

From Appendix II, we get the following ΔH^{o} values:

$$CaCO_3(s) = -1207.6 \frac{kJ}{mol}$$

$$CaO \ (s) = -634.9 \frac{kJ}{mol}$$

$$CO_2 \ (g) = -393.5 \ \frac{kJ}{mol}$$

$$\Delta H^o_{rxn} = \sum (n\Delta H^o_f)_{prod} - \sum (n\Delta H^o_f)_{react}$$

$$\Delta H^o_{rxn} = \left[\left(-634.9 \frac{kJ}{mol} \right) + \left(-393.5 \ \frac{kJ}{mol} \right) \right] - \left[\left(-1207.6 \ \frac{kJ}{mol} \right) \right] = \mathbf{179.2} \ \boldsymbol{\frac{kJ}{mol}}$$

82. Calculate the ΔH^o_{rxn} for the following reaction using the data presented in Appendix II:

$$2H_2S \ (g) + 3O_2 \ (g) \rightarrow 2SO_2 \ (g) + 2H_2O \ (l)$$

From Appendix II, we get the following ΔH^o values:

$$H_2S \ (g) = -20.6 \ \frac{kJ}{mol}$$

$$O_2 \ (g) = 0.0 \frac{kJ}{mol}$$

$$SO_2 \ (g) = -296.8 \ \frac{kJ}{mol}$$

$$H_2O \ (l) = -285.8 \ \frac{kJ}{mol} \ .$$

$$\Delta H^o_{rxn} = \sum (n\Delta H^o_f)_{prod} - \sum (n\Delta H^o_f)_{react}$$

$$\Delta H^o_{rxn} = \left[\left(2 \times -296.8 \ \frac{kJ}{mol} \right) + \left(2 \times -285.8 \ \frac{kJ}{mol} \right) \right] - \left[\left(2 \times -20.6 \ \frac{kJ}{mol} \right) + \left(3 \times 0.0 \ \frac{kJ}{mol} \right) \right]$$

$$= \mathbf{-1124.0} \ \boldsymbol{\frac{kJ}{mol}}$$

THE ENTHALPY OF BONDING

83. Use bond energies from Table 12.4 to estimate the enthalpy of reaction for the following:

$$H_2(g) + O_2(g) \rightarrow H_2O_2(g)$$

We estimate the reaction enthalpy by subtracting the sum of the bond energies of the bonds which are formed in a reaction from that of the bonds which are broken. In thise case we see that there is 1 $H - H$ single bond and 1 $O = O$ double bond broken, while there are 2 $O - H$ and 1 $O - O$ single bonds formed. Therefore:

$$\Delta H_{rxn} = \sum \left(n \Delta H_{BE} \right)_{broken} - \sum \left(n \Delta H_{BE} \right)_{formed}$$

$$\Delta H_{rxn} = \left[\left(436 \ kJ \right) + \left(498 \ kJ \right) \right] - \left[2 \left(464 \ kJ \right) + \left(142 \ kJ \right) \right]$$

$$\Delta H_{rxn} = -136 \ kJ \ / \ mol$$

84. Use bond energies from Table 12.4 to estimate the enthalpy of reaction for the following:

$$N_2 (g) + 3 \ H_2 (g) \rightarrow 2 \ NH_3 (g)$$

We estimate the reaction enthalpy by subtracting the sum of the bond energies of the bonds which are formed in a reaction from that of the bonds which are broken. In this case we see that there is 1 $N \equiv N$ triple bond and 3 $H - H$ single bonds broken, while there are 6 $N - H$ single bonds formed. Therefore:

$$\Delta H_{rxn} = \sum \left(n \Delta H_{BE} \right)_{broken} - \sum \left(n \Delta H_{BE} \right)_{formed}$$

$$\Delta H_{rxn} = \left[\left(947 \ kJ \right) + 3 \left(435 \ kJ \right) \right] - \left[6 \left(388 \ kJ \right) \right]$$

$$\Delta H_{rxn} = -76 \ kJ \ / \ mol$$

85. Arrange the following in order of increasing lattice energy:
    a. *MgO*
    b. *CaO*
    c. *RbBr*
    d. *CsBr*

Because ionic charge is of greater impact on the magnitude of lattice energy than is ionic radius we can assume the doubly charged ions have a greater lattice energy than the singly charged ions.

$$(RbBr, \ CsBr) < (MgO, \ CaO)$$

Because *Cs* has a greater ionic radius than does *Rb*:

$$CsBr < RbBr < (MgO, \ CaO)$$

Because *Ca* has a greater ionic radius than does *Mg*:

$$CsBr < RbBr < CaO < MgO$$

86. Arrange the following in order of increasing lattice energy:
    a. *MgO*
    b. *SrS*
    c. *NaF*
    d. *RbBr*

Because ionic charge is of greater impact on the magnitude of lattice energy than is ionic radius we can assume the doubly charged ions have a greater lattice energy than the singly charged ions.

$$(NaF, RbBr) < (MgO, SrS)$$

Because the sum of the ionic radii of Rb and Br is greater than that of Na and F:

$$RbBr < NaF < (MgO, SrS)$$

Because the sum of the ionic radii of Sr and S is greater than that of Mg and O:

CsBr < RbBr < SrS < MgO

87. Use the Born-Haber cycle and data from Appendix II and Chapter 7 to calculate the lattice energy of KCl. The heat of sublimation and the first ionization energy of potassium are 89.1 kJ/mol and 418.7 kJ/mol respectively.

$$K(s) + \frac{1}{2}Cl_2(g) \rightarrow KCl(s)$$

Standard heat of formation: $\Delta H_f^o = -436.7 \ kJ$

Heat of sublimation of potassium: $\Delta H_{sub} = 89.1 \ kJ$

Bond energy of chlorine: $\frac{1}{2}\Delta H_{BE} = \frac{1}{2}(242.6 \ kJ) = 121.3 \ kJ$

First ionization energy of potassium: $\Delta H_{IE} = 418.8 \ kJ$

Electron affinity of chlorine: $\Delta H_{EA} = -348.6 \ kJ$

$$\Delta H_f^o = \Delta H_{sub} + \frac{1}{2}\Delta H_{BE} + \Delta H_{IE} + \Delta H_{EA} + \Delta H_{Lattice}$$

$$\Delta H_{Lattice} = \Delta H_f^o - \Delta H_{sub} - \frac{1}{2}\Delta H_{BE} - \Delta H_{IE} - \Delta H_{EA}$$

$$\Delta H_{Lattice} = (-436.7 \ kJ) - (89.1 \ kJ) - \frac{1}{2}(242.6 \ kJ) - (418.8 \ kJ) - (-348.6 \ kJ)$$

$$\Delta H_{Lattice} = -717 \ kJ$$

$$Lattice \ Energy = -\Delta H_{Lattice} = 717 \ kJ$$

88. Use the Born-Haber cycle and data from Appendix II and Chapter 7 to calculate the lattice energy of MgF_2 ($\Delta H_f^\circ = -1123.8$ kJ). The heat of sublimation of magnesium is 147.1 kJ/mol and the electron affinity of fluorine is –328.1 kJ/mol. Additionally, diatomic fluorine has a bond energy of 155.0 kJ/mol.

$$Mg(s) + F_2(g) \rightarrow MgF(s)$$

Standard heat of formation: $\Delta H_f^\circ = -1123.8$ kJ

Heat of sublimation of magnesium: $\Delta H_{sub} = 147.1$ kJ

Bond energy of fluorine: $\Delta H_{BE} = 155.0$ kJ

First ionization energy of magnesium: $\Delta H_{IE}^{'} = 737.5$ kJ

Second ionization energy of magnesium: $\Delta H_{IE}^{''} = 1451$ kJ

Electron affinity of fluorine: $2\ \Delta H_{EA} = 2(-328.1$ kJ$)$

$$\Delta H_f^\circ = \Delta H_{sub} + \Delta H_{BE} + \Delta H_{IE}^{'} + \Delta H_{IE}^{''} + \Delta H_{EA} + \Delta H_{Lattice}$$

$$\Delta H_{Lattice} = \Delta H_f^\circ - \Delta H_{sub} - \Delta H_{BE} - \Delta H_{IE}^{'} - \Delta H_{IE}^{''} - 2\Delta H_{EA}$$

$$\Delta H_{Lattice} = (-1123.8 \text{ kJ}) - (147.1 \text{ kJ}) - (155.0 \text{ kJ}) - (737.5 \text{ kJ}) - (1451 \text{ kJ}) - 2(-328.1 \text{ kJ})$$

$$\Delta H_{Lattice} = \textbf{--2958 kJ}$$

$$\textbf{\textit{Lattice Energy}} = -\Delta H_{Lattice} = \textbf{2958 kJ}$$

SPONTANEITY, ENTROPY, AND THE SECOND LAW OF THERMODYNAMICS

89. Indicate the sign of ΔS_{rxn} for each of the following:

a. $2\ KCl(s) + 3\ O_2(g) \rightarrow 2\ KClO_3(s)$

Since there is a net reduction in the moles of gaseous molecules in this reaction, $\Delta S < 0$.

b. $CaCO_3(s) \rightarrow CaO(s) + CO_2(g)$

Since there is a net increase in the moles of gaseous molecules in this reaction, $\Delta S > 0$.

90. Indicate the sign of ΔS_{rxn} for each of the following:

    a. $NH_4Cl(s) \rightarrow HCl(g) + NH_3(g)$

    Since there is a net increase in the moles of gaseous molecules in this reaction, $\Delta S > 0$.

    b. $N_2(g) + 3\ H_2(g) \rightarrow 2\ NH_3(g)$

    Since there is a net reduction in the moles of gaseous molecules in this reaction, $\Delta S < 0$.

91. Calculate ΔS_{surr} for each of the following reactions at 298 K:

    a. $\Delta H^o_{rxn} = -165.7\ kJ$

    $$\Delta S_{surr} = -\frac{\Delta H^o_{rxn}}{T} = -\frac{-165.7\frac{kJ}{mol}}{298\ K} \times \frac{1000\ J}{1\ kJ} = \mathbf{556}\ \frac{\boldsymbol{J}}{\boldsymbol{mol\ \circ K}}$$

    b. $\Delta H^o_{rxn} = -14.23\ kJ$

    $$\Delta S_{surr} = -\frac{\Delta H^o_{rxn}}{T} = -\frac{-14.23\frac{kJ}{mol}}{298\ K} \times \frac{1000\ J}{1\ kJ} = \mathbf{47.75}\ \frac{\boldsymbol{J}}{\boldsymbol{mol\ \circ K}}$$

    c. $\Delta H^o_{rxn} = +165.7\ kJ$ a

    $$\Delta S_{surr} = -\frac{\Delta H^o_{rxn}}{T} = -\frac{165.7\frac{kJ}{mol}}{298\ K} \times \frac{1000\ J}{1\ kJ} = \mathbf{-556}\ \frac{\boldsymbol{J}}{\boldsymbol{mol\ \circ K}}$$

    d. $\Delta H^o_{rxn} = +14.23\ kJ$

    $$\Delta S_{surr} = -\frac{\Delta H^o_{rxn}}{T} = -\frac{+14.23\frac{kJ}{mol}}{298\ K} \times \frac{1000\ J}{1\ kJ} = \mathbf{-47.75}\ \frac{\boldsymbol{J}}{\boldsymbol{mol\ \circ K}}$$

92. Calculate ΔS_{surr} for each of the following reactions at 100 K:

    a. $\Delta H^o_{rxn} = -165.7\ kJ$

    $$\Delta S_{surr} = -\frac{\Delta H^o_{rxn}}{T} = -\frac{-165.7\frac{kJ}{mol}}{100\ K} \times \frac{1000\ J}{1\ kJ} = \mathbf{1657}\ \frac{\boldsymbol{J}}{\boldsymbol{mol\ \circ K}}$$

    b. $\Delta H^o_{rxn} = -14.23\ kJ$

    $$\Delta S_{surr} = -\frac{\Delta H^o_{rxn}}{T} = -\frac{-14.23\frac{kJ}{mol}}{100\ K} \times \frac{1000\ J}{1\ kJ} = \mathbf{142.3}\ \frac{\boldsymbol{J}}{\boldsymbol{mol\ \circ K}}$$

c. $\Delta H^o_{rxn} = +165.7 \ kJ$

$$\Delta S_{surr} = -\frac{\Delta H^o_{rxn}}{T} = -\frac{165.7\frac{kJ}{mol}}{100 \ K} \times \frac{1000 \ J}{1 \ kJ} = \mathbf{-1657} \ \frac{\textbf{J}}{\textbf{mol} \circ \textbf{K}}$$

d. $\Delta H^o_{rxn} = +14.23 \ kJ$

$$\Delta S_{surr} = -\frac{\Delta H^o_{rxn}}{T} = -\frac{14.23\frac{kJ}{mol}}{100 \ K} \times \frac{1000 \ J}{1 \ kJ} = \mathbf{-142.3} \ \frac{\textbf{J}}{\textbf{mol} \circ \textbf{K}}$$

93. Calculate ΔS_{univ} for each of the following reactions and indicate whether the reaction will proceed spontaneously:

a. $\Delta H^o_{rxn} = +120.0 \ kJ; \ \Delta S^o_{rxn} = -310J \ / \ mol \cdot K; \ T = 298 \ K$

$$\Delta S_{surr} = -\frac{\Delta H^o_{rxn}}{T} = -\frac{120.0\frac{kJ}{mol}}{298 \ K} \times \frac{1000 \ J}{1 \ kJ} = -402.7 \ \frac{J}{mol \cdot K}$$

$$\Delta S_{univ} = \Delta S^o_{rxn} + \Delta S_{surr} = -310\frac{J}{mol \cdot K} - 402.7\frac{J}{mol \cdot K} = \mathbf{-712.7}\frac{\textbf{J}}{\textbf{mol} \circ \textbf{K}}$$

$\Delta S_{univ} < 0$, therefore, the reaction is not spontaneous.

b. $\Delta H^o_{rxn} = -120.0 \ kJ; \ \Delta S^o_{rxn} = +310J \ / \ K; \ T = 298 \ K$

$$\Delta S_{surr} = -\frac{\Delta H^o_{rxn}}{T} = -\frac{-120.0\frac{kJ}{mol}}{298 \ K} \times \frac{1000 \ J}{1 \ kJ} = +402.7 \ \frac{J}{mol \cdot K}$$

$$\Delta S_{univ} = \Delta S^o_{rxn} + \Delta S_{surr} = +310\frac{J}{mol \cdot K} + 402.7\frac{J}{mol \cdot K} = \mathbf{712.7}\frac{\textbf{J}}{\textbf{mol} \circ \textbf{K}}$$

$\Delta S_{univ} > 0$, therefore, the reaction is spontaneous.

c. $\Delta H^o_{rxn} = -120.0 \ kJ; \ \Delta S^o_{rxn} = -310J \ / \ K; \ T = 100 \ K$

$$\Delta S_{surr} = -\frac{\Delta H^o_{rxn}}{T} = -\frac{-120.0\frac{kJ}{mol}}{100 \ K} \times \frac{1000 \ J}{1 \ kJ} = +1200. \ \frac{J}{mol \cdot K}$$

$$\Delta S_{univ} = \Delta S^o_{rxn} + \Delta S_{surr} = -310\frac{J}{mol \cdot K} + 1200.\frac{J}{mol \cdot K} = \mathbf{890}\frac{\textbf{J}}{\textbf{mol} \circ \textbf{K}}$$

$\Delta S_{univ} > 0$, therefore, the reaction is spontaneous.

d. $\Delta H^{o}_{rxn} = -120.0 \; kJ; \; \Delta S^{o}_{rxn} = -310 J \; / \; K; \; T = 500 K$

$$\Delta S_{surr} = -\frac{\Delta H^{o}_{rxn}}{T} = -\frac{-120.0\frac{kJ}{mol}}{500 \; K} \times \frac{1000 \; J}{1 \; kJ} = -1200. \; \frac{J}{mol \cdot K}$$

$$\Delta S_{univ} = \Delta S^{o}_{rxn} + \Delta S_{surr} = -310\frac{J}{mol \cdot K} - 1200.\frac{J}{mol \cdot K} = \mathbf{-1510\frac{J}{mol \; \circ K}}$$

$\Delta S_{univ} < 0$, **therefore, the reaction is not spontaneous.**

94. Calculate the ΔS^{o}_{rxn} for the following reaction using the data presented in Appendix II:

$$C \; (s) + H_2O \; (g) \rightarrow CO \; (g) + H_2 \; (g)$$

From Appendix II, we get the following S^{o} values:

$$C \; (s) = 5.7\frac{J}{mol \cdot K}$$

$$H_2O \; (g) = 188.8\frac{J}{mol \cdot K}$$

$$CO \; (g) = 197.7\frac{J}{mol \cdot K}$$

$$H_2 \; (g) = 130.7 \; \frac{J}{mol \cdot K}$$

$$\Delta S^{o}_{rxn} = \sum (nS^{o})_{prod} - \sum (nS^{o})_{react}$$

$$\Delta S^{o}_{rxn} = \left[\left(197.7 \; \frac{J}{mol \cdot K}\right) + \left(130.7 \; \frac{J}{mol \cdot K}\right)\right] - \left[\left(5.7\frac{J}{mol \cdot K}\right) + \left(188.8\frac{J}{mol \cdot K}\right)\right] = \mathbf{133.9 \; \frac{J}{mol \; \circ K}}$$

95. Calculate the ΔS^{o}_{rxn} for the following reaction using the data presented in Appendix II:

$$N_2 \; (g) + O_2 \; (g) \rightarrow 2NO \; (g)$$

From Appendix II, we get the following S^{o} values:

$$N_2 \; (g) = 191.6\frac{J}{mol \cdot K}$$

$$O_2 \; (g) = 205.2\frac{J}{mol \cdot K}$$

$$NO \; (g) = 210.8\frac{J}{mol \cdot K}$$

$$\Delta S^o_{rxn} = \sum (nS^o)_{prod} - \sum (nS^o)_{react}$$

$$\Delta S^o_{rxn} = \left[2 \times \left(210.8 \frac{J}{mol \cdot K} \right) \right] - \left[\left(191.6 \frac{J}{mol \cdot K} \right) + \left(205.2 \frac{J}{mol \cdot K} \right) \right] = 24.8 \ \frac{J}{mol \cdot K}$$

96. Calculate the ΔS^o_{rxn} for the following reaction using the data presented in Appendix II:

$$CaCO_3 \ (s) \rightarrow CaO \ (s) + CO_2 \ (g)$$

From Appendix II, we get the following S^o values:

$$CaCO_3 \ (s) = 91.7 \ \frac{J}{mol \cdot K}$$

$$CaO \ (s) = 38.1 \frac{J}{mol \cdot K}$$

$$CO_2 \ (g) = 213.8 \ \frac{J}{mol \cdot K}$$

$$\Delta S^o_{rxn} = \sum (nS^o)_{prod} - \sum (nS^o)_{react}$$

$$\Delta S^o_{rxn} = \left[\left(38.1 \frac{J}{mol \cdot K} \right) + \left(213.8 \ \frac{J}{mol \cdot K} \right) \right] - \left[\left(91.7 \ \frac{J}{mol \cdot K} \right) \right] = 160.2 \ \frac{J}{mol \cdot K}$$

97. Calculate the ΔS^o_{rxn} for the following reaction using the data presented in Appendix II:

$$2H_2S \ (g) + 3O_2 \ (g) \rightarrow 2SO_2 \ (g) + 2H_2O \ (l)$$

From Appendix II, we get the following S^o values:

$$H_2S \ (g) = 205.8 \ \frac{J}{mol \cdot K}$$

$$O_2 \ (g) = 205.2 \frac{J}{mol \cdot K}$$

$$SO_2 \ (g) = 248.2 \ \frac{J}{mol \cdot K}$$

$$H_2O \ (l) = 69.9 \ \frac{J}{mol \cdot K}$$

$$\Delta S^o_{rxn} = \sum (nS^o)_{prod} - \sum (nS^o)_{react}$$

$$\Delta S^o_{rxn} = \left[\left(2 \times 248.2 \ \frac{J}{mol \cdot K} \right) + \left(2 \times 69.9 \ \frac{J}{mol \cdot K} \right) \right] - \left[\left(2 \times 205.8 \ \frac{J}{mol \cdot K} \right) + \left(3 \times 205.2 \ \frac{J}{mol \cdot K} \right) \right]$$

$$= -391.0 \ \frac{J}{mol \cdot K}$$

THE GIBBS FREE ENERGY

98. What is meant by "free" energy?

"Free" energy is the maximum amount of available energy to do work.

99. Would you predict a particular reaction would or would not be spontaneous if you knew that it had a negative ΔH and a positive ΔS?

A negative ΔH and a positive ΔS would indicate an exothermic system which would be spontaneous at any temperature.

100. Would you predict a particular reaction would or would not be spontaneous if you knew that it had a negative ΔH and a negative ΔS?

A negative ΔH and a negative ΔS would mean that the system would be spontaneous only at lower temperatures.

101. Would you predict a particular reaction would or would not be spontaneous if you knew that it had a positive ΔH and a positive ΔS?

A positive ΔH and a positive ΔS would mean that the system would be spontaneous only at higher temperatures.

102. Would you predict a particular reaction would or would not be spontaneous if you knew that it had a positive ΔH and a negative ΔS?

A positive ΔH and a negative ΔS would result in an endothermic system which would be nonspontaneous at any temperature.

103. A particular reaction carried out at 298 K has a $\Delta H = -108\ kJ$ and $\Delta S = +286\ J\ /\ K$. What is the Gibbs free energy of the reaction? Is the reaction spontaneous? If not, at what temperature would this reaction be spontaneous?

First, we convert entropy from J/K to kJ/K:

$$\frac{286\ J}{K} \times \frac{1\ kJ}{1000\ J} = 0.286\frac{kJ}{K}$$

Now we solve for the Gibbs free energy:

$$\Delta G^{o}_{rxn} = \Delta H^{o}_{rxn} - T\Delta S^{o}_{rxn}$$

$$\Delta G = (-108\ kJ) - \left(298\ K \times 0.286\frac{kJ}{K}\right)$$

$$\Delta G^{o}_{rxn} = \mathbf{-193\ kJ}$$

Since we have a negative ΔG, this reaction is spontaneous, and because it has a negative ΔH with a positive ΔS we expect this reaction to be spontaneous at any temperature.

104. A particular reaction has a $\Delta H = -108\ kJ$ and $\Delta S = -286\ J/K$ and is carried out at 298 K. What is the Gibbs free energy of the reaction? Is the reaction spontaneous? If not, at what temperature would this reaction be spontaneous?

First, we convert entropy from J/K to kJ/K:

$$\frac{-286\ J}{K} \times \frac{1\ kJ}{1000\ J} = -0.286\frac{kJ}{K}$$

Now we solve for the Gibbs free energy:

$$\Delta G^o_{rxn} = \Delta H^o_{rxn} - T\Delta S^o_{rxn}$$

$$\Delta G^o_{rxn} = (-108\ kJ) - (298\ K)\left(-0.286\frac{kJ}{K}\right)$$

$$\Delta G^o_{rxn} = \textbf{-23 kJ}$$

Since we have a negative ΔG, this reaction is spontaneous at this temperature. However, to determine the temperature at which this reaction becomes nonspontaneous, we simply set ΔG to zero and solve for temperature.

$$\Delta G_{rxn} = \Delta H_{rxn} - T\Delta S_{rxn}$$

$$T = \frac{\Delta G_{rxn} - \Delta H_{rxn}}{-\Delta S_{rxn}}$$

$$T = \frac{0 - (-108\ kJ)}{0.286\frac{kJ}{K}} = 378\ K$$

This reaction is spontaneous at temperatures below 378 K. Temperatures higher than 378 K result in a nonspontaneous reaction.

105. A particular reaction has a $\Delta H = +108\ kJ$ and $\Delta S = +286\ J/K$ and is carried out at 298 K. What is the Gibbs free energy of the reaction? Is the reaction spontaneous? If not, at what temperature would this reaction be spontaneous?

First, we convert entropy from J/K to kJ/K:

$$\frac{286\ J}{K} \times \frac{1\ kJ}{1000\ J} = 0.286\frac{kJ}{K}$$

Now we solve for the Gibbs free energy:

$$\Delta G^o_{rxn} = \Delta H^o_{rxn} - T\Delta S^o_{rxn}$$

$$\Delta G = (+108\ kJ) - \left(298\ K \times 0.286\frac{kJ}{K}\right)$$

$$\Delta G^o_{rxn} = \textbf{+23 kJ}$$

Since we have a positive ΔG, this reaction is nonspontaneous. To determine the temperature at which this reaction becomes spontaneous, we simply set ΔG to zero and solve for temperature.

$$\Delta G_{rxn} = \Delta H_{rxn} - T\Delta S_{rxn}$$

$$T = \frac{\Delta G_{rxn} - \Delta H_{rxn}}{-\Delta S_{rxn}}$$

$$T = \frac{0 - (+108\ )kJ}{-0.286\dfrac{kJ}{K}} = 378\ K$$

This reaction becomes spontaneous at a temperature at or above 378 K.

106. Calculate the Gibbs free energy for the following reaction at 298 K:

$$C\ (s) + H_2O\ (g) \rightarrow CO\ (g) + H_2\ (g)$$

$$\Delta H^o_{rxn} = 131.3\ kJ;\ \Delta S^o_{rxn} = 133.9\ J/K$$

We convert entropy from J/K to kJ/K:

$$\frac{133.9\ J}{K} \times \frac{1\ kJ}{1000\ J} = 0.1339\ \frac{kJ}{K}$$

$$\Delta G^o_{rxn} = \Delta H^o_{rxn} - T\Delta S^o_{rxn}$$

$$\Delta G = (+131.3\ kJ) - \left(298\ K \times 0.1339\frac{kJ}{K} \right)$$

$$\Delta G^o_{rxn} = \textbf{+91.4 kJ}$$

107. Calculate the Gibbs free energy for the following reaction at 298 K:

$$N_2\ (g) + O_2\ (g) \rightarrow 2NO\ (g)$$

$$\Delta H^o_{rxn} = 182.6\ kJ;\ \Delta S^o_{rxn} = 24.8\ J/K$$

We convert entropy from J/K to kJ/K:

$$\frac{24.8\ J}{K} \times \frac{1\ kJ}{1000\ J} = 0.0248\frac{kJ}{K}$$

$$\Delta G^o_{rxn} = \Delta H^o_{rxn} - T\Delta S^o_{rxn}$$

$$\Delta G = (+182.6\ kJ) - \left(298\ K \times 0.0248\frac{kJ}{K} \right)$$

$$\Delta G^o_{rxn} = \textbf{+175.2 kJ}$$

108. Calculate the Gibbs free energy for the following reaction at 298 K:

$$CaCO_3 \ (s) \rightarrow CaO \ (s) + CO_2 \ (g)$$

$$\Delta H^o_{rxn} = 179.2 \ kJ; \ \Delta S^o_{rxn} = 160.2 \ J \ / \ K$$

We convert entropy from J/K to kJ/K:

$$\frac{160.2 \ J}{K} \times \frac{1 \ kJ}{1000 \ J} = 0.1602 \frac{kJ}{K}$$

$$\Delta G^o_{rxn} = \Delta H^o_{rxn} - T\Delta S^o_{rxn}$$

$$\Delta G = (+179.2 \ kJ) - \left(298 \ K \times 0.1602 \frac{kJ}{K} \right)$$

$$\Delta G^o_{rxn} = \textbf{+131.5 } \textbf{\textit{kJ}}$$

109. Calculate the Gibbs free energy for the following reaction at 298 K:

$$2H_2S \ (g) + 3O_2 \ (g) \rightarrow 2SO_2 \ (g) + 2H_2O \ (l)$$

$$\Delta H^o_{rxn} = -1124.0 \ kJ; \ \Delta S^o_{rxn} = -391.0 \ J/K$$

We convert entropy from J/K to kJ/K:

$$\frac{-391.0 \ J}{K} \times \frac{1 \ kJ}{1000 \ J} = -0.3910 \frac{kJ}{K}$$

$$\Delta G^o_{rxn} = \Delta H^o_{rxn} - T\Delta S^o_{rxn}$$

$$\Delta G = (-1124.0 \ kJ) - \left(298 \ K \times -0.3910 \frac{kJ}{K} \right)$$

$$\Delta G^o_{rxn} = \textbf{-1007.5 } \textbf{\textit{kJ}}$$

GIBBS FREE ENERGY AND NONSTANDARD CONDITIONS

110. Consider the reaction depicted in the following chemical equation at 298 K:

$$N_2 \ (g) + O_2 \ (g) \rightarrow 2 \ NO \ (g) \qquad \Delta G^o_{rxn} = 175.2 \ kJ \cdot mol^{-1}$$

a. Calculate the equilibrium constant for this reaction at 298 K.

$$\Delta G^{o}_{rxn} = -RT\ln K$$

$$\ln K = \frac{\Delta G^{o}_{rxn}}{-RT}$$

$$\ln K = \frac{-\left(175.2\dfrac{kJ}{mol}\right)}{\left(8.314\dfrac{J}{mol \cdot K}\right)\left(\dfrac{1\ kJ}{1000\ J}\right)(298\ K)} = -70.71$$

$$K = e^{-70.71} = \mathbf{1.95 \times 10^{-31}}$$

b. If the initial partial pressures of the reactants and products are as listed below, calculate ΔG_{rxn} under these conditions and predict whether the reaction will be expected to proceed spontaneously in the forward direction as written.

$$P_{N_2} = 0.650\ atm$$

$$P_{O_2} = 0.150\ atm$$

$$P_{NO} = 0.450\ atm$$

$$\Delta G_{rxn} = \Delta G^{o}_{rxn} + RT\ln Q$$

$$Q = \frac{\left(P_{NO}\right)^2}{P_{O_2} \cdot P_{N_2}} = \frac{(0.450)^2}{(0.150)(0.650)} = 2.077$$

$$\Delta G_{rxn} = 175.2\frac{kJ}{mol} + \left(8.314\frac{J}{mol \cdot K}\right)\left(\frac{1\ kJ}{1000\ J}\right)(298\ K)\ln 2.077 = \mathbf{177\ kJ \cdot mol^{-1}}$$

Nonspontaneous

111. Consider the reaction depicted in the following chemical equation at 298 K:

$$C\ (s) + H_2O\ (g) \rightarrow CO\ (g) + H_2\ (g) \qquad \Delta G^{o}_{rxn} = 91.4\ kJ \cdot mol^{-1}$$

a. Calculate the equilibrium constant for this reaction at 298 K.

$$\Delta G^{o}_{rxn} = -RT\ln K$$

$$\ln K = \frac{\Delta G^{o}_{rxn}}{-RT}$$

$$\ln K = \frac{-\left(91.4\dfrac{kJ}{mol}\right)}{\left(8.314\dfrac{J}{mol \cdot K}\right)\left(\dfrac{1\ kJ}{1000\ J}\right)(298\ K)} = -36.89$$

$$K = e^{-36.89} = \mathbf{9.53 \times 10^{-17}}$$

b. If the initial partial pressures of the reactants and products are as listed below, calculate ΔG_{rxn} under these conditions and predict whether the reaction will be expected to proceed spontaneously in the forward direction as written.

$$P_{H_2O} = 0.250 \ atm$$

$$P_{H_2} = 0.250 \ atm$$

$$P_{CO} = 0.250 \ atm$$

$$\Delta G_{rxn} = \Delta G_{rxn}^{o} + RT \ln Q$$

$$Q = \frac{P_{H_2} \cdot P_{CO}}{P_{H_2O}} = \frac{(0.250)^2}{(0.250)} = 0.250$$

$$\Delta G_{rxn} = 91.4 \frac{kJ}{mol} + \left(8.314 \frac{J}{mol \cdot K} \right) \left(\frac{1 \ kJ}{1000 \ J} \right) (298 \ K) \ln 0.250 = \textbf{88.0 } \textit{kJ} \circ \textit{mol}^{-1}$$

Nonspontaneous

112. Consider the reaction depicted in the following chemical equation at 298 K:

$$Br_2(g) + Cl_2(g) \rightarrow 2 \ BrCl(g) \qquad \Delta G_{rxn}^{o} = -1.1 \ kJ \cdot mol^{-1}$$

a. Calculate the equilibrium constant for this reaction at 298 K.

$$\Delta G_{rxn}^{o} = -RT \ln K$$

$$\ln K = \frac{\Delta G_{rxn}^{o}}{-RT}$$

$$\ln K = \frac{-\left(-1.1 \frac{kJ}{mol} \right)}{\left(8.314 \frac{J}{mol \cdot K} \right) \left(\frac{1 \ kJ}{1000 \ J} \right) (298 \ K)} = 0.444$$

$$K = e^{0.444} = \textbf{1.56}$$

b. If the initial partial pressures of the reactants and products are as listed below, calculate ΔG_{rxn} under these conditions and predict whether the reaction will be expected to proceed spontaneously in the forward direction as written.

$$P_{Br_2} = 0.500 \ atm$$

$$P_{Cl_2} = 0.100 \ atm$$

$$P_{BrCl} = 1.00 \ atm$$

$$\Delta G_{rxn} = \Delta G_{rxn}^{o} + RT\ln Q$$

$$Q = \frac{\left(P_{BrCl}\right)^2}{P_{Cl_2} \cdot P_{Br_2}} = \frac{(1.00)^2}{(0.100)(0.500)} = 20.0$$

$$\Delta G_{rxn} = -1.1\frac{kJ}{mol} + \left(8.314\frac{J}{mol \cdot K}\right)\left(\frac{1\,kJ}{1000\,J}\right)(298\,K)\ln 20.0 = \textbf{6.32 kJ} \circ \textbf{mol}^{-1}$$

Nonspontaneous

113. The enthalpy (ΔH_{rxn}^{o}) for a reaction is –20.5 kJ/mol. If the equilibrium constant of this reaction is 3.2×10^3 at 298 K, what is the equilibrium constant at 400 K?

$$\ln\frac{K_2}{K_1} = -\frac{\Delta H^{o}}{R}\left(\frac{1}{T_2} - \frac{1}{T_1}\right)$$

$$\ln K_2 = \ln K_1 - \frac{\Delta H^{o}}{R}\left(\frac{1}{T_2} - \frac{1}{T_1}\right)$$

$$\ln K_2 = \ln(3200) - \frac{\left(-20.5\frac{kJ}{mol}\right)}{\left(8.314\frac{J}{mol \cdot K}\right)\left(\frac{1\,kJ}{1000\,J}\right)}\left(\frac{1}{400\,K} - \frac{1}{298\,K}\right)$$

$$\ln K_2 = 5.96098$$

$$K_2 = e^{5.96098}$$

$$\boldsymbol{K_2 = 388}$$

114. A reaction has an equilibrium constant of 30.2 at 298 K, what is ΔH_{rxn}^{o} if the equilibrium constant at 800 K is 1455?

$$\ln\frac{K_2}{K_1} = -\frac{\Delta H^{o}}{R}\left(\frac{1}{T_2} - \frac{1}{T_1}\right)$$

$$\Delta H^{o} = \frac{-R\left(\ln\frac{K_2}{K_1}\right)}{\left(\frac{1}{T_2} - \frac{1}{T_1}\right)} = \frac{-\left(8.314\frac{J}{mol \cdot K}\right)\left(\frac{1\,kJ}{1000\,J}\right)\left(\ln\frac{30.2}{1455}\right)}{\left(\frac{1}{800\,K} - \frac{1}{298\,K}\right)} = \textbf{–15.3 kJ} \cdot \textbf{mol}^{-1}$$

$$\ln K_2 = \ln(3200) - \frac{\left(-20.5\frac{kJ}{mol}\right)}{\left(8.314\frac{J}{mol \cdot K}\right)\left(\frac{1\,kJ}{1000\,J}\right)}\left(\frac{1}{400\,K} - \frac{1}{298\,K}\right)$$

$$\ln K_2 = 5.96098$$

$$K_2 = e^{5.96098}$$

$$\boldsymbol{K_2 = 388}$$

KEY TERMS

Bomb calorimetry (also called Constant-volume calorimetry) Calorimetry experiments wherein measurements are made using an apparatus commonly referred to as a bomb calorimeter.

Bomb calorimeter A piece of equipment specifically designed to measure ΔE, most commonly for combustion reactions.

Bond energy The energy required to homolytically break a particular bond in 1 mole of a molecule in the gaseous state.

Bond strength See bond energy.

Born-Haber cycle A method for calculating lattice energies of ionic solids. The method takes its name from its developers, Max Born (Chapter 7) and Fritz Haber, and is based on Hess's Law. For any given ionic solid, a series of theoretical steps can be defined which precede the formation of the solid lattice from gaseous ions.

Calorie A unit of energy defined as the energy required to raise the temperature of 1 gram of water by 1°C.

Calorimetry An apparatus which is used to perform chemical reactions under controlled conditions such that temperature changes can be carefully measured.

Calorimetry The scientific discipline directed toward the measurement of heat.

Chemical energy The potential energy associated with chemical composition, the relative distributions of electrons and nuclei in atoms and molecules.

Coffee cup calorimetry (also called constant-pressure calorimetry) In a typical experiment, reactants are delivered into the reactor (all reactant solutions at the same initial temperature). The reaction mixture is stirred, and the temperature is monitored, and a final temperature is recorded. Again, we are not directly measuring a temperature change for the system but for the surroundings. Also, because such experiments are carried out under constant pressure (atmospheric pressure), coffee cup calorimetry experiments are used to determine the enthalpies of reaction (ΔH_{rxi}).

Constant-pressure calorimetry Calorimetry measurements carried out under conditions of constant pressure wherein measurements are made using an apparatus commonly referred to as a coffee cup calorimeter. Also, because such experiments are carried out under constant pressure (atmospheric pressure), coffee cup calorimetry experiments are used to determine the enthalpies of reaction (ΔH_{rxi}).

Constant-volume calorimetry Calorimetry measurements carried out under conditions of constant volume wherein measurements are made using an apparatus commonly referred to as a bomb calorimeter.

Endothermic A term referring to chemical reactions which exhibit a positive reaction enthalpy.

Energy The capacity to do work.

Enthalpy The sum of the internal energy of a system plus the product of its pressure and volume under conditions of constant pressure.

Enthalpy of reaction   The enthalpy change for a chemical reaction.

Enthalpy of solution   The heat (absorbed or released) when a solute is dissolved in a solvent.

Entropy   The measure of the distribution or dispersal of energy within a system at a given temperature. This can be understood a little more informally as a measure of the "disorder" of a system.

Exothermic   A term referring to chemical reactions which exhibit a negative reaction enthalpy.

Extensive property   A property that depends on the mass or amount of matter in the system.

First law of thermodynamics   The total energy in the universe is a constant and cannot be altered due to any process. In other words, energy can neither be created nor destroyed.

Formation reaction   The formation of *1 mole* of a compound from its constituent elements in their standard states.

Gibbs free energy   The enthalpy of a system minus the product of temperature (in Kelvin) and the entropy at constant temperature.

Heat   The transfer of thermal energy (measured in joules) between two objects due to a temperature difference (or gradient).

Heat capacity   The amount of energy required to raise the temperature of the system by 1°C (assuming ΔT is measured in °C).

Heat of hydration   The change in enthalpy associated with solvation (by water) of 1 mole of ions in the gaseous state.

Heat of reaction   See enthalpy of reaction.

Heat of solution   See enthalpy of solution.

Heat of solvation   The change in enthalpy associated with solvation of 1 mole of ions in the gaseous state.

Hess's law   The enthalpy change of an overall chemical process is equal to the sum of the enthalpy changes for individual steps in that process.

Intensive properties   A property that does not depend on the mass or amount of matter in the system.

Internal energy   The internal energy of a system is defined as the sum of all of the potential and kinetic energies of all the particles which constitute the system.

Joule   A unit of energy equal to 1 newton-meter.

Kinetic energy   The energy associated with, or due to, motion.

Lattice energy   The energy required to separate 1 mole of an ionic solid into ions in the gaseous state.

Potential energy   The energy associated with, or due to, composition or position.

Pressure-volume work   Work done through expansion or compression of gases.

Second law of thermodynamics   Entropy of the universe increases due to a spontaneous process.

Specific heat capacity   An *intensive* property and given in units of $\dfrac{J}{g \cdot {}^\circ C}$. The specific heat capacity is the amount of heat (in joules) required to raise the temperature of 1 gram of a substance by 1°C.

Spontaneous   A process which proceeds without any outside intervention.

Standard enthalpy of formation   The enthalpy change associated with the standard formation reaction of a substance.

Standard enthalpy of reaction   The enthalpy change corresponding to a reaction at constant pressure (1 bar) wherein all reactants and products are in their respective standard states.

Standard entropy of reaction   The entropy change corresponding to a reaction at constant pressure (1 bar) wherein all reactants and products are in their respective standard states.

Standard free energy of formation   The free energy change associated with the standard formation reaction of a substance.

Standard free energy of reaction   The change in free energy for a reaction under standard conditions wherein reactants and products are in their standard states.

Standard heat of formation   See standard enthalpy of formation.

Standard heat of reaction   See standard enthalpy of reaction.

Standard molar entropy   The absolute entropy of 1 mole of substance in its standard state.

State function   A property that depends only on the current state of the system in question.

Surroundings   Everything in the Universe which is outside the system.

System   The portion of the Universe which is under observation.

Thermochemical equation   A balanced chemical equation which includes the enthalpy change which corresponds to the chemical change described by the equation.

Thermochemistry   The field of thermodynamics which deals with the energy changes associated with chemical changes.

Thermodynamics   The scientific discipline that is concerned with the transfer of energy from one system to another, and its transformation from one form to another.

Thermal equilibrium   The circumstance wherein the system and surroundings have reached the same temperature and there is no longer any net transfer of thermal energy or heat.

Third law of thermodynamics   The entropy of perfect crystalline substance is zero at a temperature of 0 K, absolute zero.

Work   A force acting over a distance.

Oxidation-Reduction and Electrochemistry

CHAPTER

13

KEY CONCEPTS

- Oxidation-Reduction Reactions
- Oxidation Numbers and Their Assignment
- Identifying Redox Reactions from Oxidation Number Assignments
- Oxidizing and Reducing Agents
- Balancing Redox Reactions under Acidic and Basic Conditions Using the Half-Reaction Method
- Galvanic Cells
- Standard Reduction Potentials and Cell Potentials
- Standard Reduction Potentials and Gibbs Free Energy
- Standard Reduction Potentials and Equilibrium Constants
- Electrolysis and Electrolytic Cells

OXIDATION-REDUCTION (REDOX) REACTIONS

1. What is reduction?

   The gain of electrons is referred to as reduction.

2. What is oxidation?

   Oxidation is defined as the loss of electrons.

3. What is an oxidation number?

   We define oxidation numbers as imaginary charges which are assigned based on a set of rules. These are determined by assigning shared (bonding) electrons in covalent species to the atoms with greatest electronegativity.

4. How do we use oxidation numbers to identify redox reactions?

   Redox reactions are characterized by the transfer of electrons from one element to another. Elements undergoing oxidation or reduction will necessarily exhibit different oxidation states in the reactants and products, indicating a redox reaction has occurred. Elements will have higher oxidation numbers in the products when they have undergone oxidation and vice versa.

5. Define the term reducing agent.

   The reactant which contains the element which is reduced is referred to as the oxidizing agent (electron acceptor).

6. Define the term oxidizing agent.

   The reactant containing the element which is oxidized is the reducing agent (electron donor).

7. Assign oxidation numbers to the elements in the following:
   a. *CsBr*

      $Cs = +1$

      $Br = -1$

      The first specific rule states that cesium will have an O.N. of +1. General rule 3 therefore requires the oxidation number of Cl to be -1.

   b. H_2CO_3

      $H = +1$

      $O = -2$

      $C = +4$

      Specific rules 4 and 5 tell us that hydrogen will have an oxidation number of +1 and oxygen will have an oxidation number -2. General rule 3 therefore requires that carbon is assigned an oxidation number of +4.

c. Na_2O_2

$Na = +1$

$O = -1$

8. Assign oxidation numbers to the elements in the following:

a. $SrBr_2$

$Sr = +2$

$Br = -1$

b. H_2SO_4

$H = +1$

$O = -2$

$S = +6$

c. $KMnO_4$

$K = +1$

$Mn = +7$

$O = -2$

9. Assign oxidation numbers to the elements in the following:

a. Cl_2

$Cl = 0$

b. Mg^{2+}

$Mg^{2+} = +2$

c. NO_2

$N = +4$

$O = -2$

10. Assign oxidation numbers to the elements in the following:

a. PCl_5

$P = +5$

$Cl = -1$

b. BrO_3^-

$O = -2$

$Br = +5$

c. H_3BO_3

$H = +1$

$B = +3$

$O = -2$

11. Determine whether the following reaction is a redox reaction. If so, identify the oxidizing and reducing agents.

$$2\ Na(s) + Cl_2(g) \rightarrow 2NaCl(s)$$

$$\overset{0}{2\ Na(s)} + \overset{0}{Cl_2} \rightarrow \overset{+1\ \ -1}{2\ NaCl(s)}$$

We can see from the assignment of oxidation numbers that sodium is oxidized and chlorine is reduced. Therefore, this is a redox reaction and:

$Na(s)$ = reducing agent

$Cl_2(g)$ = oxidizing agent .

12. Determine whether the following reaction is a redox reaction. If so, identify the oxidizing and reducing agents.

$$Mg(s) + 2\ H_2O(l) \rightarrow Mg(OH)_2(aq) + H_2(g)$$

$$\overset{0}{Mg(s)} + \overset{+1\ \ -2}{2\ H_2O(l)} \rightarrow \overset{+2\ -2\ +1}{Mg(OH)_2(aq)} + \overset{0}{H_2(g)}$$

We can see from the assignment of oxidation numbers that magnesium is oxidized and hydrogen is reduced. Therefore this is a redox reaction and:

$Mg(s)$ = reducing agent

$H_2O(l)$ = oxidizing agent .

13. Determine whether the following reaction is a redox reaction. If so, identify the oxidizing and reducing agents.

$$2\ NaOH(aq) + H_2SO_4(aq) \rightarrow Na_2SO_4(aq) + 2\ H_2O(l)$$

$$\overset{+1-2+1}{2\ NaOH(aq)} + \overset{+1+6-2}{H_2SO_4(aq)} \rightarrow \overset{+1+6-2}{Na_2SO_4(aq)} + \overset{+1\ -2}{2\ H_2O(l)}$$

Not a redox reaction.

14. Determine whether the following reaction is a redox reaction. If so, identify the oxidizing and reducing agents.

$$C_3H_8(g) + 5\ O_2(g) \rightarrow 3\ CO_2(g) + 4\ H_2O(g)$$

$$\overset{-\frac{8}{3}+1}{C_3H_8(g)} + \overset{0}{5\ O_2(g)} \rightarrow \overset{+4-2}{3\ CO_2(g)} + \overset{+1\ -2}{4\ H_2O(g)}$$

In this case we have a fractional oxidation number for carbon. This indicates that there are mixed oxidation states respecting carbon in this compound. Nevertheless, we clearly see that carbon is oxidized and oxygen is reduced. We therefore have a redox reaction:

$C_3H_8(g)$ = reducing agent

$O_2(g)$ = oxidizing agent .

BALANCING REDOX REACTIONS

15. Define the term half-reaction.

A redox reaction can be divided into two chemical reactions, one representing oxidation and the other reduction. These are referred to as half-reactions.

16. Balance the following half-reactions:

    a. $NiO_2(s) \rightarrow Ni^{2+}(aq)$ (acidic conditions)

First, we see that all "non-hydrogen" and "non-oxygen" atoms are already balanced. So we balance oxygen atoms by adding waters:

$$NiO_2(s) \rightarrow Ni^{2+}(aq) + 2\ H_2O(l)$$

We then balance hydrogens with hydrogen cations:

$$NiO_2(s) + 4\ H^+(aq) \rightarrow Ni^{2+}(aq) + 2\ H_2O(l)$$

Since we are under acidic conditions we are now finished with balancing according to mass. We now add electrons in order to balance according to charge.

$$\mathbf{NiO_2(s) + 4\ H^+(aq) + 2\ e^- \rightarrow Ni^{2+}(aq) + 2\ H_2O(l)}$$

We now have a properly balanced half-reaction under acidic conditions with a balanced net charge of +2 on both the reactant and product side of the reaction arrow.

    b. $N_2H_4(aq) \rightarrow N_2(g)$ (basic conditions)

First, we see that all "non-hydrogen" and "non-oxygen" atoms are already balanced. So we balance hydrogens with hydrogen cations:

$$N_2H_4(aq) \rightarrow N_2(g) + 4\ H^+(aq)$$

We are now finished with balancing according to mass. We now add electrons in order to balance according to charge:

$$N_2H_4(aq) \rightarrow N_2(g) + 4\ H^+(aq) + 4\ e^-$$

We now have a properly balanced half-reaction under acidic conditions with a balanced net charge of 0 on both the reactant and product side of the reaction arrow. However, this reaction is to be balanced under basic conditions so we will neutralize all hydrogen cations with hydroxide anions:

$$\mathbf{N_2H_4(aq) + 4\ OH^-(aq) \rightarrow N_2(g) + 4\ H_2O(l) + 4\ e^-}$$

We now have a properly balanced half-reaction under basic conditions.

17. Balance the following half-reactions:

    a. $IO_3^-(aq) \rightarrow I^-(aq)$ (acidic conditions)

First, we see that all "non-hydrogen" and "non-oxygen" atoms are already balanced. So we balance oxygen atoms by adding waters:

$$IO_3^-(aq) \rightarrow I^-(aq) + 3\ H_2O(l)$$

We then balance hydrogens with hydrogen cations:

$$IO_3^- (aq) + 6\ H^+(aq) \rightarrow I^-(aq) + 3\ H_2O(l)$$

Since we are under acidic conditions we are now finished with balancing according to mass. We now add electrons in order to balance according to charge:

$$\boldsymbol{IO_3^- (aq) + 6\ H^+(aq) + 6\ e^- \rightarrow I^-(aq) + 3\ H_2O(l)}$$

We now have a properly balanced half-reaction under acidic conditions with a balanced net charge of −1 on both the reactant and product side of the reaction arrow.

b. $ClO^- (aq) \rightarrow Cl^- (aq)$ (basic conditions)

First, we see that all "non-hydrogen" and "non-oxygen" atoms are already balanced. So we balance oxygen atoms by adding waters:

$$ClO^- (aq) \rightarrow Cl^- (aq) + H_2O(l)$$

We then balance hydrogens with hydrogen cations:

$$ClO^- (aq) + 2\ H^+ (aq) \rightarrow Cl^- (aq) + H_2O(l)$$

We are now finished with balancing according to mass. We now add electrons in order to balance according to charge:

$$ClO^- (aq) + 2\ H^+ (aq) + 2\ e^- \rightarrow Cl^- (aq) + H_2O(l)$$

We now have a properly balanced half-reaction under acidic conditions with a balanced net charge of −1 on both the reactant and product side of the reaction arrow. However, this reaction is to be balanced under basic conditions so we will neutralize all hydrogen cations with hydroxide anions:

$$\boldsymbol{ClO^- (aq) + H_2O(l) + 2\ e^- \rightarrow Cl^- (aq) + 2\ OH^- (aq)}$$

We now have a properly balanced half-reaction under basic conditions.

18. Balance the following half-reactions:

a. $Ag(s) \rightarrow Ag_2O(s)$ (basic conditions)

Balance non-hydrogen and non-oxygen atoms:

$$2\ Ag(s) \rightarrow Ag_2O(s)$$

Balance oxygen atoms with waters:

$$2\ Ag(s) + H_2O(l) \rightarrow Ag_2O(s)$$

Balance hydrogen atoms with H^+:

$$2\ Ag(s) + H_2O(l) \rightarrow Ag_2O(s) + 2\ H^+(aq)$$

Balance charges by adding electrons:

$$2\ Ag(s) + H_2O(l) \rightarrow Ag_2O(s) + 2\ H^+(aq) + 2\ e^-$$

Under basic conditions neutralize protons with hydroxide:

$$\mathbf{2\ Ag(s) + 2\ OH^-(aq) \rightarrow Ag_2O(s) + H_2O(l) + 2\ e^-}$$

b. $H_2O_2(aq) \rightarrow H_2O(l)$ (acidic conditions)

There are no non-hydrogen and non-oxygen atoms:

$$H_2O_2(aq) \rightarrow H_2O(l)$$

Balance oxygen atoms with waters:

$$H_2O_2(aq) \rightarrow 2\ H_2O(l)$$

Balance hydrogen atoms with H^+:

$$H_2O_2(aq) + 2\ H^+(aq) \rightarrow 2\ H_2O(l)$$

Balance charges by adding electrons:

$$\mathbf{H_2O_2(aq) + 2\ H^+(aq) + 2\ e^- \rightarrow 2\ H_2O(l)}$$

19. Balance the following half-reactions:

a. $Cr(s) \rightarrow Cr^{3+}(aq)$

Balance all non-hydrogen and non-oxygen atoms:

$$Cr(s) \rightarrow Cr^{3+}(aq)$$

Balance charges by adding electrons:

$$\mathbf{Cr(s) \rightarrow Cr^{3+}(aq) + 3\ e^-}$$

b. $MnO_4^-(aq) \rightarrow MnO_2(s)$ (basic conditions)

Balance non-hydrogen and non-oxygen atoms:

$$MnO_4^-(aq) \rightarrow MnO_2(s)$$

Balance oxygen atoms with waters:

$$MnO_4^- (aq) \rightarrow MnO_2(s) + 2\ H_2O(l)$$

Balance hydrogen atoms with H^+:

$$MnO_4^- (aq) + 4\ H^+(aq) \rightarrow MnO_2(s) + 2\ H_2O(l)$$

Balance charges by adding electrons:

$$MnO_4^- (aq) + 4\ H^+(aq) + 3\ e^- \rightarrow MnO_2(s) + 2\ H_2O(l)$$

Under basic conditions neutralize protons with hydroxide:

$$\mathbf{MnO_4^-\ (aq) + 2\ H_2O(l) + 3\ e^- \rightarrow MnO_2(s) + 4\ OH^-\ (aq)}$$

20. Balance the following redox reactions using the half-reaction method under acidic conditions:

a. $Al^{3+}(aq) + Cu(s) \rightarrow Al(s) + Cu^{2+}(aq)$

Separate the redox reaction into oxidation and reduction half-reactions:

Oxidation: $\qquad Cu(s) \rightarrow Cu^{2+}(aq)$

Reduction: $\qquad Al^{3+}(aq) \rightarrow Al(s)$

Everything is already balanced by mass. So simply balance each by charge:

Oxidation: $\qquad Cu(s) \rightarrow Cu^{2+}(aq) + 2\ e^-$

Reduction: $\qquad Al^{3+}(aq) + 3\ e^- \rightarrow Al(s)$

Multiply each reaction by the appropriate factor to realize equal numbers of electrons produced and consumed:

Oxidation: $\qquad 3\ Cu(s) \rightarrow 3\ Cu^{2+}(aq) + 6\ e^-$

Reduction: $\qquad 2\ Al^{3+}(aq) + 6\ e^- \rightarrow 2\ Al(s)$

Combine the half-reactions, cancelling electrons and any identical species which appear on both sides of the reaction arrow:

$$\mathbf{2\ Al^{3+}(aq) + 3\ Cu(s) \rightarrow 2\ Al(s) + 3\ Cu^{2+}(aq)}$$

b. $Ag(s) + Fe^{3+}(aq) \rightarrow Ag^+(aq) + Fe(s)$

Separate the redox reaction into oxidation and reduction half-reactions:

Oxidation: $\qquad Ag(s) \rightarrow Ag^+(aq)$

Reduction: $\qquad Fe^{3+}(aq) \rightarrow Fe(s)$

Everything is already balanced by mass. So simply balance each by charge:

Oxidation: $\qquad Ag(s) \rightarrow Ag^+(aq) + e^-$

Reduction: $\qquad Fe^{3+}(aq) + 3\ e^- \rightarrow Fe(s)$

Multiply each reaction by the appropriate factor to realize equal numbers of electrons produced and consumed:

Oxidation: $\qquad 3\ Ag(s) \rightarrow 3\ Ag^+(aq) + 3\ e^-$

Reduction: $\qquad Fe^{3+}(aq) + 3\ e^- \rightarrow Fe(s)$

Combine the half-reactions, cancelling electrons and any identical species which appear on both sides of the reaction arrow:

$3\ Ag(s) + Fe^{3+}(aq) \rightarrow 3\ Ag^+(aq) + Fe(s)$

c. $NO_3^-(aq) + Cd(s) \rightarrow NO(g) + Cd^{2+}(aq)$

Separate the redox reaction into oxidation and reduction half-reactions:

Oxidation: $\qquad Cd(s) \rightarrow Cd^{2+}(aq)$

Reduction: $\qquad NO_3^-(aq) \rightarrow NO(g)$

Balance oxygen atoms by adding waters:

Oxidation: $\qquad Cd(s) \rightarrow Cd^{2+}(aq)$

Reduction: $\qquad NO_3^-(aq) \rightarrow NO(g) + 2\ H_2O(l)$

Balance hydrogen atoms with protons:

Oxidation: $\qquad Cd(s) \rightarrow Cd^{2+}(aq)$

Reduction: $\qquad NO_3^-(aq) + 4\ H^+(aq) \rightarrow NO(g) + 2\ H_2O(l)$

Everything is already balanced by mass. So simply balance each by charge:

Oxidation: $\qquad Cd(s) \rightarrow Cd^{2+}(aq) + 2\ e^-$

Reduction: $\qquad NO_3^-(aq) + 4\ H^+(aq) + 3\ e^- \rightarrow NO(g) + 2\ H_2O(l)$

Multiply each reaction by the appropriate factor to realize equal numbers of electrons produced and consumed:

Oxidation: $\qquad 3\ Cd(s) \rightarrow 3\ Cd^{2+}(aq) + 6\ e^-$

Reduction: $\qquad 2\ NO_3^-(aq) + 8\ H^+(aq) + 6\ e^- \rightarrow 2\ NO(g) + 4\ H_2O(l)$

Combine the half-reactions, cancelling electrons and any identical species which appear on both sides of the reaction arrow:

$$\mathbf{2\ NO_3^-\ (aq) + 3\ Cd\ (s) + 8\ H^+\ (aq) \rightarrow 2\ NO\ (g) + 3\ Cd^{2+}\ (aq) + 4\ H_2O\ (l)}\ .$$

21. Balance the following redox reactions using the half-reaction method under acidic conditions:

a. $H_2O_2(aq) + Zn(s) \rightarrow H_2O(l) + Zn^{2+}(aq)$

Separate the redox reaction into oxidation and reduction half-reactions:

Oxidation: $\qquad Zn(s) \rightarrow Zn^{2+}(aq)$

Reduction: $\qquad H_2O_2(aq) \rightarrow H_2O(l)$

Balance oxygen atoms by adding waters:

Oxidation: $\qquad Zn(s) \rightarrow Zn^{2+}(aq)$

Reduction: $\qquad H_2O_2(aq) \rightarrow 2\ H_2O(l)$

Balance hydrogen atoms with protons:

Oxidation: $\qquad Zn(s) \rightarrow Zn^{2+}(aq)$

Reduction: $\qquad H_2O_2(aq) + 2\ H^+(aq) \rightarrow 2\ H_2O(l)$

Everything is already balanced by mass. So simply balance each by charge:

Oxidation: $\qquad Zn(s) \rightarrow Zn^{2+}(aq) + 2\ e^-$

Reduction: $\qquad H_2O_2(aq) + 2\ H^+(aq) + 2\ e^- \rightarrow 2\ H_2O(l)$

Multiply each reaction by the appropriate factor to realize equal numbers of electrons produced and consumed:

Oxidation: $\qquad Zn(s) \rightarrow Zn^{2+}(aq) + 2\ e^{-}$

Reduction: $\qquad H_2O_2(aq) + 2\ H^{+}(aq) + 2\ e^{-} \rightarrow 2\ H_2O(l)$

Combine the half-reactions, cancelling electrons and any identical species which appear on both sides of the reaction arrow:

$$H_2O_2(aq) + Zn(s) + 2\ H^{+} \rightarrow 2\ H_2O(l) + Zn^{2+}(aq)$$

b. $BrO_3^{-}(aq) + Fe(s) \rightarrow Br_2(l) + Fe^{2+}(aq)$

Separate the redox reaction into oxidation and reduction half-reactions and balance any non-hydrogen and non-oxygen atoms:

Oxidation: $\qquad Fe(s) \rightarrow Fe^{2+}(aq)$

Reduction: $\qquad 2\ BrO_3^{-}(aq) \rightarrow Br_2(l)$

Balance oxygen atoms by adding waters:

Oxidation: $\qquad Fe(s) \rightarrow Fe^{2+}(aq)$

Reduction: $\qquad 2\ BrO_3^{-}(aq) \rightarrow Br_2(l) + 6\ H_2O(l)$

Balance hydrogen atoms with protons:

Oxidation: $\qquad Fe(s) \rightarrow Fe^{2+}(aq)$

Reduction: $\qquad 2\ BrO_3^{-}(aq) + 12\ H^{+}(aq) \rightarrow Br_2(l) + 6\ H_2O(l)$

Everything is already balanced by mass. So simply balance each by charge:

Oxidation: $\qquad Fe(s) \rightarrow Fe^{2+}(aq) + 2\ e^{-}$

Reduction: $\qquad 2\ BrO_3^{-}(aq) + 12\ H^{+}(aq) + 10\ e^{-} \rightarrow Br_2(l) + 6\ H_2O(l)$

Multiply each reaction by the appropriate factor to realize equal numbers of electrons produced and consumed:

Oxidation: $\qquad 5\ Fe(s) \rightarrow 5\ Fe^{2+}(aq) + 10\ e^{-}$

Reduction: $\qquad 2\ BrO_3^{-}(aq) + 12\ H^{+}(aq) + 10\ e^{-} \rightarrow Br_2(l) + 6\ H_2O(l)$

Combine the half-reactions, cancelling electrons and any identical species which appear on both sides of the reaction arrow:

$$2\ BrO_3^{-}(aq) + 5\ Fe(s) + 12\ H^{+}(aq) \rightarrow Br_2(l) + 5\ Fe^{2+}(aq) + 6\ H_2O(l)$$

c. $Cu^{2+}(aq) + N_2H_5^+(aq) \rightarrow N_2(g) + Cu(s)$

Separate the redox reaction into oxidation and reduction half-reactions and balance any non-hydrogen and non-oxygen atoms:

Oxidation: $N_2H_5^+(aq) \rightarrow N_2(g)$

Reduction: $Cu^{2+}(aq) \rightarrow Cu(s)$

Balance hydrogen atoms with protons:

Oxidation: $N_2H_5^+(aq) \rightarrow N_2(g) + 5\ H^+(aq)$

Reduction: $Cu^{2+}(aq) \rightarrow Cu(s)$

Everything is already balanced by mass. So simply balance each by charge:

Oxidation: $N_2H_5^+(aq) \rightarrow N_2(g) + 5\ H^+(aq) + 4\ e^-$

Reduction: $Cu^{2+}(aq) + 2\ e^- \rightarrow Cu(s)$

Multiply each reaction by the appropriate factor to realize equal numbers of electrons produced and consumed:

Oxidation: $N_2H_5^+(aq) \rightarrow N_2(g) + 5\ H^+(aq) + 4\ e^-$

Reduction: $2\ Cu^{2+}(aq) + 4\ e^- \rightarrow 2\ Cu(s)$

Combine the half-reaction, cancelling electrons and any identical species which appear on both sides of the reaction arrow:

$2\ Cu^{2+}(aq) + N_2H_5^+(aq) \rightarrow N_2(g) + 2\ Cu(s) + 5\ H^+(aq)$

22. Balance the following redox reactions using the half-reaction method under acidic conditions:

a. $MnO_4^-(aq) + Ca(s) \rightarrow MnO_2(s) + Ca^{2+}(aq)$

Separate the redox reaction into oxidation and reduction half-reactions and balance any non-hydrogen and non-oxygen atoms:

Oxidation: $Ca(s) \rightarrow Ca^{2+}(aq)$

Reduction: $MnO_4^-(aq) \rightarrow MnO_2(s)$

Balance oxygen atoms by adding waters:

Oxidation: $Ca(s) \rightarrow Ca^{2+}(aq)$

Reduction: $MnO_4^-(aq) \rightarrow MnO_2(s) + 2\ H_2O(l)$

Balance hydrogen atoms with protons:

Oxidation: $\quad Ca(s) \rightarrow Ca^{2+}(aq)$

Reduction: $\quad MnO_4^-(aq) + 4\ H^+(aq) \rightarrow MnO_2(s) + 2\ H_2O(l)$

Everything is already balanced by mass. So simply balance each by charge:

Oxidation: $\quad Ca(s) \rightarrow Ca^{2+}(aq) + 2\ e^-$

Reduction: $\quad MnO_4^-(aq) + 4\ H^+(aq) + 3\ e^- \rightarrow MnO_2(s) + 2\ H_2O(l)$

Multiply each reaction by the appropriate factor to realize equal numbers of electrons produced and consumed:

Oxidation: $\quad 3\ Ca(s) \rightarrow 3\ Ca^{2+}(aq) + 6\ e^-$

Reduction: $\quad 2\ MnO_4^-(aq) + 8\ H^+(aq) + 6\ e^- \rightarrow 2\ MnO_2(s) + 4\ H_2O(l)$

Combine the half-reactions, cancelling electrons and any identical species which appear on both sides of the reaction arrow:

$$2\ MnO_4^-(aq) + 3\ Ca(s) + 8\ H^+(aq) \rightarrow 2\ MnO_2(s) + 3\ Ca^{2+}(aq) + 4\ H_2O(l)$$

b. $\quad PbO_2(s) + I^-(aq) \rightarrow Pb^{2+}(aq) + I_2(s)$

Separate the redox reaction into oxidation and reduction half-reactions and balance any non-hydrogen and non-oxygen atoms:

Oxidation: $\quad 2\ I^-(aq) \rightarrow I_2(s)$

Reduction: $\quad PbO_2(s) \rightarrow Pb^{2+}(aq)$

Balance oxygen atoms by adding waters:

Oxidation: $\quad 2\ I^-(aq) \rightarrow I_2(s)$

Reduction: $\quad PbO_2(s) \rightarrow Pb^{2+}(aq) + 2\ H_2O(l)$

Balance hydrogen atoms with protons:

Oxidation: $\quad 2\ I^-(aq) \rightarrow I_2(s)$

Reduction: $\quad PbO_2(s) + 4\ H^+(aq) \rightarrow Pb^{2+}(aq) + 2\ H_2O(l)$

Everything is already balanced by mass. So simply balance each by charge:

Oxidation: $\quad 2\ I^-(aq) \rightarrow I_2(s) + 2\ e^-$

Reduction: $\quad PbO_2(s) + 4\ H^+(aq) + 2\ e^- \rightarrow Pb^{2+}(aq) + 2\ H_2O(l)$

Multiply each reaction by the appropriate factor to realize equal numbers of electrons produced and consumed:

Oxidation: $2\ I^-(aq) \rightarrow I_2(s) + 2\ e^-$

Reduction: $PbO_2(s) + 4\ H^+(aq) + 2\ e^- \rightarrow Pb^{2+}(aq) + 2\ H_2O(l)$

Combine the half-reactions, cancelling electrons and any identical species which appear on both sides of the reaction arrow:

$$PbO_2(s) + 2\ I^-(aq) + 4\ H^+(aq) \rightarrow Pb^{2+}(aq) + I_2(s) + 2\ H_2O(l)$$

c. $Cr_2O_7^{2-}(aq) + Fe(s) \rightarrow Cr^{3+}(aq) + Fe^{3+}(aq)$

Separate the redox reaction into oxidation and reduction half-reactions and balance any non-hydrogen and non-oxygen atoms:

Oxidation: $Fe(s) \rightarrow Fe^{3+}(aq)$

Reduction: $Cr_2O_7^{2-}(aq) \rightarrow 2\ Cr^{3+}(aq)$

Balance oxygen atoms by adding waters:

Oxidation: $Fe(s) \rightarrow Fe^{3+}(aq)$

Reduction: $Cr_2O_7^{2-}(aq) \rightarrow 2\ Cr^{3+}(aq) + 7\ H_2O(l)$

Balance hydrogen atoms with protons:

Oxidation: $Fe(s) \rightarrow Fe^{3+}(aq)$

Reduction: $Cr_2O_7^{2-}(aq) + 14\ H^+(aq) \rightarrow 2\ Cr^{3+}(aq) + 7\ H_2O(l)$

Everything is already balanced by mass. So simply balance each by charge:

Oxidation: $Fe(s) \rightarrow Fe^{3+}(aq) + 3\ e^-$

Reduction: $Cr_2O_7^{2-}(aq) + 14\ H^+(aq) + 6\ e^- \rightarrow 2\ Cr^{3+}(aq) + 7\ H_2O(l)$

Multiply each reaction by the appropriate factor to realize equal numbers of electrons produced and consumed:

Oxidation: $2\ Fe(s) \rightarrow 2\ Fe^{3+}(aq) + 6\ e^-$

Reduction: $Cr_2O_7^{2-}(aq) + 14\ H^+(aq) + 6\ e^- \rightarrow 2\ Cr^{3+}(aq) + 7\ H_2O(l)$

Combine the half-reactions, cancelling electrons and any identical species which appear on both sides of the reaction arrow:

$$Cr_2O_7^{2-}(aq) + 2\ Fe(s) + 14\ H^+(aq) \rightarrow 2\ Cr^{3+}(aq) + 2\ Fe^{3+}(aq) + 7\ H_2O(l)$$

23. Balance the following redox reactions using the half-reaction method under basic conditions:

a. $MnO_2(s) + Cl_2(g) \rightarrow MnO_4^-(aq) + Cl^-(aq)$

Separate the redox reaction into oxidation and reduction half-reactions and balance any non-hydrogen and non-oxygen atoms:

Oxidation: $\qquad MnO_2(s) \rightarrow MnO_4^-(aq)$

Reduction: $\qquad Cl_2(g) \rightarrow 2\, Cl^-(aq)$

Balance oxygen atoms by adding waters:

Oxidation: $\qquad MnO_2(s) + 2\, H_2O(l) \rightarrow MnO_4^-(aq)$

Reduction: $\qquad Cl_2(g) \rightarrow 2\, Cl^-(aq)$

Balance hydrogen atoms with protons:

Oxidation: $\qquad MnO_2(s) + 2\, H_2O(l) \rightarrow MnO_4^-(aq) + 4\, H^+(aq)$

Reduction: $\qquad Cl_2(g) \rightarrow 2\, Cl^-(aq)$

Everything is already balanced by mass. So simply balance each by charge:

Oxidation: $\qquad MnO_2(s) + 2\, H_2O(l) \rightarrow MnO_4^-(aq) + 4\, H^+(aq) + 3\, e^-$

Reduction: $\qquad Cl_2(g) + 2\, e^- \rightarrow 2\, Cl^-(aq)$

Multiply each reaction by the appropriate factor to realize equal numbers of electrons produced and consumed:

Oxidation: $\qquad 2\, MnO_2(s) + 4\, H_2O(l) \rightarrow 2\, MnO_4^-(aq) + 8\, H^+(aq) + 6\, e^-$

Reduction: $\qquad 3\, Cl_2(g) + 6\, e^- \rightarrow 6\, Cl^-(aq)$

Combine the half-reactions, cancelling electrons and any identical species which appear on both sides of the reaction arrow:

$2\, MnO_2(s) + 4\, H_2O(l) + 3\, Cl_2(g) \rightarrow 2\, MnO_4^-(aq) + 6\, Cl^-(aq) + 8\, H^+(aq)$

This reaction is to be balanced under basic conditions so we will neutralize all hydrogen cations with hydroxide anions:

$\mathbf{2\ MnO_2(s) + 3\ Cl_2(g) + 8\ OH^-(aq) \rightarrow 2\ MnO_4^-(aq) + 6\ Cl^-(aq) + 4\ H_2O(l)}$

b. $ClO^-(aq) + Fe(s) \rightarrow Cl^-(aq) + Fe^{3+}(aq)$

Separate the redox reaction into oxidation and reduction half-reactions and balance any non-hydrogen and non-oxygen atoms:

Oxidation: $Fe(s) \rightarrow Fe^{3+}(aq)$

Reduction: $ClO^-(aq) \rightarrow Cl^-(aq)$

Balance oxygen atoms by adding waters:

Oxidation: $Fe(s) \rightarrow Fe^{3+}(aq)$

Reduction: $ClO^-(aq) \rightarrow Cl^-(aq) + H_2O(l)$

Balance hydrogen atoms with protons:

Oxidation: $Fe(s) \rightarrow Fe^{3+}(aq)$

Reduction: $ClO^-(aq) + 2\ H^+(aq) \rightarrow Cl^-(aq) + H_2O(l)$

Everything is already balanced by mass. So simply balance each by charge:

Oxidation: $Fe(s) \rightarrow Fe^{3+}(aq) + 3\ e^-$

$2\text{-}1 + 1 = 2$

Reduction: $ClO^-(aq) + 2\ H^+(aq) + 2\ e^- \rightarrow Cl^-(aq) + H_2O(l)$

Multiply each reaction by the appropriate factor to realize equal numbers of electrons produced and consumed:

Oxidation: $2\ Fe(s) \rightarrow 2\ Fe^{3+}(aq) + 6\ e^-$

Reduction: $3\ ClO^-(aq) + 6\ H^+(aq) + 6\ e^- \rightarrow 3\ Cl^-(aq) + 3\ H_2O(l)$

Combine the half-reactions, cancelling electrons and any identical species which appear on both sides of the reaction arrow:

$3\ ClO^-(aq) + 6\ H^+(aq) + 2\ Fe(s) \rightarrow 3\ Cl^-(aq) + 2\ Fe^{3+}(aq) + 3\ H_2O(l)$

This reaction is to be balanced under basic conditions so we will neutralize all hydrogen cations with hydroxide anions:

$3\ ClO^-(aq) + 3\ H_2O(l) + 2\ Fe(s) \rightarrow 3\ Cl^-(aq) + 2\ Fe^{3+}(aq) + 6\ OH^-(aq)$

24. Balance the following redox reactions using the half-reaction method under basic conditions:

a. $MnO_4^-(aq) + I^-(aq) \rightarrow MnO_2(s) + I_2(g)$

Separate the redox reaction into oxidation and reduction half-reactions and balance any non-hydrogen and non-oxygen atoms:

Oxidation: $\qquad 2\,I^-(aq) \rightarrow I_2(g)$

Reduction: $\qquad MnO_4^-(aq) \rightarrow MnO_2(s)$

Balance oxygen atoms by adding waters:

Oxidation: $\qquad 2\,I^-(aq) \rightarrow I_2(g)$

Reduction: $\qquad MnO_4^-(aq) \rightarrow MnO_2(s) + 2\,H_2O(l)$

Balance hydrogen atoms with protons:

Oxidation: $\qquad 2\,I^-(aq) \rightarrow I_2(g)$

Reduction: $\qquad MnO_4^-(aq) + 4\,H^+(aq) \rightarrow MnO_2(s) + 2\,H_2O(l)$

Everything is already balanced by mass. So simply balance each by charge:

Oxidation: $\qquad 2\,I^-(aq) \rightarrow I_2(g) + 2\,e^-$

Reduction: $\qquad MnO_4^-(aq) + 4\,H^+(aq) + 3\,e^- \rightarrow MnO_2(s) + 2\,H_2O(l)$

Multiply each reaction by the appropriate factor to realize equal numbers of electrons produced and consumed:

Oxidation: $\qquad 6\,I^-(aq) \rightarrow 3\,I_2(g) + 6\,e^-$

Reduction: $\qquad 2\,MnO_4^-(aq) + 8\,H^+(aq) + 6\,e^- \rightarrow 2\,MnO_2(s) + 4\,H_2O(l)$

Combine the half-reactions, cancelling electrons and any identical species which appear on both sides of the reaction arrow:

$2\,MnO_4^-(aq) + 8\,H^+(aq) + 6\,I^-(aq) \rightarrow 2\,MnO_2(s) + 3\,I_2(g) + 4\,H_2O(l)$

This reaction is to be balanced under basic conditions so we will neutralize all hydrogen cations with hydroxide anions:

$2\,MnO_4^-(aq) + 4\,H_2O(l) + 6\,I^-(aq) \rightarrow 2\,MnO_2(s) + 3\,I_2(g) + 8\,OH^-(aq)$

b. $Mn^{2+}(aq) + H_2O_2(aq) \rightarrow MnO_2(s) + H_2O(l)$

Separate the redox reaction into oxidation and reduction half-reactions and balance any non-hydrogen and non-oxygen atoms:

Oxidation: $Mn^{2+}(aq) \rightarrow MnO_2(s)$

Reduction: $H_2O_2(aq) \rightarrow H_2O(l)$

Balance oxygen atoms by adding waters:

Oxidation: $Mn^{2+}(aq) + 2\ H_2O(l) \rightarrow MnO_2(s)$

Reduction: $H_2O_2(aq) \rightarrow 2\ H_2O(l)$

Balance hydrogen atoms with protons:

Oxidation: $Mn^{2+}(aq) + 2\ H_2O(l) \rightarrow MnO_2(s) + 4\ H^+(aq)$

Reduction: $H_2O_2(aq) + 2\ H^+ \rightarrow 2\ H_2O(l)$

Everything is already balanced by mass. So simply balance each by charge:

Oxidation: $Mn^{2+}(aq) + 2\ H_2O(l) \rightarrow MnO_2(s) + 4\ H^+(aq) + 2\ e^-$

Reduction: $H_2O_2(aq) + 2\ H^+(aq) + 2\ e^- \rightarrow 2\ H_2O(l)$

Multiply each reaction by the appropriate factor to realize equal numbers of electrons produced and consumed:

Oxidation: $Mn^{2+}(aq) + 2\ H_2O(l) \rightarrow MnO_2(s) + 4\ H^+(aq) + 2\ e^-$

Reduction: $H_2O_2(aq) + 2\ H^+(aq) + 2\ e^- \rightarrow 2\ H_2O(l)$

Combine the half-reactions, cancelling electrons and any identical species which appear on both sides of the reaction arrow:

$H_2O_2(aq) + Mn^{2+}(aq) \rightarrow MnO_2(s) + 2\ H^+(aq)$

This reaction is to be balanced under basic conditions so we will neutralize all hydrogen cations with hydroxide anions:

$\mathbf{H_2O_2(aq) + Mn^{2+}(aq) + 2\ OH^-(aq) \rightarrow MnO_2(s) + 2\ H_2O(l)}$

25. Balance the following redox reactions using the half-reaction method under basic conditions:

a. $ClO^-(aq) + Cr(OH)_4^-(aq) \rightarrow CrO_4^{2-}(aq) + Cl^-(aq)$

Separate the redox reaction into oxidation and reduction half-reactions and balance any non-hydrogen and non-oxygen atoms:

Oxidation: $Cr(OH)_4^-(aq) \rightarrow CrO_4^{2-}(aq)$

Reduction: $ClO^-(aq) \rightarrow Cl^-(aq)$

Balance oxygen atoms by adding waters:

Oxidation: $Cr(OH)_4^-(aq) \rightarrow CrO_4^{2-}(aq)$

Reduction: $ClO^-(aq) \rightarrow Cl^-(aq) + H_2O(l)$

Balance hydrogen atoms with protons:

Oxidation: $Cr(OH)_4^-(aq) \rightarrow CrO_4^{2-}(aq) + 4\ H^+(aq)$

Reduction: $ClO^-(aq) + 2\ H^+(aq) \rightarrow Cl^-(aq) + H_2O(l)$

Everything is already balanced by mass. So simply balance each by charge:

Oxidation: $Cr(OH)_4^-(aq) \rightarrow CrO_4^{2-}(aq) + 4\ H^+(aq) + 3\ e^-$

Reduction: $ClO^-(aq) + 2\ H^+(aq) + 2\ e^- \rightarrow Cl^-(aq) + H_2O(l)$

Multiply each reaction by the appropriate factor to realize equal numbers of electrons produced and consumed:

Oxidation: $2\ Cr(OH)_4^-(aq) \rightarrow 2\ CrO_4^{2-}(aq) + 8\ H^+(aq) + 6\ e^-$

Reduction: $3\ ClO^-(aq) + 6\ H^+(aq) + 6\ e^- \rightarrow 3\ Cl^-(aq) + 3\ H_2O(l)$

Combine the half-reactions, cancelling electrons and any identical species which appear on both sides of the reaction arrow:

$2\ Cr(OH)_4^-(aq) + 3\ ClO^-(aq) \rightarrow 2\ CrO_4^{2-}(aq) + 2\ H^+(aq) + 3\ Cl^-(aq) + 3\ H_2O(l)$

This reaction is to be balanced under basic conditions so we will neutralize all hydrogen cations with hydroxide anions:

$\mathbf{2\ Cr(OH)_4^-(aq) + 3\ ClO^-(aq) + 2\ OH^-(aq) \rightarrow 2\ CrO_4^{2-}(aq) + 3\ Cl^-(aq) + 5\ H_2O(l)}$

b. $Br_2(l) \rightarrow BrO_3^-(aq) + Br^-(aq)$

Separate the redox reaction into oxidation and reduction half-reactions and balance any non-hydrogen and non-oxygen atoms:

Oxidation: $Br_2(l) \rightarrow 2\ BrO_3^-(aq)$

Reduction: $Br_2(l) \rightarrow 2\ Br^-(aq)$

Balance oxygen atoms by adding waters:

Oxidation: $Br_2(l) + 6\ H_2O(l) \rightarrow 2\ BrO_3^-(aq)$

Reduction: $Br_2(l) \rightarrow 2\ Br^-(aq)$

Balance hydrogen atoms with protons:

Oxidation: $Br_2(l) + 6\ H_2O(l) \rightarrow 2\ BrO_3^-(aq) + 12\ H^+(aq)$

Reduction: $Br_2(l) \rightarrow 2\ Br^-(aq)$

Everything is already balanced by mass. So simply balance each by charge:

Oxidation: $Br_2(l) + 6\ H_2O(l) \rightarrow 2\ BrO_3^-(aq) + 12\ H^+(aq) + 10\ e^-$

Reduction: $Br_2(l) + 2\ e^- \rightarrow 2\ Br^-(aq)$

Multiply each reaction by the appropriate factor to realize equal numbers of electrons produced and consumed:

Oxidation: $Br_2(l) + 6\ H_2O(l) \rightarrow 2\ BrO_3^-(aq) + 12\ H^+(aq) + 10\ e^-$

Reduction: $5\ Br_2(l) + 10\ e^- \rightarrow 10\ Br^-(aq)$

Combine the half-reaction, cancelling electrons and any identical species which appear on both sides of the reaction arrow:

$6\ Br_2(l) + 6\ H_2O(l) \rightarrow 2\ BrO_3^-(aq) + 10\ Br^-(aq) + 12\ H^+(aq)$

This reaction is to be balanced under basic conditions so we will neutralize all hydrogen cations with hydroxide anions:

$6\ Br_2(l) + 12\ OH^-(aq) \rightarrow 2\ BrO_3^-(aq) + 10\ Br^-(aq) + 6\ H_2O(l)$

GALVANIC (VOLTAIC) CELLS

26. What is an electrode?

Electrodes are conductive materials which facilitate the flow of electrons to and from each of the half-cells.

27. Define the terms anode and cathode.

The anode is the electrode where oxidation occurs in all electrochemical cells.

The cathode is the electrode where reduction occurs in all electrochemical cells.

28. Define the terms half-cell.

Half-cells are the two separate compartments of the galvanic cell, one containing the oxidation half-reaction and the other containing the reduction half-reaction.

29. Describe the difference between a galvanic (voltaic) cell and an electrolytic cell.

Galvanic cells (also referred to as voltaic cells) are devices which use spontaneous redox reactions to generate an electric current which is then used to do work. Electrolytic cells are devices which use an external electric current to drive redox reactions which are not spontaneous.

30. What is the standard hydrogen electrode? What is its significance?

The standard hydrogen electrode (SHE) is characterized by an inert metal electrode (platinum) submerged in a 1 M HCl solution, bathed in hydrogen gas at a pressure of 1 atm (hydrogen gas is bubbled over the electrode). When employed in a galvanic cell the SHE is described by the following balanced half-reaction:

$$2\,H^{+}(aq) + 2\,e^{-} \rightarrow H_{2}(g) \qquad E^{o}_{cathode} = 0.00\ V$$

The SHE is the reference potential against which all half-cell standard reduction potentials are measured.

31. What is the relation between the spontaneity of a redox reaction and the cell potential, E^{o}_{cell}?

Electrochemical cells with $E^{o}_{cell} > 0$ proceed spontaneously and the redox reaction on which they are based have a negative gibb's free energy. These two quantities are related mathematically as follows:

$$\Delta G^{o} = -nFE^{o}_{cell},$$

where F is the faraday constant and n is the number of moles of electrons exchanged in the reaction.

32. Write the cell diagram that describes an electrochemical cell consisting of a silver electrode submerged in a 1 M solution of silver nitrate and a copper electrode submerged in a 1 M solution of copper(II) sulfate.

Because copper is a weaker oxidizer than silver, the Cu^{2+} / Cu half-cell will serve as the anode.

$$Cu(s)\left|Cu^{2+}(aq)\right|\left|Ag^{+}(aq)\right|Ag(s)$$

33. Write the cell diagram that describes an electrochemical cell consisting of a zinc electrode submerged in a 1 M solution of zinc sulfate and a magnesium electrode submerged in a 1 M solution of magnesium nitrate.

Because magnesium is a weaker oxidizer than zinc, the Mg^{2+} / Mg half-cell will serve as the anode.

$$Mg(s)\left|Mg^{2+}(aq)\right|\left|Zn^{2+}(aq)\right|Zn(s)$$

34. Arrange the following in order of increasing reducing strength:
    a. Cu
    b. Zn
    c. Fe
    d. Pb

$$Cu < Pb < Fe < Zn$$

35. Arrange the following in order of increasing oxidizing strength:
    a. Li^+
    b. Cr^{2+}
    c. Ti^{2+}
    d. Sn^{2+}

$$Li^+ < Ti^{2+} < Cr^{2+} < Sn^{2+}$$

36. Use the standard electrode potentials in Table 13.1 to calculate the standard cell potential for a Galvanic cell based on the reaction described by the following balanced equation at 25°C (assume acidic conditions).

$$2\ ClO_2(g) + 2\ I^-(aq) \rightarrow 2\ ClO_2^-(aq) + I_2(s)$$

Separate the redox reaction into oxidation and reduction half-reactions:

Oxidation: $2\ I^-(aq) \rightarrow I_2(s)$

Reduction: $ClO_2(g) \rightarrow ClO_2^-(aq)$

Separate the redox reaction into oxidation and reduction half-reactions:

Oxidation: $2\ I^-(aq) \rightarrow I_2(s)$

Reduction: $ClO_2(g) \rightarrow ClO_2^-(aq)$

We can now look up the standard reduction potentials for these two half-reactions:

Oxidation: $2\ I^-(aq) \rightarrow I_2(s) + 2\ e^-$ $E^o = 0.54\ V$

Reduction: $ClO_2(g) + e^- \rightarrow ClO_2^-(aq)$ $E^o = 0.95\ V$

Multiply each reaction by the appropriate factor to realize equal numbers of electrons produced and consumed:

Oxidation: $\quad 2\,I^-(aq) \rightarrow I_2(s) + 2\,e^- \qquad\qquad\qquad E^o = 0.54\ V$

Reduction: $\quad 2\,ClO_2(g) + 2\,e^- \rightarrow 2\,ClO_2^-(aq) \qquad\quad E^o = 0.95\ V$

Combine the half-reactions, cancelling electrons and any identical species which appear on both sides of the reaction arrow:

$$2\,ClO_2(g) + 2\,I^-(aq) \rightarrow 2\,ClO_2^-(aq) + I_2(s)$$

$$E^o_{cell} = E^o_{cathode} - E^o_{anode} = 0.95\ V - 0.54\ V = 0.41\ V$$

37. Use the standard electrode potentials in Table 13.1 to calculate the standard cell potential for a Galvanic cell based on the reaction described by the following balanced equation at 25°C.

$$Zn(s) + 2\,H^+(aq) \rightarrow Zn^{2+}(aq) + H_2(g)$$

Separate the redox reaction into oxidation and reduction half-reactions:

Oxidation: $\quad Zn(s) \rightarrow Zn^{2+}(aq)$

Reduction: $\quad 2\,H^+(aq) \rightarrow H_2(g)$

Everything is already balanced by mass. So simply balance each by charge:

Oxidation: $\quad Zn(s) \rightarrow Zn^{2+}(aq) + 2\,e^-$

Reduction: $\quad 2\,H^+(aq) + 2\,e^- \rightarrow H_2(g)$

We can now look up the standard reduction potentials for these two half-reactions:

Oxidation: $\quad Zn(s) \rightarrow Zn^{2+}(aq) + 2\,e^- \qquad\qquad E^o = -0.76\ V$

Reduction: $\quad 2\,H^+(aq) + 2\,e^- \rightarrow H_2(g) \qquad\qquad E^o = 0.00\ V$

Multiply each reaction by the appropriate factor to realize equal numbers of electrons produced and consumed:

Oxidation: $\quad Zn(s) \rightarrow Zn^{2+}(aq) + 2\,e^- \qquad\qquad E^o = -0.76\ V$

Reduction: $\quad 2\,H^+(aq) + 2\,e^- \rightarrow H_2(g) \qquad\qquad E^o = 0.00\ V$

Combine the half-reactions, cancelling electrons and any identical species which appear on both sides of the reaction arrow:

$$Zn(s) + 2\,H^+(aq) \rightarrow Zn^{2+}(aq) + H_2(g)$$

$$E^o_{cell} = E^o_{cathode} - E^o_{anode} = 0.00\ V - (-0.76\ V) = 0.76\ V$$

38. Use the standard electrode potentials in Table 13.1 to calculate the standard cell potential and write the overall balanced equation for a Galvanic cell based on the reaction described by the following cell diagram at 25°C. Assume acidic conditions and that all solutes are 1 M and all partial pressures are 1 atm.

$$Zn(s)\left|Zn^{2+}(aq)\right|\left|Ni^{2+}(aq)\right|Ni(s)$$

Separate the redox reaction into oxidation and reduction half-reactions:

Oxidation: $\quad Zn(s) \rightarrow Zn^{2+}(aq)$

Reduction: $\quad Ni^{2+}(aq) \rightarrow Ni(s)$

Everything is already balanced by mass. So simply balance each by charge:

Oxidation: $\quad Zn(s) \rightarrow Zn^{2+}(aq) + 2\ e^-$

Reduction: $\quad Ni^{2+}(aq) + 2\ e^- \rightarrow Ni(s)$

We can now look up the standard reduction potentials for these two half-reactions:

Oxidation: $\quad Zn(s) \rightarrow Zn^{2+}(aq) + 2\ e^- \qquad\qquad E^o = -0.76\ V$

Reduction: $\quad Ni^{2+}(aq) + 2\ e^- \rightarrow Ni(s) \qquad\qquad E^o = -0.26\ V$

Multiply each reaction by the appropriate factor to realize equal numbers of electrons produced and consumed:

Oxidation: $\quad Zn(s) \rightarrow Zn^{2+}(aq) + 2\ e^- \qquad\qquad E^o = -0.76\ V$

Reduction: $\quad Ni^{2+}(aq) + 2\ e^- \rightarrow Ni(s) \qquad\qquad E^o = -0.26\ V$

Combine the half-reactions, cancelling electrons and any identical species which appear on both sides of the reaction arrow:

$$Zn(s) + Ni^{2+}(aq) \rightarrow Ni(s) + Zn^{2+}(aq)$$

$$E^o_{cell} = E^o_{cathode} - E^o_{anode} = -0.26\ V - (-0.76\ V) = 0.50\ V$$

39. Use the standard electrode potentials in Table 13.1 to calculate the standard cell potential and write the overall balanced equation for a Galvanic cell based on the reaction described by the following cell diagram at 25°C. Assume acidic conditions and that all solutes are 1 M and all partial pressures are 1 atm.

$$Pb(s)\left|Pb^{2+}(aq)\right|\left|Ag^+(aq)\right|Ag(s)$$

Separate the redox reaction into oxidation and reduction half-reactions:

Oxidation: $Pb(s) \rightarrow Pb^{2+}(aq)$

Reduction: $Ag^+(aq) \rightarrow Ag(s)$

Everything is already balanced by mass. So simply balance each by charge:

Oxidation: $Pb(s) \rightarrow Pb^{2+}(aq) + 2\,e^-$

Reduction: $Ag^+(aq) + e^- \rightarrow Ag(s)$

We can now look up the standard reduction potentials for these two half-reactions:

Oxidation: $Pb(s) \rightarrow Pb^{2+}(aq) + 2\,e^-$ $\quad\quad\quad E^o = -0.13\ V$

Reduction: $Ag^+(aq) + e^- \rightarrow Ag(s)$ $\quad\quad\quad E^o = 0.80\ V$

Multiply each reaction by the appropriate factor to realize equal numbers of electrons produced and consumed:

Oxidation: $Pb(s) \rightarrow Pb^{2+}(aq) + 2\,e^-$ $\quad\quad\quad E^o = -0.13\ V$

Reduction: $2\ Ag^+(aq) + 2\,e^- \rightarrow 2\ Ag(s)$ $\quad\quad\quad E^o = 0.80\ V$

Combine the half-reactions, cancelling electrons and any identical species which appear on both sides of the reaction arrow:

$$Pb(s) + 2\ Ag^+(aq) \rightarrow 2\ Ag(s) + Pb^{2+}(aq)$$

$$E^o_{cell} = E^o_{cathode} - E^o_{anode} = 0.80\ V - (-0.13\ V) = 0.93\ V$$

40. Use the standard electrode potentials in Table 13.1 to calculate the standard cell potential for a Galvanic cell based on the reaction described by the following cell diagrams at 25°C (acidic conditions):

a. $Cu(s) \mid Cu^{2+}(aq) \mid\mid MnO_4^-(aq) \mid MnO_2(s) \mid Pt(s)$

$E^o_{cell} = E^o_{cathode} - E^o_{anode} = 1.67\ V - (0.34\ V) = 1.33\ V$

b. $Cr(s) \mid Cr^{3+}(aq) \mid\mid Fe^{3+}(aq) \mid Fe(s)$

$E^o_{cell} = E^o_{cathode} - E^o_{anode} = -0.036\ V - (-0.74\ V) = 0.704\ V$

c. $Mg(s) \mid Mg^{2+}(aq) \mid\mid Ni^{2+}(aq) \mid Ni(s)$

$E^o_{cell} = E^o_{cathode} - E^o_{anode} = -0.26\ V - (-2.37\ V) = 2.11V$

41. Use the standard electrode potentials in Table 13.1 to calculate the standard cell potential for a Galvanic cell based on the reaction described by the following cell diagrams at 25°C (acidic conditions):

a. $Fe(s)\left|Fe^{2+}(aq)\right|\left|H^{+}(aq)\right|H_{2}(g)\mid Pt(s)$

$E_{cell}^{o}=E_{cathode}^{o}-E_{anode}^{o}=0.00\ V-(-0.45\ V)=0.45\ V$

b. $Zn(s)\left|Zn^{2+}(aq)\right|\left|Sn^{2+}(aq)\right|Sn(s)$

$E_{cell}^{o}=E_{cathode}^{o}-E_{anode}^{o}=-0.14\ V-(-0.76\ V)=0.62\ V$

c. $Al(s)\left|Al^{3+}(aq)\right|\left|Fe^{2+}(aq)\right|Fe(s)$

$E_{cell}^{o}=E_{cathode}^{o}-E_{anode}^{o}=-0.45\ V-(-1.66\ V)=1.21\ V$

42. Determine E_{cell}^{o} for the following balanced reaction equations and indicate whether they will proceed spontaneously as written:

a. $MnO_{2}(s)+4\ H^{+}(aq)+Zn(s)\rightarrow Mn^{2+}(aq)+2\ H_{2}O(l)+Zn^{2+}(aq)$

$E_{cell}^{o}=E_{cathode}^{o}-E_{anode}^{o}=1.22\ V-(-0.76\ V)=1.98\ V$

$E_{cell}^{o}>0$ Therefore, the reaction will proceed spontaneously as written.

b. $Ca(s)+Cd^{2+}(aq)\rightarrow Ca^{2+}+Cd(s)$

$E_{cell}^{o}=E_{cathode}^{o}-E_{anode}^{o}=-0.40\ V-(-2.87\ V)=2.47\ V$

$E_{cell}^{o}>0$ Therefore, the reaction will proceed spontaneously as written.

c. $5\ Fe^{2+}(aq)+2\ Mn^{2+}(aq)+8\ H_{2}O(l)\rightarrow 5\ Fe(s)+2\ MnO_{4}^{-}(aq)+16\ H^{+}(aq)$

$E_{cell}^{o}=E_{cathode}^{o}-E_{anode}^{o}=-0.45\ V-(1.51\ V)=-1.96\ V$

$E_{cell}^{o}<0$ Therefore, the reaction will not proceed spontaneously as written.

43. Balance the following reaction equations and determine E_{cell}^{o} for each reaction. Indicate whether they will proceed spontaneously as written:

a. $Fe(s)+Cr_{2}O_{7}^{2-}(aq)\rightarrow Fe^{2+}(aq)+Cr^{3+}(aq)$ (acidic)

$3\ Fe(s)+Cr_{2}O_{7}^{2-}(aq)+7\ H_{2}O(l)\rightarrow 3\ Fe^{2+}(aq)+2\ Cr^{3+}(aq)+14\ OH^{-}(aq)$

$E_{cell}^{o}=E_{cathode}^{o}-E_{anode}^{o}=1.23\ V-(-0.45\ V)=1.68\ V$

$E_{cell}^{o}>0$ Therefore, the reaction will proceed spontaneously as written.

b. $MnO_2(s) + Ag^+(aq) \rightarrow MnO_4^-(aq) + Ag(s)$ (basic)

$MnO_2(s) + 3\ Ag^+(aq) + 4\ OH^-(aq) \rightarrow MnO_4^-(aq) + 3\ Ag(s) + 2\ H_2O(l)$

$E^o_{cell} = E^o_{cathode} - E^o_{anode} = 0.80\ V - (0.60\ V) = 0.20\ V$

$E^o_{cell} > 0$ Therefore, the reaction will proceed spontaneously as written.

c. $Co^{2+}(aq) + H_2O_2(aq) \rightarrow O_2(g) + Co(s)$ (acidic)

$Co^{2+}(aq) + H_2O_2(aq) \rightarrow O_2(g) + Co(s) + 2\ H^+(aq)$

$E^o_{cell} = E^o_{cathode} - E^o_{anode} = -0.28\ V - (0.70\ V) = -0.98\ V$

$E^o_{cell} < 0$ Therefore, the reaction will not proceed spontaneously as written.

44. Combine the following half-reactions into the balanced equation for a spontaneous redox reaction and calculate E^o_{cell}:

$N_2O(g) + 2\ H^+(aq) + 2\ e^- \rightarrow N_2(g) + H_2O(l)$ $E^o = 1.73\ V$

$I_2(s) + 2\ e^- \rightarrow 2\ I^-(aq)$ $E^o = 0.54\ V$

The half-cell with the most positive standard reduction potential will serve as the cathode:

$N_2O(g) + 2\ I^-(aq) + 2\ H^+(aq) \rightarrow N_2(g) + I_2(s) + H_2O(l)$

$E^o_{cell} = E^o_{cathode} - E^o_{anode} = 1.73\ V - (0.54\ V) = 1.19\ V$

45. Combine the following half-reactions into the balanced equation for a spontaneous redox reaction and calculate E^o_{cell}:

$MnO_4^-(aq) + 4\ H^+(aq) + 3\ e^- \rightarrow MnO_2(s) + 2\ H_2O(l)$ $E^o = 1.67\ V$

$Fe^{2+}(aq) + 2\ e^- \rightarrow Fe(s)$ $E^o = -0.45\ V$

The half-cell with the most positive standard reduction potential will serve as the cathode:

$2\ MnO_4^-(aq) + 3\ Fe(s) + 8\ H^+(aq) \rightarrow 2\ MnO_2(s) + 3\ Fe^{2+}(aq) + 4\ H_2O(l)$

$E^o_{cell} = E^o_{cathode} - E^o_{anode} = 1.67\ V - (-0.45\ V) = 2.12\ V$

GIBBS FREE ENERGY, EQUILIBRIUM, AND CELL POTENTIAL

46. Use standard reduction potentials to calculate ΔG^o for the following reactions:

a. $Br_2(l) + 2\ I^-(aq) \rightarrow 2\ Br^-(aq) + I_2(s)$

Identify the oxidation and reduction half-reactions and look up the standard reduction potentials for each in Table 13.1.

Oxidation half-reaction:

$2\ I^-(aq) \rightleftharpoons I_2(s) + 2\ e^-$ $\qquad\qquad\qquad E^o = 0.54\ V$

Reduction half-reaction:

$Br_2(l) + 2\ e^- \rightleftharpoons 2\ Br^-(aq)$ $\qquad\qquad\qquad E^o = 1.09\ V$

Use the standard reduction potentials to determine E^o_{cell}.

$E^o_{cell} = E^o_{cathode} - E^o_{anode} = \textbf{1.09 V} - (\textbf{0.54 V}) = \textbf{0.55 V}$

We now calculate ΔG^o:

$\Delta G^o = -nFE^o_{cell}$,

$\Delta G^o = -\left(2\ mol\ e^-\right)\left(\dfrac{96,485\ C}{mol\ e^-}\right)\left(0.55\dfrac{J}{C}\right) = \textbf{--1.06} \times \textbf{10}^{\textbf{5}}\ \textbf{J}$

b. $Cu^{2+}(aq) + Pb(s) \rightarrow Pb^{2+}(aq) + Cu(s)$

Identify the oxidation and reduction half-reactions and look up the standard reduction potentials for each in Table 13.1.

Oxidation half-reaction:

$Pb(s) \rightleftharpoons Pb^{2+}(aq) + 2\ e^-$ $\qquad\qquad\qquad E^o = -0.13\ V$

Reduction half-reaction:

$Cu^{2+}(aq) + 2\ e^- \rightleftharpoons Cu(s)$ $\qquad\qquad\qquad E^o = 0.15\ V$

Use the standard reduction potentials to determine E^o_{cell}.

$E^o_{cell} = E^o_{cathode} - E^o_{anode} = \textbf{0.15 V} - (\textbf{--0.13 V}) = \textbf{0.28 V}$

We now calculate ΔG^o.

$\Delta G^o = -nFE^o_{cell}$,

$\Delta G^o = -\left(2\ mol\ e^-\right)\left(\dfrac{96,485\ C}{mol\ e^-}\right)\left(0.28\dfrac{J}{C}\right) = \textbf{--5.40} \times \textbf{10}^{\textbf{4}}\ \textbf{J}$

47. Use standard reduction potentials to calculate ΔG° for the following reactions:

a. $2\ Al(s) + Ni^{2+}(aq) \rightarrow 2\ Al^{+}(aq) + Ni(s)$

Identify the oxidation and reduction half-reactions and look up the standard reduction potentials for each in Table 13.1.

Oxidation half-reaction:

$$Al(s) \rightleftharpoons Al^{3+}(aq) + 3\ e^{-} \qquad\qquad E^{\circ} = -1.66\ V$$

Reduction half-reaction:

$$Ni^{2+}(aq) + 2\ e^{-} \rightleftharpoons Ni(s) \qquad\qquad E^{\circ} = -0.26\ V$$

Use the standard reduction potentials to determine E°_{cell}.

$$E^{\circ}_{cell} = E^{\circ}_{cathode} - E^{\circ}_{anode} = -0.26\ V - (-1.66\ V) = 1.40\ V$$

We now calculate ΔG°.

$$\Delta G^{\circ} = -nFE^{\circ}_{cell}$$

$$\Delta G^{\circ} = -\left(6\ mol\ e^{-}\right)\left(\frac{96,485\ C}{mol\ e^{-}}\right)\left(1.40\frac{J}{C}\right) = -8.10 \times 10^{5}\ J$$

b. $Ca(s) + Pb^{2+}(aq) \rightarrow Ca^{2+}(aq) + Pb(s)$

Identify the oxidation and reduction half-reactions and look up the standard reduction potentials for each in Table 13.1.

Oxidation half-reaction:

$$Ca(s) \rightleftharpoons Ca^{2+}(aq) + 2\ e^{-} \qquad\qquad E^{\circ} = -2.87\ V$$

Reduction half-reaction:

$$Pb^{2+}(aq) + 2\ e^{-} \rightleftharpoons Pb(s) \qquad\qquad E^{\circ} = -0.13\ V$$

Use the standard reduction potentials to determine E°_{cell}.

$$E^{\circ}_{cell} = E^{\circ}_{cathode} - E^{\circ}_{anode} = -0.13\ V - (-2.87\ V) = 2.74\ V$$

We now calculate ΔG°.

$$\Delta G^{\circ} = -nFE^{\circ}_{cell}$$

$$\Delta G^{\circ} = -\left(2\ mol\ e^{-}\right)\left(\frac{96,485\ C}{mol\ e^{-}}\right)\left(2.74\frac{J}{C}\right) = -5.29 \times 10^{5}\ J$$

48. Use standard reduction potentials to calculate ΔG^o for the following reactions:

    a. $MnO_2(s) + 4\ H^+(aq) + Sn(s) \rightarrow Mn^{2+}(aq) + 2\ H_2O(l) + Sn^{2+}(aq)$

    $$\Delta G^o = -\left(2\ mol\ e^-\right)\left(\frac{96,485\ C}{mol\ e^-}\right)\left(1.36\frac{J}{C}\right) = -2.62 \times 10^5\ J$$

    b. $Co(s) + Fe^{3+}(aq) \rightarrow Co^{2+}(aq) + Fe(s)$

    $$\Delta G^o = -\left(6\ mol\ e^-\right)\left(\frac{96,485\ C}{mol\ e^-}\right)\left(0.24\frac{J}{C}\right) = -1.39 \times 10^5\ J$$

49. Use standard reduction potentials to calculate ΔG^o for the following reactions:

    a. $O_2(g) + 2\ H_2O(l) + 2\ Sn(s) \rightarrow 4\ OH^-(aq) + 2\ Sn^{2+}(aq)$

    $$\Delta G^o = -\left(4\ mol\ e^-\right)\left(\frac{96,485\ C}{mol\ e^-}\right)\left(0.54\frac{J}{C}\right) = -2.08 \times 10^5\ J$$

    b. $2\ H^+(aq) + Sn(s) \rightarrow H_2(g) + Sn^{2+}$

    $$\Delta G^o = -\left(2\ mol\ e^-\right)\left(\frac{96,485\ C}{mol\ e^-}\right)\left(0.14\frac{J}{C}\right) = -2.70 \times 10^4\ J$$

50. Determine the equilibrium constant, K, for the reactions (25°C) in problem 46.

    a. $Br_2(l) + 2\ I^-(aq) \rightarrow 2\ Br^-(aq) + I_2(s)$

    $$E^o_{cell} = \frac{0.0592\ V}{n}\log K$$

    $$\log K = \frac{nE^o_{cell}}{0.0592\ V} = \frac{(2)(0.55\ V)}{0.0592\ V} = 18.58108$$

    $$K = 10^{18.58108} = 3.81 \times 10^{18}$$

    b. $Cu^{2+}(aq) + Pb(s) \rightarrow Pb^{2+}(aq) + Cu(s)$

    $$E^o_{cell} = \frac{0.0592\ V}{n}\log K$$

    $$\log K = \frac{nE^o_{cell}}{0.0592\ V} = \frac{(2)(0.28\ V)}{0.0592\ V} = 9.45946$$

    $$K = 10^{9.45946} = 2.88 \times 10^9$$

51. Determine the equilibrium constant, K, for the reactions in problem 47.

a. $2\ Al(s) + Ni^{2+}(aq) \rightarrow 2\ Al^{+}(aq) + Ni(s)$

$$E^{o}_{cell} = \frac{0.0592\ V}{n}\log K$$

$$\log K = \frac{nE^{o}_{cell}}{0.0592\ V} = \frac{(6)(1.40\ V)}{0.0592\ V} = 141.8919$$

$$K = 10^{141.8919} = \mathbf{7.80 \times 10^{141}}$$

b. $Ca(s) + Pb^{2+}(aq) \rightarrow Ca^{2+}(aq) + Pb(s)$

$$E^{o}_{cell} = \frac{0.0592\ V}{n}\log K$$

$$\log K = \frac{nE^{o}_{cell}}{0.0592\ V} = \frac{(2)(2.74\ V)}{0.0592\ V} = 92.5676$$

$$K = 10^{92.5676} = \mathbf{3.69 \times 10^{92}}$$

52. Determine the equilibrium constant, K, for the reactions in problem 48.

a. $MnO_2(s) + 4\ H^{+}(aq) + Sn(s) \rightarrow Mn^{2+}(aq) + 2\ H_2O(l) + Sn^{2+}(aq)$

$$E^{o}_{cell} = \frac{0.0592\ V}{n}\log K$$

$$\log K = \frac{nE^{o}_{cell}}{0.0592\ V} = \frac{(2)(1.36\ V)}{0.0592\ V} = 45.94594$$

$$K = 10^{45.94594} = \mathbf{8.83 \times 10^{45}}$$

b. $3\ Co(s) + 2\ Fe^{3+}(aq) \rightarrow 3\ Co^{2+}(aq) + 2\ Fe(s)$

$$E^{o}_{cell} = \frac{0.0592\ V}{n}\log K$$

$$\log K = \frac{nE^{o}_{cell}}{0.0592\ V} = \frac{(6)(0.24\ V)}{0.0592\ V} = 24.2143243$$

$$K = 10^{24.2143243} = \mathbf{2.11 \times 10^{24}}$$

53. Determine the equilibrium constant, K, for the reactions in problem 49.

a. $O_2(g) + 2\ H_2O(l) + 2\ Sn(s) \rightarrow 4\ OH^{-}(aq) + 2\ Sn^{2+}(aq)$

$$E^{o}_{cell} = \frac{0.0592\ V}{n}\log K$$

$$\log K = \frac{nE^o_{cell}}{0.0592\ V} = \frac{(4)(0.54\ V)}{0.0592\ V} = 36.48649$$

$$K = 10^{36.48649} = \mathbf{3.07 \times 10^{36}}$$

b. $2\ H^+(aq) + Sn(s) \rightarrow H_2(g) + Sn^{2+}$

$$E^o_{cell} = \frac{0.0592\ V}{n}\log K$$

$$\log K = \frac{nE^o_{cell}}{0.0592\ V} = \frac{(2)(0.14\ V)}{0.0592\ V} = 4.7297$$

$$K = 10^{4.7297} = \mathbf{5.37 \times 10^4}$$

54. Calculate E^o_{cell} for the following reaction at 25°C under the given sets of conditions:

$$Pb^{2+}(aq) + Mn(s) \rightarrow Pb(s) + Mn^{2+}(aq)$$

a.   Standard conditions: $[Pb^{2+}] = 1.00\ M;\ [Mn^{2+}] = 1.00\ M$

Oxidation half-reaction:

$Mn(s) \rightleftharpoons Mn^{2+}(aq) + 2\ e^-$ $\qquad\qquad\qquad\qquad$ $E^o = -1.19\ V$

Reduction half-reaction:

$Pb^{2+}(aq) + 2\ e^- \rightleftharpoons Pb(s)$ $\qquad\qquad\qquad\qquad$ $E^o = -0.13\ V$

$$\mathbf{E^o_{cell} = E^o_{cathode} - E^o_{anode} = -0.13\ V - (-1.19\ V) = 1.06\ V}$$

b. $[Pb^{2+}] = 0.0150\ M;\ [Mn^{2+}] = 1.50\ M$

$$E_{cell} = E^o_{cell} - \frac{0.0592\ V}{n}\log Q$$

$$\mathbf{E_{cell} = 1.06\ V - \frac{0.0592\ V}{2}\log\frac{[Mn^{2+}]}{[Pb^{2+}]} = 1.06\ V - \frac{0.0592\ V}{2}\log\frac{(1.50)}{(0.0150)} = 1.00\ V}$$

c. $[Pb^{2+}] = 1.50\ M;\ [Mn^{2+}] = 0.0150\ M$

$$E_{cell} = E^o_{cell} - \frac{0.0592\ V}{n}\log Q$$

$$\mathbf{E_{cell} = 1.06\ V - \frac{0.0592\ V}{2}\log\frac{[Mn^{2+}]}{[Pb^{2+}]} = 1.06\ V - \frac{0.0592\ V}{2}\log\frac{(0.0150)}{(1.50)} = 1.12\ V}$$

55. Calculate E^o_{cell} for the following reaction at 25°C under the given sets of conditions:

$$2\ Fe^{3+}(aq) + 3\ Zn(s) \rightarrow 2\ Fe(s) + 3\ Zn^{2+}(aq)$$

a. Standard conditions: $[Fe^{3+}] = 1.00\ M;\ [Zn^{2+}] = 1.00\ M$

Oxidation half-reaction:

$$Zn(s) \rightleftharpoons Zn^{2+}(aq) + 2\ e^- \qquad\qquad E^o = -0.76\ V$$

Reduction half-reaction:

$$Fe^{3+}(aq) + 3\ e^- \rightleftharpoons Fe(s) \qquad\qquad E^o = -0.036\ V$$

$$E^o_{cell} = E^o_{cathode} - E^o_{anode} = -0.036\ V - (-0.76\ V) = 0.724\ V$$

b. $[Fe^{3+}] = 0.00100\ M;\ [Zn^{2+}] = 3.00\ M$

$$E_{cell} = E^o_{cell} - \frac{0.0592\ V}{n} \log Q$$

$$E_{cell} = E^o_{cell} - \frac{0.0592\ V}{6} \log\frac{\left[Zn^{2+}\right]^3}{\left[Fe^{3+}\right]^2} = 0.724\ V - \frac{0.0592\ V}{6} \log\frac{(3.00)^3}{(0.00100)^2} = 0.65\ V$$

c. $[Fe^{3+}] = 2.25\ M;\ [Zn^{2+}] = 0.00320\ M$

$$E_{cell} = E^o_{cell} - \frac{0.0592\ V}{n} \log Q$$

$$E_{cell} = E^o_{cell} - \frac{0.0592\ V}{6} \log\frac{\left[Zn^{2+}\right]^3}{\left[Fe^{3+}\right]^2} = 0.724\ V - \frac{0.0592\ V}{6} \log\frac{(0.00320)^3}{(2.25)^2} = 0.80\ V$$

56. At 25°C, one of the half-cells in a galvanic cell consists of a copper electrode submerged into a 3.75 × 10⁻³ M aqueous solution of copper(II) nitrate, while the other half-cell consists of a zinc electrode in a 0.375 M solution of zinc nitrate. Calculate E_{cell} for this galvanic cell.

$$Cu^{2+}(aq) + Zn(s) \rightarrow Zn^{2+}(aq) + Cu(s)$$

$$E^o_{cell} = E^o_{cathode} - E^o_{anode} = 0.34\ V - (-0.76\ V) = 1.10\ V$$

$$E_{cell} = E^o_{cell} - \frac{0.0592\ V}{2} \log\frac{\left[Zn^{2+}\right]}{\left[Fe^{3+}\right]} = 1.10\ V - \frac{0.0592\ V}{2} \log\frac{(0.375)}{(0.00375)} = 1.04\ V$$

57. At 25°C, one of the half-cells in a galvanic cell consists of a lead electrode submerged into a 0.0350 M aqueous solution of lead(II) nitrate, while the other half-cell consists of a silver electrode in a 0.375 M solution of silver nitrate. Calculate E^o_{cell} for this galvanic cell.

$$2\ Ag^+(aq) + Pb(s) \rightarrow Pb^{2+}(aq) + 2\ Ag(s)$$

$$E^o_{cell} = E^o_{cathode} - E^o_{anode} = 0.80\ V - (-0.13\ V) = 0.93\ V$$

$$E_{cell} = E^o_{cell} - \frac{0.0592\ V}{2}\log\frac{\left[Pb^{2+}\right]}{\left[Ag^+\right]^2} = 0.93\ V - \frac{0.0592\ V}{2}\log\frac{(0.0350)}{(0.375)^2} = \mathbf{0.95\ V}$$

ELECTROLYSIS

58. Consider the following generic electrolytic cell:

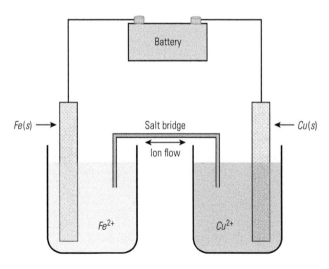

Sketch this cell and:

a. Write the balanced half-reaction for the cathode.

The half-cell with the most negative reduction potential will be reduced in an electrolytic cell. Therefore:

Cathode (Reduction): $\qquad Fe^{2+}(aq) + 2\ e^- \rightarrow Fe(s) \qquad\qquad E^o = -0.45\ V$

b. Write the balanced half-reaction for the anode.

The half-cell with the most positive reduction potential according to Table 13.1 will be oxidized in an electrolytic cell. Therefore:

Anode (Oxidation): $\qquad Cu(s) \rightarrow Cu^{2+}(aq) + 2\ e^- \qquad\qquad E^o = +0.34\ V$

c. Label the cathode and anode half-cells, label the battery terminals as positive or negative, and draw the flow of electrons.

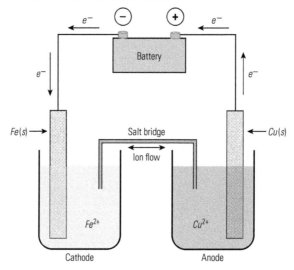

59. Sketch a cell similar to that in problem 59 except replace the Cu^{2+} / Cu cell with Mg^{2+} / $Mg(s)$ ·

a. Write the balanced half-reaction for the cathode.

The half-cell with the most negative reduction potential will be reduced in an electrolytic cell. Therefore:

Cathode (Reduction): $Mg^{2+}(aq) + 2\ e^- \rightarrow Mg(s)$ $E^0 = -2.37\ V$

b. Write the balanced half-reaction for the anode.

The half-cell with the most positive reduction potential according to Table 13.1 will be oxidized in an electrolytic cell. Therefore:

Anode (Oxidation): $Fe(s) \rightarrow Fe^{2+}(aq) + 2\ e^-$ $E^0 = -0.45\ V$

c. Label the battery terminals as positive or negative and draw the flow of electrons.

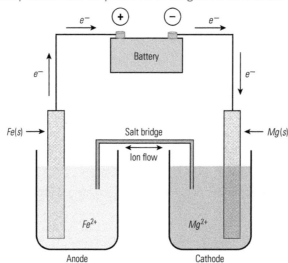

60. Write the half-reactions that occur at the anode and cathode during electrolysis of molten sodium iodide.

    In the electrolysis of a salt, the cation is reduced and the anion is oxidized, therefore:

    Cathode (reduction): $Na^+ + e^- \rightarrow Na$

    Anode (oxidation): $2\ I^- \rightarrow I_2 + 2\ e^-$

61. Write the half-reactions that occur at the anode and cathode during electrolysis of molten potassium chloride.

    In the electrolysis of a salt, the cation is reduced and the anion is oxidized, therefore:

    Cathode (reduction): $K^+ + e^- \rightarrow K$

    Anode (oxidation): $2\ Cl^- \rightarrow Cl_2 + 2\ e^-$

62. In the electrolysis of aqueous potassium chloride, is chlorine gas or oxygen more likely to evolve from the anode? Why?

    Chlorine gas.

    Even though water has a lower reduction potential than that of chloride (at neutral pH), overvoltage results in an apparent potential of water that is approximately 1.4 V, which is slightly higher than that of chloride ($E = 1.34\ V$). As such, chloride is preferentially oxidized at the anode, resulting a chlorine gas as the product.

63. In the electrolysis of aqueous magnesium chloride, is magnesium metal or hydrogen gas more likely to evolve from the cathode? Why?

    Hydrogen gas.

    Water has a more positive reduction potential than that of magnesium (at neutral pH), and overvoltage does not change this. As such, water is preferentially reduced at the cathode, resulting a hydrogen gas as the product.

64. Write the half-reactions that occur at the anode and cathode during electrolysis of aqueous copper(II) chloride.

    There are two possible half reactions at the cathode, reduction of copper(II) or the reduction of water. Because the electrode potential of the reduction of water is less than that of copper(II), copper(II) will be preferentially reduced at the cathode.

    Cathode: $Cu^{2+}(aq) + 2\ e^- \rightarrow Cu(s)$

    There are two possible half reactions at the anode, oxidation of chloride or the oxidation of water. Because the reduction potential of water is less than that of chlorine, we would predict it will be oxidized. However, due to overvoltage, we find the apparent electrode potential for the oxidation of water ($E = 0.82 + 0.6 \approx 1.4\ V$) to be slightly greater than that for chloride ($E = 1.34\ V$). As such, chloride is oxidized preferentially.

    Anode: $2\ Cl^-(aq) \rightarrow Cl_2(g) + 2\ e^-$

65. Write the half-reactions that occur at the anode and cathode during electrolysis of aqueous copper(II) bromide.

There are two possible half reactions at the cathode, reduction of copper(II) or the reduction of water. Because the electrode potential of the reduction of water is less than that of copper(II), copper(II) will be preferentially reduced at the cathode.

Cathode: $Cu^{2+}(aq) + 2\ e^- \rightarrow Cu(s)$

There are two possible half reactions at the anode, oxidation of bromide or the oxidation of water. Because the reduction potential of water is less than that of bromide, we would predict it will be preferentially oxidized. However, due to overvoltage, we find the apparent electrode potential for the oxidation of water ($E = 0.82 + 0.6 \approx 1.4\ V$) to be greater than that for bromide ($E = 1.09\ V$). As such, bromide is oxidized preferentially.

Anode: $2\ Br^-(aq) \rightarrow Br_2(g) + 2\ e^-$

66. Write the half-reactions that occur at the anode and cathode during electrolysis of aqueous nickel(II) iodide.

There are two possible half reactions at the cathode, reduction of nickel(II) or the reduction of water. Because the electrode potential of the reduction of water ($E = -0.42\ V$) is less than that of nickel(II) ($E = -0.26\ V$), nickel(II) will be preferentially reduced at the cathode.

Cathode: $Ni^{2+}(aq) + 2\ e^- \rightarrow Ni(s)$

There are two possible half reactions at the anode, oxidation of iodide or the oxidation of water. Because the reduction potential of water is less than that of iodide, we would predict it will be preferentially oxidized. However, due to overvoltage, we find the apparent electrode potential for the oxidation of water ($E = 0.82 + 0.6 \approx 1.4\ V$) to be greater than that for iodide ($E = 0.54\ V$). As such, iodide is oxidized preferentially.

Anode: $2\ I^-(aq) \rightarrow I_2(g) + 2\ e^-$

67. Write the half-reactions that occur at the anode and cathode during electrolysis of aqueous calcium chloride.

There are two possible half reactions at the cathode, reduction of calcium cation or the reduction of water. Because the electrode potential of the reduction of water ($E = -0.42\ V$) is greater than that of Ca^{2+} ($E = -2.87\ V$), water will be preferentially reduced at the cathode.

Cathode: $2\ H_2O(l) + 2\ e^- \rightarrow H_2(g) + 2\ OH^-$

There are two possible half reactions at the anode, oxidation of iodide or the oxidation of water. Because the reduction potential of water is less than that of chloride, we would predict it will be preferentially oxidized. However, due to overvoltage, we find the apparent electrode potential for the oxidation of water ($E = 0.82 + 0.6 \approx 1.4\ V$) to be greater than that for chloride ($E = 1.36\ V$). As such, chloride is oxidized preferentially.

Anode: $2\ I^-(aq) \rightarrow I_2(g) + 2\ e^-$

68. Electrolysis and electroplating is the chemical means by which many metals are produced. If electrolysis of a solution of a silver salt is carried out with a current of 2.0 amps, what mass of silver metal will be produced over a time interval of 1.50 hours?

$$Ag^+(aq) + e^- \rightarrow Ag(s)$$

$$1.50 \ hrs \times \frac{60 \ min}{1 \ hr} \times \frac{60 \ s}{1 \ min} \times \frac{2.00 \ C}{1 \ s} \times \frac{1 \ mol \ e^-}{96,485 \ C} \times \frac{1 \ mol \ Ag}{1 \ mol \ e^-} \times \frac{107.87 \ g \ Ag}{1 \ mol \ Ag} = \textbf{12.1 g Ag}$$

69. If electrolysis of a solution of Zn^{2+} is carried out with a current of 1.35 amps, what mass of zinc will be produced over a time interval of 45.25 minutes?

$$Zn^{2+}(aq) + 2 \ e^- \rightarrow Zn(s)$$

$$45.25 \ min \times \frac{60 \ s}{1 \ min} \times \frac{1.35 \ C}{1 \ s} \times \frac{1 \ mol \ e^-}{96,485 \ C} \times \frac{1 \ mol \ Zn}{2 \ mol \ e^-} \times \frac{65.38 \ g \ Zn}{1 \ mol \ Zn} = \textbf{1.24 g Zn}$$

70. If electrolysis of a solution of Fe^{3+} is carried out with a current of 1.75 amps, how long would it take to produce 4.35 g of iron metal?

$$Fe^{3+}(aq) + 3 \ e^- \rightarrow Fe(s)$$

$$4.35 \ g \ Fe \times \frac{1 \ mol \ Fe}{55.85 \ g \ Fe} \times \frac{3 \ mol \ e^-}{1 \ mol \ Fe} \times \frac{96,485 \ C}{1 \ mol \ e^-} \times \frac{1 \ s}{1.75 \ C} \times \frac{1 \ min}{60 \ s} \times \frac{1 \ hr}{60 \ min} = \textbf{3.58 hrs.}$$

71. If electrolysis of a solution of Na^+ is carried out with a current of 2.00 amps, how long would it take to produce 10.00 g of sodium metal?

$$Na^+(aq) + e^- \rightarrow Na(s)$$

$$10.00 \ g \ Na \times \frac{1 \ mol \ Na}{22.99 \ g \ Na} \times \frac{1 \ mol \ e^-}{1 \ mol \ Na} \times \frac{96,485 \ C}{1 \ mol \ e^-} \times \frac{1 \ s}{2.00 \ C} \times \frac{1 \ min}{60 \ s} \times \frac{1 \ hr}{60 \ min} = \textbf{5.83 hrs.}$$

KEY TERMS

Alkaline battery   A subset of batteries collectively known as *dry-cell batteries* that are constructed with no fluid components. These include the common AAA, AA, C, and D batteries used in small handheld or mobile devices such as flashlights, radios, etc.

Ampere   We measure electric current through a medium in units of charge per unit time. The commonly used unit of current is the ampere (amp) which is defined as 1 C/s.

Anode   The electrode where oxidation occurs in all electrochemical cells.

Battery   A housing which encloses one or more electrochemical cells which can be used as a source of electric power.

Cathode   The electrode where reduction occurs in all electrochemical cells.

Cell diagram   A standard cell notation which is used as a shorthand in describing a galvanic cell. The notation defines oxidation (anode) on the left and reduction (cathode) on the right.

Cell notation   See cell diagram.

Cell potential   The potential difference between two electrodes in an electrochemical cell which is often denoted by the symbol, E_{cell}.

Concentration cell   An electrochemical cell wherein both half-cells consist of the same half reaction but the solutes are present in different concentrations.

Corrosion   The unwanted oxidation of metals caused by oxidizing agents present in nearly all natural environments.

Coulomb   A unit used to measure electric charge. It is defined as 1 ampere-second.

Electrochemical cells   Devices that rely on redox reactions to generate electrical current.

Electrochemistry   The study of electrical work and its relation to chemical change.

Electrode   Conductive materials which facilitate the flow of electrons to and from each of the half-cells.

Electrolysis   The use of electrical energy to force a redox reaction which is otherwise not spontaneous.

Electrolytic cells   Systems which use an external electric current to produce chemical changes.

Electromotive force   See cell potential.

Faraday constant   A constant which represents the total charge of 1 mole of electrons.

Fuel cells   An electrochemical cell wherein the reactant components of the redox reaction are continuously fed into the cell like a fuel.

Galvanic cells   Devices which use spontaneous redox reactions to generate an electric current which is then used to do work.

Half-cell   The two separate compartments of the galvanic cell, one containing the oxidation half-reaction and, the other, containing the reduction half-reaction.

Half-reaction   Half-reaction refers to either the oxidation or reduction process (reaction) in an oxidation-reduction reaction.

Inert electrode   A conductive material which serves as an electron source or drop, without playing any chemical role in the redox process.

Nernst equation   A mathematical expression which allows the determination of E_{cell} from non-standard reactant and product concentrations in redox reactions.

Overvoltage   The voltage, over and above that which is otherwise expected based on the standard electrode potentials, which is required to drive a nonspontaneous redox reaction in an electrolytic process.

Oxidation   The loss of electrons.

Oxidation number   Imaginary charges which are assigned based on a set of rules.

Oxidation state   See oxidation number.

Oxidation-reduction reaction   Reactions characterized by the exchange of electrons.

Oxidizing agent   In a redox reaction, the reactant which contains the element which is reduced is referred to as the *oxidizing agent* (electron acceptor).

Redox reactions   (short for Oxidation-reduction reaction) Reactions characterized by the exchange of electrons.

Reducing agent   In a redox reaction, the reactant containing the element which is oxidized is the **reducing agent** (electron donor).

Reduction   The gain of electrons.

Sacrificial electrode   A metal which has a more negative reduction potential (listed lower on Table 13.1) in contact with iron. This creates a situation where this other metal will preferentially oxidize in place of the iron, thereby preventing corrosion of the iron.

Salt bridge   A salt bridge typically contains an electrolyte in solution and held between two permeable plugs or discs, which allows free flow of counter ions between each half-cell of an electrochemical cell while maintaining their separation.

Standard cell potential   The expected cell potential calculated from the standard reduction potentials of the half-cells comprising an electrochemical cell.

Standard electrode potential   The potential of a half-cell written as a reduction, measured against the standard hydrogen electrode.

Standard hydrogen electrode   The electrode which serves to define the standard reference potential of 0. The standard hydrogen electrode is characterized by an inert metal electrode (platinum) submerged in a 1 M *HCl* solution, bathed in hydrogen gas at a pressure of 1 atm (hydrogen gas is bubbled over the electrode).

Standard reduction potential   See standard electrode potential.

Volt   A unit for measuring the electric potential energy difference is an electrochemical cell. It is defined as 1 joule-per-coulomb.

Voltaic cells   See galvanic cells.

CHAPTER 14

Chemical Kinetics

KEY CONCEPTS

- Reaction Rates as a Function of Reactant Concentrations

- Instantaneous Rates

- The Rate Law and Integrated Rate Laws

- Reaction Half Life

- The Temperature Dependence of Reaction Rates

- Catalytic Effects on Rate

- Reaction Mechanisms

OVERVIEW OF CHEMICAL REACTION RATES

1. What are chemical reaction rates?

   Reaction rates involve the change in either reactant or product concentrations as a function of time.

2. Define chemical kinetics.

   Chemical kinetics is the study of how fast reactants change into products by examining reaction rates.

3. Why are the rates of reactions defined as the negative of the change of reactant concentrations with respect to time, and the positive of the change of product concentrations with respect to time?

   The rates of reactions are defined as the negative of the change of reactant concentrations with respect to time because the reactants are decreasing as the reaction proceeds making the change a negative number. The negative sign in front of this change makes the overall rate of reaction positive (as it should be). The rates of reactions can also be defined as the positive of the change of product concentrations with respect to time because products increase as the reaction proceeds, making the change positive as well as the rate of reaction (again, as it should be).

4. Express the rate of reaction with respect to each reactant and product given the following hypothetical generic chemical equation:

   $$A + B \rightarrow C + D$$

   $$Rate\ of\ reaction = -\frac{\Delta[A]}{\Delta t} = -\frac{\Delta[B]}{\Delta t} = \frac{\Delta[C]}{\Delta t} = \frac{\Delta[D]}{\Delta t}$$

5. Express the rate of reaction with respect to each reactant and product given the following hypothetical generic chemical equation:

   $$A + 3B \rightarrow 2C + 2D$$

   $$Rate\ of\ reaction = -\frac{\Delta[A]}{\Delta t} = -\frac{1}{3}\frac{\Delta[B]}{\Delta t} = \frac{1}{2}\frac{\Delta[C]}{\Delta t} = \frac{1}{2}\frac{\Delta[D]}{\Delta t}$$

6. Express the rate expression with respect to the highlighted reactant or product in the balanced chemical equations listed below:

   a. $CH_4(g) + 2O_2(g) \rightarrow CO_2(g) + 2H_2O(g)$

   b. $P_4(s) + 3O_2(g) \rightarrow 2P_2O_3(s)$

   c. $2Fe_2O_3(s) + 3C(s) \rightarrow 4Fe(s) + 3CO_2(g)$

   d. $2H_2(g) + V_2O_5(s) \rightarrow V_2O_3(s) + 2H_2O(l)$

   a. $Rate\ of\ reaction = -\dfrac{\Delta CH_4}{\Delta t}$

   b. $Rate\ of\ reaction = -\dfrac{1}{3}\dfrac{\Delta O_2}{\Delta t}$

c. $\text{Rate of reaction} = \dfrac{1}{4}\dfrac{\Delta Fe}{\Delta t}$

d. $\text{Rate of reaction} = \dfrac{1}{2}\dfrac{\Delta H_2O}{\Delta t}$

7. Express the rate expression with respect to the highlighted reactant or product in the balanced chemical equations listed below:

a. $4NH_3(g) + 5O_2(g) \rightarrow 4NO\,(g) + 6H_2O(g)$

b. $3Cl_2(g) + 6NaOH\,(aq) \rightarrow 5NaCl\,(aq) + NaClO_3\,(aq) + 3H_2O\,(l)$

c. $2Fe\,(s) + O_2\,(g) + 2H_2O\,(l) \rightarrow 2Fe(OH)_2\,(s)$

d. $C_6H_6\,(l) + 15H_2O_2\,(l) \rightarrow 6CO_2\,(g) + 18H_2O\,(l)$

a. $\text{Rate of reaction} = -\dfrac{1}{4}\dfrac{\Delta NH_3}{\Delta t}$

b. $\text{Rate of reaction} = -\dfrac{1}{6}\dfrac{\Delta NaOH}{\Delta t}$

c. $\text{Rate of reaction} = \dfrac{1}{2}\dfrac{\Delta Fe(OH)_2}{\Delta t}$

d. $\text{Rate of reaction} = \dfrac{1}{18}\dfrac{\Delta H_2O}{\Delta t}$

8. Using the data table below, calculate the rate of reaction with respect to reactant X in the first 10 seconds.

$$X \rightarrow Y + Z$$

Time (s)	X concentration (M)	Y concentration (M)	Z concentration (M)
0.0	3.00	0.00	0.00
10.0	2.70	0.30	0.30
20.0	2.40	0.60	0.60
30.0	2.20	0.80	0.80

$$\text{Rate of reaction} = -\frac{\Delta[X]}{\Delta t} = -\frac{([X]_2 - [X]_1)}{(t_2 - t_1)} = -\frac{(2.70 - 3.00)}{(10.0 - 0.0)} = 3.0 \times 10^{-2}\ M/s$$

9. Using the data table in problem 8, calculate the rate of reaction with respect to product Y in the last 10.0 seconds.

$$\text{Rate of reaction} = \frac{\Delta[Y]}{\Delta t} = \frac{([Y]_2 - [Y]_1)}{(t_2 - t_1)} = \frac{(0.80 - 0.60)}{(30.0 - 20.0)} = 2.0 \times 10^{-2}\ M/s$$

10. Consider the following chemical reaction:

$$2SO_2\,(g) + O_2(g) \rightarrow 2SO_3(g)$$

What is the rate of this reaction if 0.15 mols of SO_3 are produced in a 0.50 L container in the first 25.0 s?

Concentration of SO_3 produced in 25.0 s $= \dfrac{0.15\ mols\ SO_3}{0.50\ L} = 0.30\ M\ SO_3$

$Rate\ of\ reaction = \dfrac{1}{2}\dfrac{\Delta[SO_3]}{\Delta t} = \dfrac{1}{2}\dfrac{(0.30-0.00)}{(25.0-0.00)} = 6.0\times10^{-3}\ \dfrac{M}{s}$

11. Based on your answer from question 10, what is the rate of depletion of $O_2\left(\dfrac{\Delta O_2}{\Delta t}\right)$ in that reaction during the same time period?

$Rate\ of\ reaction = \dfrac{1}{2}\dfrac{\Delta[SO_3]}{\Delta t} = \dfrac{1}{2}\dfrac{(0.30-0.00)}{(25.0-0.00)} = 6.0\times10^{-3}\ \dfrac{M}{s} = -\dfrac{\Delta[O_2]}{\Delta t}$

Therefore, the rate of depletion of $O_2 = -6.0\times10^{-3}\ \dfrac{M}{s}$ (negative because O_2 is a reactant).

12. Consider the following chemical reaction:

$$2N_2O\,(g) \rightarrow 2N_2(g) + O_2(g)$$

What is the rate of this reaction if 0.25 mols of O_2 are produced in a 0.50 L container in the first 35.0 s?

Concentration of O_2 produced in 35.0 s $= \dfrac{0.25\ mols\ O_2}{0.50\ L} = 0.50\ M\ SO_3$

$Rate\ of\ reaction = \dfrac{\Delta[O_2]}{\Delta t} = \dfrac{(0.50-0.00)}{(35.0-0.00)} = 1.4\times10^{-2}\ \dfrac{M}{s}$

13. Based on your answer from question 12, what is the rate of depletion of $N_2O\left(\dfrac{\Delta N_2O}{\Delta t}\right)$ in that reaction during the same time period?

$Rate\ of\ reaction = \dfrac{\Delta[O_2]}{\Delta t} = \dfrac{(0.50-0.00)}{(35.0-0.00)} = 1.4\times10^{-2}\ \dfrac{M}{s} = -\dfrac{1}{2}\dfrac{\Delta[N_2O]}{\Delta t}$

Therefore, the rate of depletion of $N_2O = -2.9\times10^{-2}\ \dfrac{M}{s}$ (negative because N_2O is a reactant).

For questions 14–17, consider the following chemical equation:

$$C_4H_8 \rightarrow 2C_2H_4$$

This reaction was monitored and the following data was collected:

Time (seconds)	$[C_4H_8]$ (M)
0.0	1.00
20.0	0.72
40.0	0.61
60.0	0.55

14. Given the data above, what is the reaction rate between 0.0 s and 20.0 s?

$$Rate\ of\ reaction = -\frac{\Delta[C_4H_8]}{\Delta t} = -\frac{(0.72 - 1.00)}{(20.0 - 0.0)} = 1.4 \times 10^{-2}\ \frac{M}{s}$$

15. Given the data above, what is the rate of production of C_2H_4 between 0.0 s and 20.0 s?

$$Rate\ of\ reaction = -\frac{\Delta[C_4H_8]}{\Delta t} = -\frac{(0.72 - 1.00)}{(20.0 - 0.0)} = 1.4 \times 10^{-2}\ \frac{M}{s} = \frac{1}{2}\frac{\Delta[C_2H_4]}{\Delta t}$$

Therefore, the rate of production of $C_2H_4 = 2.8. \times 10^{-2}\ \frac{M}{s}$ (twice the rate of reaction).

16. Given the data above, what is the reaction rate between 20.0 s and 40.0 s?

$$Rate\ of\ reaction = -\frac{\Delta[C_4H_8]}{\Delta t} = -\frac{(0.61 - 0.72)}{(40.0 - 20.0)} = 5.5 \times 10^{-3}\ \frac{M}{s}$$

17. Given the data above, what is the rate of production of $C_2H_4 \left(\frac{\Delta[C_2H_4]}{\Delta t} \right)$ between 20.0 s and 40.0 s?

$$Rate\ of\ reaction = -\frac{\Delta[C_4H_8]}{\Delta t} = -\frac{(0.61 - 0.72)}{(40.0 - 20.0)} = 5.5 \times 10^{-3}\ \frac{M}{s} = \frac{1}{2}\frac{\Delta[C_2H_4]}{\Delta t}$$

Therefore, the rate of production of $C_2H_4 = 1.1 \times 10^{-2}\ \frac{M}{s}$ (twice the rate of reaction).

18. What is the difference between the average rate of a reaction and the instantaneous rate of a reaction?

The average rate of a reaction can be calculated between two different time points (i.e. for a given particular time interval), while the instantaneous rate of a reaction can be calculated at any one point in time. The instantaneous rate can be calculated from the slope of the line tangent to the time point of interest on a curve generated from a plot of time versus concentration.

CONCENTRATION EFFECTS ON CHEMICAL REACTION RATES

19. What is the reaction order?

    The reaction order tells us how the reaction rate depends on the reactant concentrations.

20. What is the rate law equation?

    The rate law equation defines the mathematical relationship between the reactant concentrations to the reaction rate.

21. Define the rate constant (k).

    The rate constant (k) is the proportionality constant, which is related to the slope of the line in a graph of concentration versus time.

22. What is the overall reaction order?

    The overall reaction order is the sum of the powers in the rate equation.

23. What is the rate law if reactant "A" in the following generic equation is determined to be zero-order?

    $$A \rightarrow B$$
    $$Rate = k[A]^0$$
    $$Rate = k$$

24. What is the rate law if reactant "A" in the following generic equation is determined to be first-order?

    $$A \rightarrow B$$
    $$Rate = k[A]^1$$

25. What is the rate law if reactant "A" in the following generic equation is determined to be second-order?

    $$A \rightarrow B$$
    $$Rate = k[A]^2$$

26. What are the units for the rate constant (k) in an overall zero-order reaction?

    For an overall zero-order reaction, the units for k are M/s.

27. What are the units for the rate constant (k) in an overall first-order reaction?

    For an overall first-order reaction, the units for k are s^{-1}.

28. What are the units for the rate constant (k) in an overall second-order reaction?

    For an overall second-order reaction, the units for k are $M^{-1} \cdot s^{-1}$.

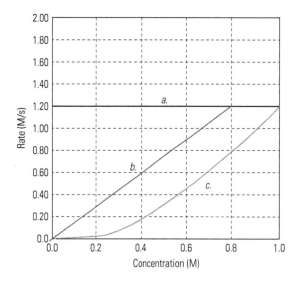

For questions 29–31, consider the following graph:

29. The line labeled "*a*" in the above graph represents what reaction order?
    a. Zero-order
    b. First-order
    c. Second-order
    d. Third-order
        Zero-order

30. The line labeled "*b*" in the above graph represents what reaction order?
    a. Zero-order
    b. First-order
    c. Second-order
    d. Third-order
        First-order

31. The line labeled "*c*" in the above graph represents what reaction order?
    a. Zero-order
    b. First-order
    c. Second-order
    d. Third-order
        Second-order

For questions 32–36, consider the following hypothetical generic chemical reaction and experimental data acquired at a particular temperature:

$$A + B \rightarrow C$$

Experiment	[A]	[B]	Initial Reaction Rate (M/s)
1	0.23	0.23	0.13
2	0.23	0.46	0.26
3	0.46	0.23	0.26

32. What is the order of "A"?

    If we compare experiments 1 and 3, we see that when the concentration of A doubles (and B is constant), so does the rate. Therefore, A is first-order.

33. What is the order of "B"

    If we compare experiments 1 and 2, we see that when the concentration of B doubles (and A is constant), so does the rate. Therefore, B is also first-order.

34. What is the overall order of the reaction?

    The overall order of the reaction is second-order (sum of the powers in the rate equation).

35. What is the value of the rate constant (k) for the reaction?

    To calculate the value of k, we can pick any of the three experiments (here we will use experiment 1) and plug in the numbers to the rate equation and solve for k as follows:

    $$Rate = k[A][B]$$

    $$k = \frac{Rate}{[A][B]} = \frac{(0.13)}{(0.23) \times (0.23)} = 2.5 \ M^{-1} \cdot s^{-1}$$

36. Write the rate law expression for this generic chemical reaction.

    $$Rate = k[A][B]$$

    $$Rate = 2.5 \ M^{-1} \cdot s^{-1} \ [A][B]$$

For questions 37–41, consider the following chemical reaction and experimental data acquired at a particular temperature:

$$2NO \ (g) + O_2 \ (g) \rightarrow 2NO_2 \ (g)$$

Experiment	[*NO*]	[*O$_2$*]	Initial Reaction Rate (M/s)
1	0.48	0.48	1.0×10^{-5}
2	0.96	0.48	4.0×10^{-5}
3	0.48	0.96	2.0×10^{-5}

37. What is the order of *NO*?

    If we compare experiments 1 and 2, we see that when the concentration of *NO* doubles (and O_2 is constant), the rate increase by a factor of 4. Therefore, *NO* is second-order.

38. What is the order of O_2?

    If we compare experiments 1 and 3, we see that when the concentration of O_2 doubles (and *NO* is constant), so does the rate. Therefore, O_2 is first-order.

39. What is the overall order of the reaction?

The overall order of the reaction is third-order (sum of the powers in the rate equation).

40. What is the value of the rate constant (k) for the reaction?

To calculate the value of k, we can pick any of the three experiments (here we will use experiment 1) and plug in the numbers to the rate equation and solve for k as follows:

$$Rate = k[NO]^2[O_2]$$

$$k = \frac{Rate}{[NO]^2[O_2]} = \frac{(1.0 \times 10^{-5})}{(0.48)^2 \times (0.48)} = 9.0 \times 10^{-5} \ M^{-2} \cdot s^{-1}$$

41. Write the rate law expression for this chemical reaction.

$$Rate = k[NO]^2[O_2]$$

$$Rate = 9.0 \times 10^{-5} \ M^{-2} \cdot s^{-1}[NO]^2[O_2]$$

42. What is the integrated rate law?

The integrated rate law utilizes the relationship between the concentrations of the reactants and time.

43. Write the mathematical expression for the zero-order integrated rate law given the following generic equation:

$$A \rightarrow B + C$$

$$[A]_t = -kt + [A]_0$$

Where $[A]_t$ is the concentration of A at any time (t), k is the rate constant and $[A]_0$ is the initial concentration of A.

44. Write the mathematical expression for the first-order integrated rate law given the following generic equation:

$$A \rightarrow B + C$$

$$ln[A]_t = -kt + ln[A]_0$$

Where $[A]_t$ is the concentration of A at any time (t), k is the rate constant and $[A]_0$ is the initial concentration of A.

45. Write the mathematical expression for the second-order integrated rate law given the following generic equation:

$$A \rightarrow B + C$$

$$\frac{1}{[A]_t} = kt + \frac{1}{[A]_0}$$

Where $[A]_t$ is the concentration of A at any time (t), k is the rate constant and $[A]_0$ is the initial concentration of A.

For questions 46–48, consider the following generic equation and various graphs:

$$A \rightarrow B + C$$

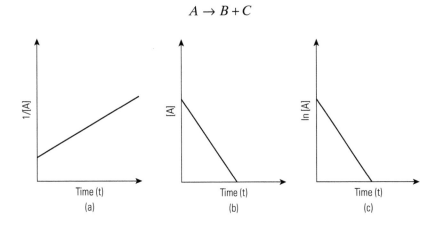

(a)   (b)   (c)

46. Which of the above plots represents the zero-order integrated rate law?

(b)

47. Which of the above plots represents the first-order integrated rate law?

(c)

48. Which of the above plots represents the second-order integrated rate law?

(a)

49. What are reaction half-lives?

Reaction half-lives refer to the time in which the concentration of a reactant decreases by half.

50. Write the mathematical expression for the half-life of a zero-order reaction given the following generic equation:

$$A \rightarrow B + C$$

$$t_{1/2} = \frac{[A]_0}{2k} = \frac{1}{k}\frac{[A]_0}{2}$$

51. Write the mathematical expression for the half-life of a first-order reaction given the following generic equation:

$$A \rightarrow B + C$$

$$t_{1/2} = \frac{0.693}{k} = \frac{1}{k}(0.693)$$

52. Write the mathematical expression for the half-life of a second-order reaction given the following generic equation:

$$A \rightarrow B + C$$

$$t_{1/2} = \frac{1}{k[A]_0} = \frac{1}{k}\frac{1}{[A]_0}$$

For questions 53–56, consider the following generic equation and experimental data:

$$A \rightarrow B + C$$

Time (s)	[A]
0	0.98
25	0.88
50	0.79
75	0.69
100	0.59
125	0.50
150	0.40
175	0.30
200	0.20

53. Determine the order of the above reaction.

First, we will generate all three plots for zero-order, first-order, and second-order. The plot that yields a straight line will tell us what the order is of this reaction.

Time	[A]	ln [A]	1/[A]
0	0.98	−0.02	1.02
25	0.88	−0.13	1.14
50	0.79	−0.24	1.27
75	0.69	−0.37	1.45
100	0.59	−0.53	1.69
125	0.50	−0.69	2.00
150	0.40	−0.92	2.50
175	0.30	−1.20	3.33
200	0.20	−1.61	5.00

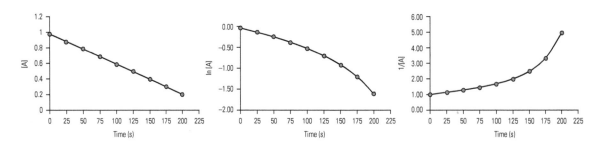

Thus, this is a zero-order reaction.

54. Given the data above, what is the value of the rate constant (k) for the reaction?

$$[A]_t = -kt + [A]_0$$

At 25 s:

$$k = \frac{[A]_t - [A]_0}{-t} = \frac{(0.88\ M) - (0.98\ M)}{-25\ s} = 4.0 \times 10^{-3}\ \frac{M}{s}$$

55. Write the rate expression for this reaction.

$$Rate = k [A]^0$$

$$Rate = k$$

$$Rate = 4.0 \times 10^{-3}\ \frac{M}{s}$$

56. Given the data above, what is the half-life of the reaction?

$$t_{1/2} = \frac{[A]_0}{2k} = \frac{1}{k} \frac{[A]_0}{2} = \frac{1}{4.0 \times 10^{-3}} \times \frac{0.98\ M}{2} = 1.2 \times 10^2\ s$$

For questions 57–60, consider the following generic equation and experimental data:

$$A \rightarrow B + C$$

Time (s)	[A]
0	0.98
25	0.79
50	0.64
75	0.53
100	0.43
125	0.35
150	0.29
175	0.24
200	0.20

57. Determine the order of the above reaction.

First, we will generate all three plots for zero-order, first-order, and second-order. The plot that yields a straight line will tell us what the order is of this reaction.

Time	[A]	ln [A]	1/[A]
0	0.98	−0.02	1.02
25	0.79	−0.24	1.27
50	0.64	−0.45	1.56
75	0.53	−0.63	1.89
100	0.43	−0.84	2.33
125	0.35	−1.05	2.86
150	0.29	−1.24	3.45
175	0.24	−1.43	4.17
200	0.20	−1.61	5.00

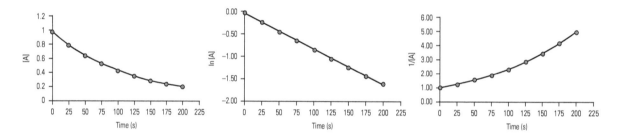

Thus, this is a first-order reaction.

58. Given the data above, what is the value of the rate constant (k) for the reaction?

$$ln[A]_t = -kt + ln[A]_0$$

At 175 s:

$$k = \frac{ln[A]_t - ln[A]_0}{-t} = \frac{ln(0.24) - ln(0.98)}{-175} = 8.0 \times 10^{-3}\,s^{-1}$$

59. Write the rate expression for this reaction.

$$Rate = k\,[A]^1$$

$$Rate = k\,[A]$$

$$Rate = 8.0 \times 10^{-3}\,s^{-1}\,[A]$$

60. Given the data above, what is the half-life of the reaction?

$$t_{1/2} = \frac{0.693}{k} = \frac{1}{k}\,(0.693) = \frac{1}{8.0 \times 10^{-3}}\,(0.693) = 87\ s$$

61. What is the collision theory of kinetics?

According to the collision theory of kinetics, reactant molecules must collide with sufficient energy and proper orientation for the reaction to take place (i.e. effective collisions).

62. What is an activated complex?

An activated complex is a temporary high energy and unstable complex which must be achieved in order for reactants to produce products.

63. What is the activation energy?

The activation energy (E_a) is defined as the energy barrier which must be overcome in order to temporarily form the activated complex as reactants are used to produce products.

64. If temperature has such a profound effect on reaction rates, why is it not present in the rate equation (i.e. **Rate** = $k[A]^x$)? Write out the Arrhenius equation.

The effect of temperature on the reaction rate is contained within the rate constant (k). We can clearly see this correlation by taking a look at the Arrhenius equation as follows:

$$k = Ae^{\frac{-E_a}{RT}}$$

65. What is the pre-exponential factor in the Arrhenius equation and what does it tell you?

A is the pre-exponential factor (or frequency factor), which represents the number of times that reactants approach the activation barrier.

66. What is the exponential factor in the Arrhenius equation and what does it tell you?

$e^{\frac{-E_a}{RT}}$ is the exponential factor, which represents the number of molecules that have enough energy to make it over the activation barrier on a given approach.

67. What are catalysts?

Catalyst increase reaction rates by lowering the activation energy of a particular reaction. They can do this without being consumed in the reaction.

68. What is a heterogeneous catalyst?

A heterogeneous catalyst is a catalyst that is in a different phase than the reactants.

69. What is a homogeneous catalyst?

A homogenous catalyst would be one in which the catalyst in the same phase as the reactants.

70. What are enzymes? Give an example.

Enzymes are biological catalysts that increase the rates of biochemical reactions. Hexokinase is an example of an enzyme.

71. What is a reaction mechanism?

A reaction mechanism is the series of individual reactions that contribute to the overall chemical reaction.

72. What are reaction intermediates?

   Reaction intermediates are produced in one step and consumed in another in a reaction mechanism, and therefore do not generally appear in the overall reaction.

73. What is a rate-limiting step?

   The rate-limiting step is a much slower reaction than the others in a particular mechanism and is often a point of regulatory control of the whole reaction mechanism.

KEY TERMS

Activated complex   A temporary high energy and unstable complex. It can be thought of as an intermediate structure along the reaction coordinate which is no longer the reactant(s) but not yet product(s).

Activation energy   The energy barrier (or activation barrier) which must be overcome in order to temporarily form the activated complex as reactants are used to produce products.

Aliquot   A sample, periodically taken from the reaction mixture through a chemical reaction.

Arrhenius equation   A mathematic expression relating the rate constant for a given reaction to its activation energy and the reaction temperature.

Catalyst   A chemical species present during a reaction (usually at very low concentration) that is not consumed by the reaction, but participates in the formation of the activated complex, lowering the activation barrier resulting in higher reaction rates at a given temperature.

Chemical kinetics   The study of how fast reactants change into products by examining reaction rates.

Collision theory of kinetics   According to this theory, reactant molecules must collide with sufficient energy and proper orientation for the reaction to take place.

Effective collisions   According to the collision theory of kinetics, reactant molecules must collide with sufficient energy and proper orientation for the reaction to take place. Effective collisions result when both of these conditions are met, which can then lead to the formation of an activated complex or transition state.

Enzymes   Proteins that serve as biological catalysts that increase the rates of biochemical reactions.

Exponential factor   In the Arrhenius equation, the exponential factor $\left(e^{\frac{-E_a}{RT}} \right)$ represents the number of molecules that have enough energy to make it over the activation barrier on a given approach.

First order integrated rate law $ln[A]_t = -kt + ln[A]_0$

First order reaction half-life   The half-life for a first-order reaction can be calculated as $t_{\frac{1}{2}} = \dfrac{0.693}{k} = \dfrac{1}{k}(0.693)$.

Frequency factor (A) The *pre-exponential* or **frequency factor (A)** in the Arrhenius equation represents the number of times that reactants approach the activation barrier.

Heterogeneous catalyst A catalyst which is in a different phase (physical state) than the reactants.

Homogeneous catalyst A catalyst which is in the same phase (physical state) as the reactants.

Integrated rate law An equation that relates the concentrations of the reactants in a chemical reaction to time.

Overall reaction order The sum of the orders of reaction with respect to each of the individual reactants.

Pre-exponential factor See frequency factor.

Rate constant The proportionality constant in the rate law for a given reaction which relates the rate of reaction the concentrations of the reactants raised to their respective powers.

Rate-determining step In a reaction mechanism this represents a much slower reaction step relative to the others in the mechanism and is often a point of regulatory control of the whole reaction mechanism. As the rate-determining step is the slowest step, it limits the overall rate of the reaction, and is therefore generally used to determine the rate law for the whole reaction mechanism.

Rate law equation The mathematical relationship between the reactant concentrations and the reaction rate.

Reaction half-life The time interval within which the concentration of a reactants in a given reaction will be decreased by half.

Reaction intermediates Within a multi-step reaction mechanism, these are chemical species or products which are produced in one step and subsequently consumed in another later step.

Reaction mechanism A series of individual reactions that contribute to the overall chemical reaction.

Reaction order The reaction order tells us how the reaction rate depends on the reactant concentrations.

Reaction rates The rate at which reactants are depleted with time in a given chemical reaction. Likewise, the rate can be defined as the rate at which products are formed.

Second order integrated rate law $\dfrac{1}{[A]_t} = kt + \dfrac{1}{[A]_0}$

Second order reaction half-life $t_{1/2} = \dfrac{1}{k[A]_0} = \dfrac{1}{k}\dfrac{1}{[A]_0}$

Transition state See activated complex.

Zero order integrated rate law $[A]_t = -kt + [A]_0$

Zero order reaction half-life $t_{1/2} = \dfrac{[A]_0}{2k} = \dfrac{1}{k}\dfrac{[A]_0}{2}$

Introduction to Organic Chemistry

KEY CONCEPTS

- Aliphatic and Aromatic Hydrocarbons
- Nomenclature
- Alkyl and Other Functional Groups
- Isomers
- Nomenclature and Properties of Aromatic Compounds

HYDROCARBONS

1. Define organic chemistry.

    Organic chemistry is the study of carbon-containing compounds, which may also contain various other elements such as hydrogen, nitrogen and oxygen to name a few.

2. When we say that carbon has the ability to "catenate", what do we mean by this?

    Carbon can bond to itself to form long chains in more ways and combinations than any other element on the periodic table.

3. What are hydrocarbons?

    Hydrocarbons are organic compounds that contain only carbon and hydrogen.

4. What are some examples of substances that contain hydrocarbons?

    Hydrocarbons can be found in a numerous substances such as gasoline, jet fuel, and candle wax as well as many aerosol sprays (i.e. volatile hydrocarbons).

5. Define alkanes, alkenes, and alkynes.

    Alkanes are hydrocarbons that contain all single bonds, while alkenes and alkynes have either a double or triple bond respectively.

6. What is the correct name of the following molecule?

    hexane

    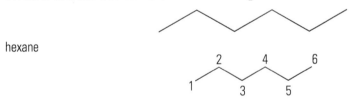

7. What is the correct name of the following molecule?

    butane

8. What is the correct name of the following molecule?

    3-nonene

    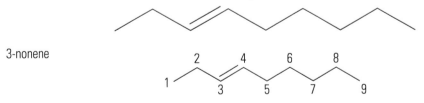

9. What is the correct name of the following molecule?

2-pentyne

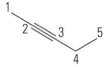

10. What is the correct name of the following molecule?

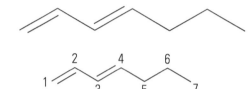

1,3-heptadiene

11. Draw the structure of propane.

12. Draw the structure of propene.

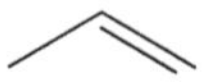

13. Draw the structure of 2-hexene.

14. Draw the structure of 2-butyne.

15. Draw the structure of 1,3-octadiene.

16. What are alkyl groups?

Alkyl groups are branches off of the continuous main chain of the structure.

17. Fill in the chart below:

Name of Alkyl Group	Number of Carbons	Condensed Formula
methyl	1	CH_3-
ethyl	2	CH_3CH_2-
propyl	3	$CH_3CH_2CH_2-$
isopropyl	3	$(CH_3)_2CH-$

n-butyl	4	$CH_3CH_2CH_2CH_2-$
sec-butyl	4	$CH_3CH_2(CH_3)CH-$
isobutyl	4	$(CH_3)_2CHCH_2-$
tert-butyl	4	$(CH_3)_3C-$

18. What is the correct name of the following molecule?

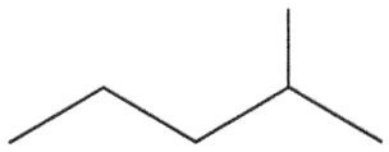

2-methylpentane

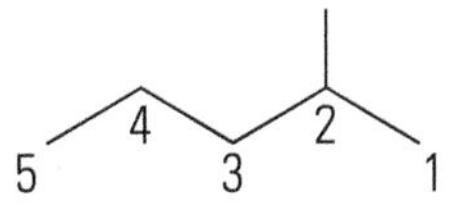

19. What is the correct name of the following molecule?

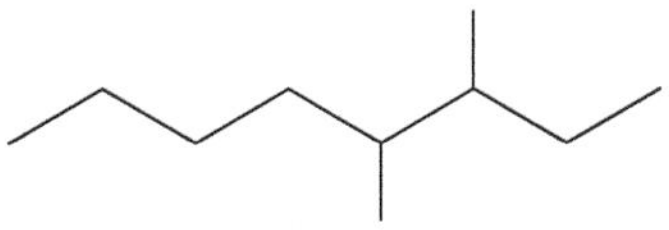

3,4-dimethyloctane

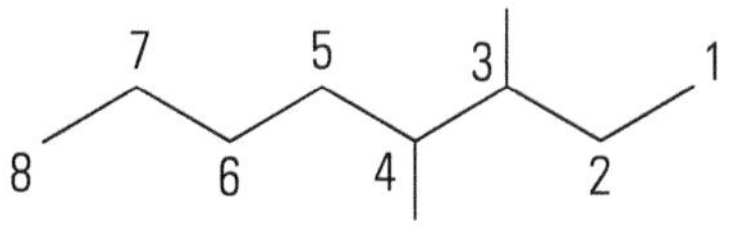

20. What is the correct name of the following molecule?

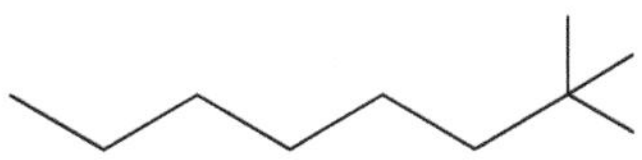

2,2-dimethyloctane

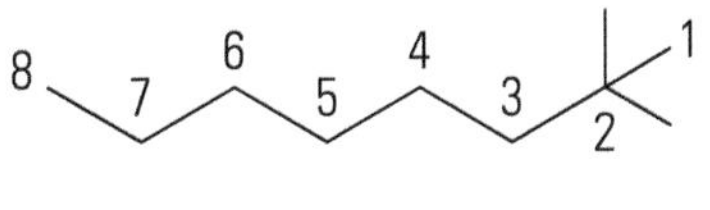

21. What is the correct name of the following molecule?

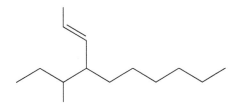

4-*sec*-butyl-2-decene

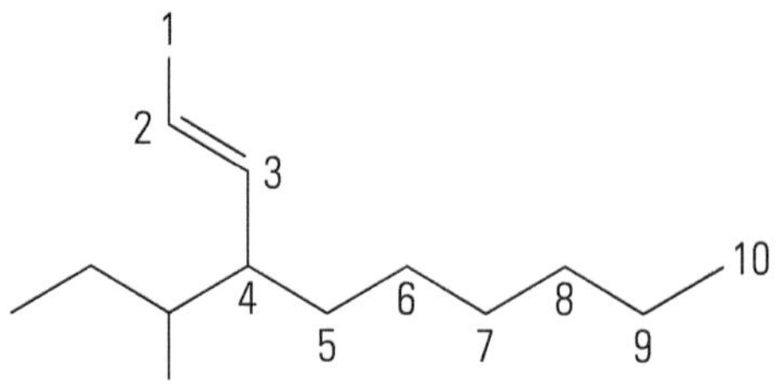

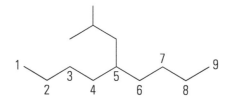

22. What is the correct name of the following molecule?

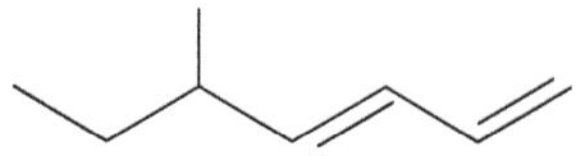

5-methyl-1,3-heptadiene

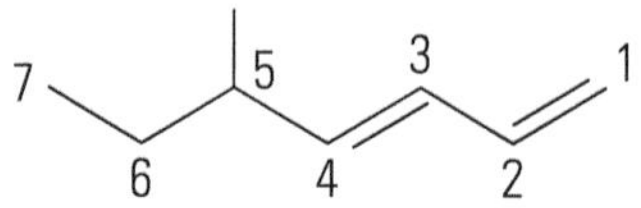

23. Draw the structure of 3-methylheptane.

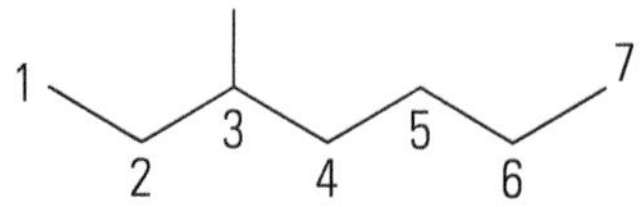

24. Draw the structure of 5-isobutylnonane.

*Can be numbered different ways and still get the same name/structure.

25. Draw the structure of 2,2,4-trimethylhexane.

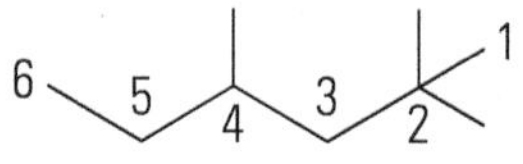

26. Draw the structure of 2,3,4-trimethyl-2-pentene.

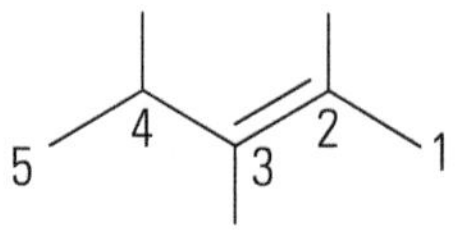

*Can be numbered different ways and still get the same name/structure.

27. Draw the structure of 5-ethyl-4-methyl-2-heptyne.

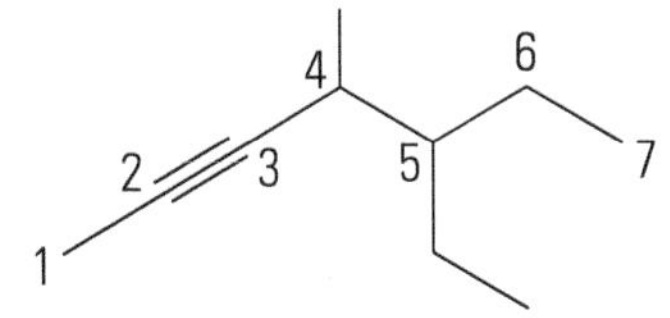

*Can be numbered different ways and still get the same name/structure.

28. What is a functional group?

A functional group inserted into a hydrocarbon is an atom, or group of atoms, which is primarily responsible for the chemical and physical properties of that particular molecule (hence the name "functional group").

29. List and define the seven major functional groups discussed in this chapter.

The seven major functional groups discussed in this chapter include alcohols (R-OH), aldehydes (contains a terminal carbonyl group), ketones (contains a carbonyl group in the middle of the structure, or between two other carbon atoms), carboxylic acids (contains carboxyl group), esters (derived from carboxylic acids in which at least one hydroxyl group is replaced by an —O—alkyl group), ethers (an oxygen atom connected to two alkyl groups), as well as amines (nitrogen-containing compounds derived from ammonia).

30. What is the correct name of the following alcohol?

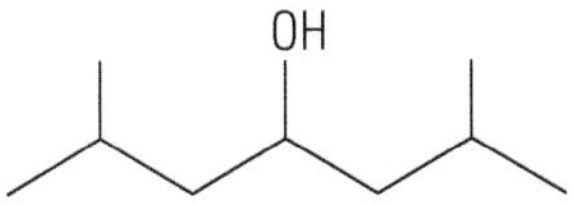

2,6-dimethyl-4-heptanol

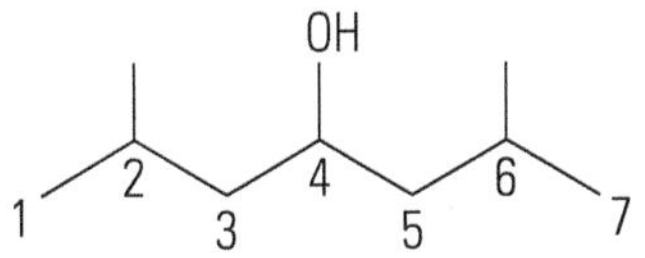

*Can be numbered different ways and still get the same name/structure.

31. What is the correct name of the following alcohol?

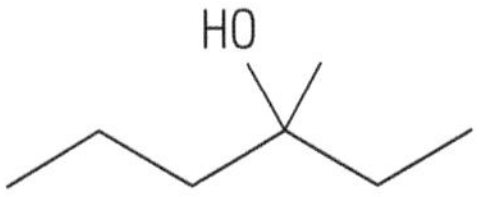

3-methyl-3-hexanol

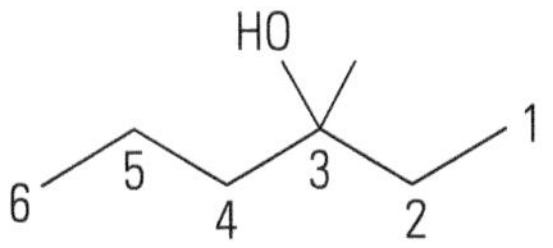

32. Draw the structure of 2-hexanol.

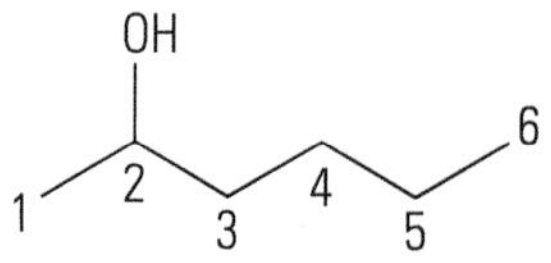

33. Draw the structure of 2-methyl-3-pentanol.

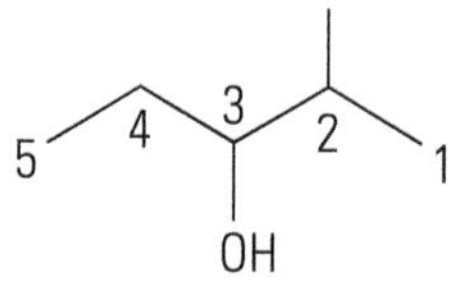

34. What is the correct name of the following aldehyde?

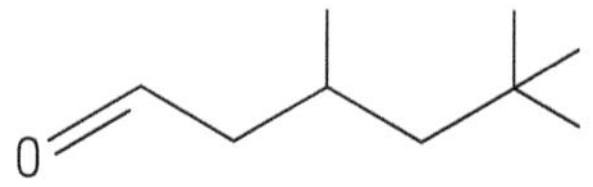

3,5,5-trimethylhexanal

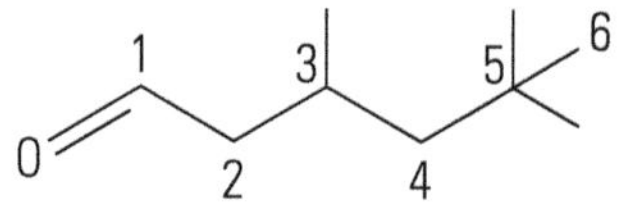

*Can be numbered different ways and still get the same name/structure.

35. What is the correct name of the following aldehyde?

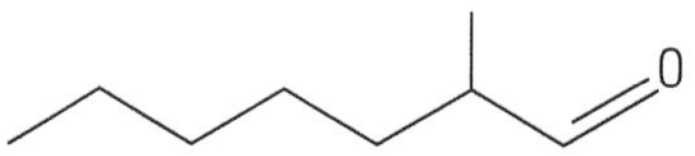

2-methylheptanal

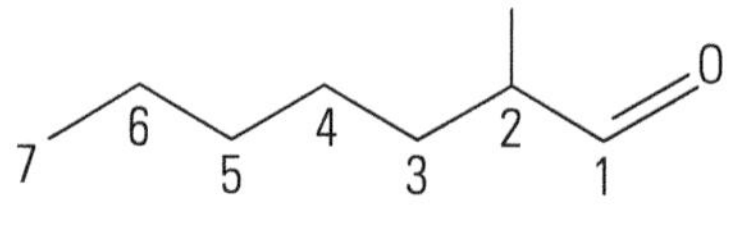

36. Draw the structure of butanal.

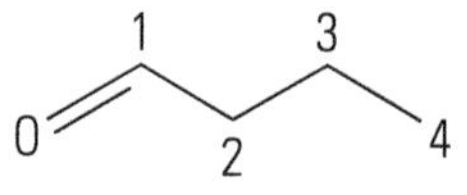

37. Draw the structure of 2-methylpropanal.

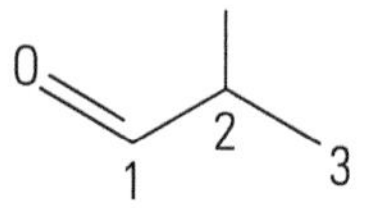

38. What is the correct name of the following ketone?

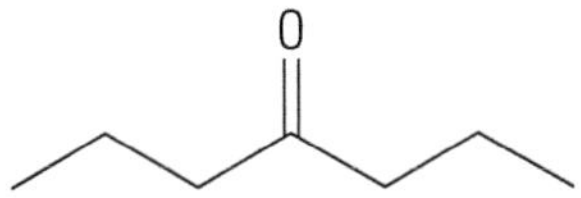

4-heptanone

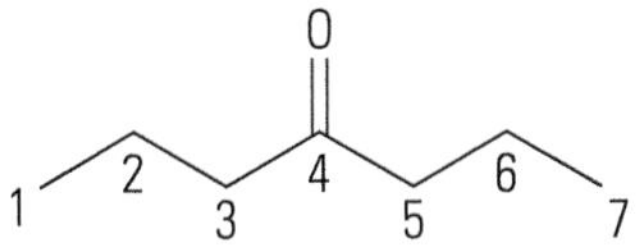

*Can be numbered different ways and still get the same name/structure.

39. What is the correct name of the following ketone?

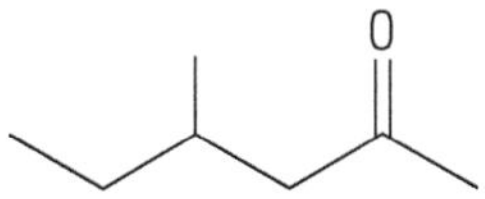

4-methyl-2-hexanone

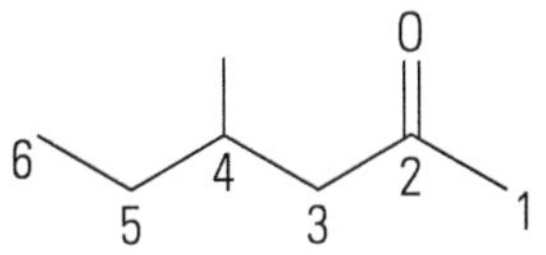

40. Draw the structure of butanone.

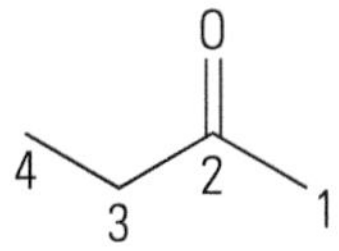

41. Draw the structure of 2-pentanone.

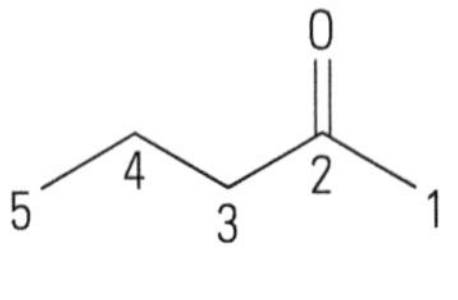

42. What is the correct name of the following carboxylic acid?

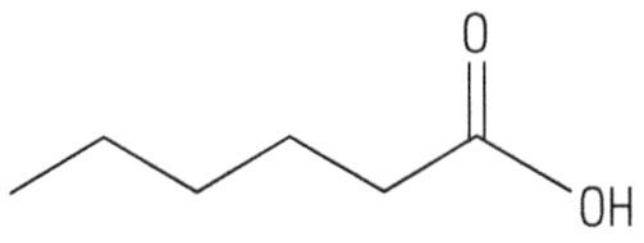

hexanoic acid

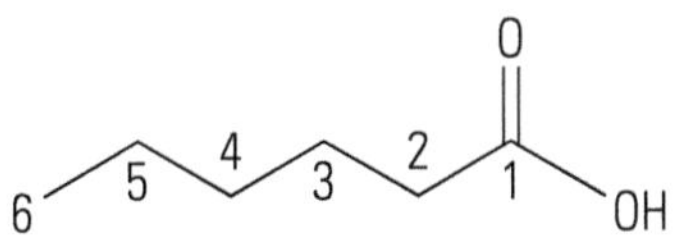

43. What is the correct name of the following carboxylic acid?

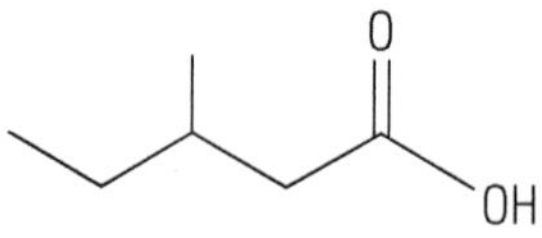

3-methylpentanoic acid

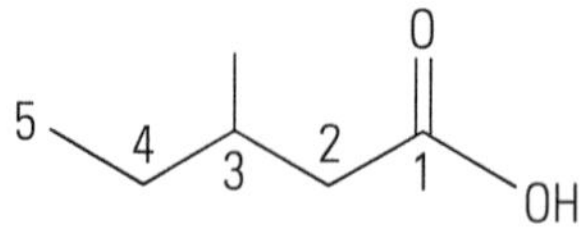

44. Draw the structure of methanoic acid.

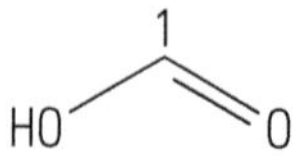

45. Draw the structure of ethanoic acid.

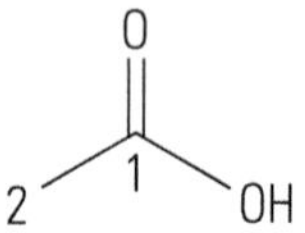

46. What is the correct name of the following ester?

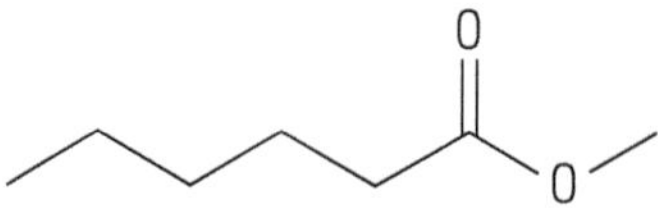

methyl hexanoate

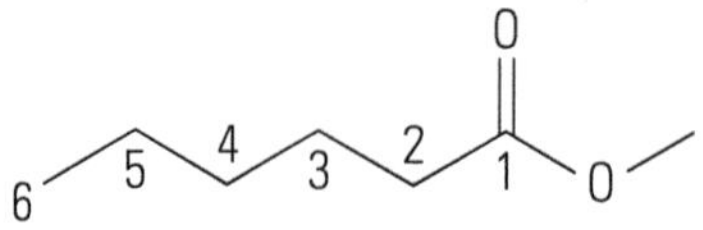

47. What is the correct name of the following ester?

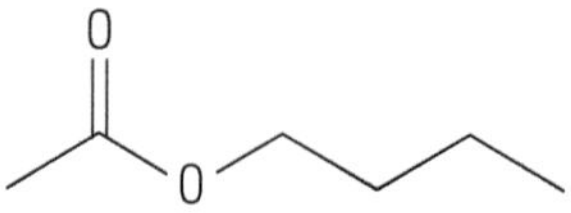

butyl ethanoate

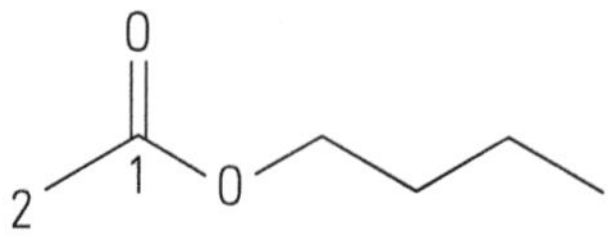

48. Draw the structure of methyl propanoate.

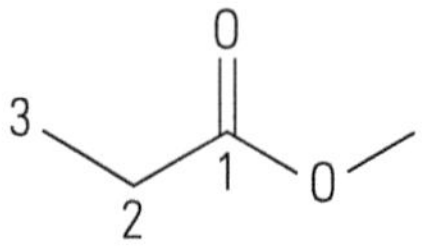

49. Draw the structure of ethyl propanoate.

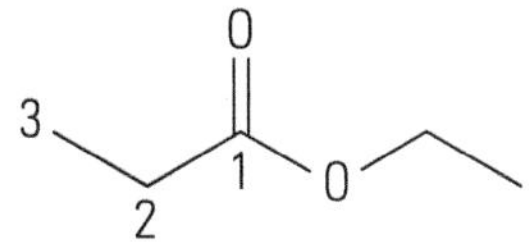

50. What is the correct name of the following ether?

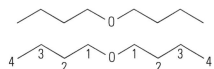

methyl hexyl ether

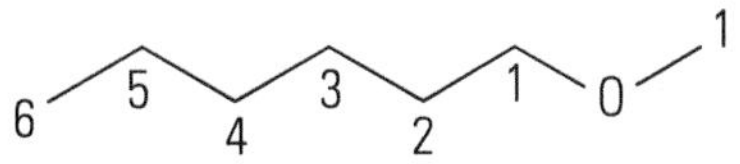

51. What is the correct name of the following ether?

dibutyl ether

52. Draw the structure of ethyl methyl ether.

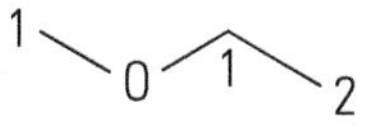

53. Draw the structure of ethyl propyl ether.

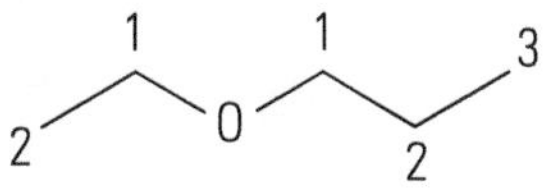

54. What is the correct name of the following amine?

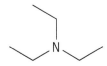

triethylamine

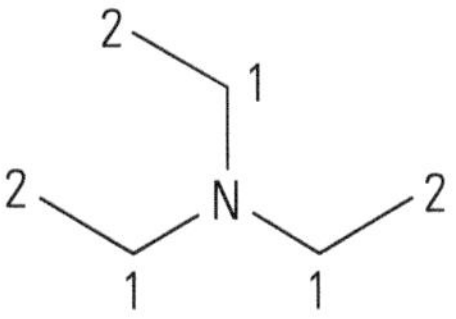

55. What is the correct name of the following amine?

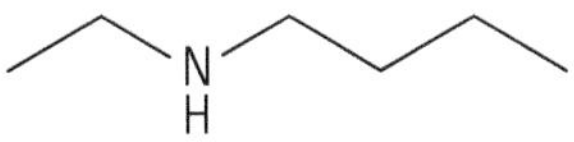

butylethylamine

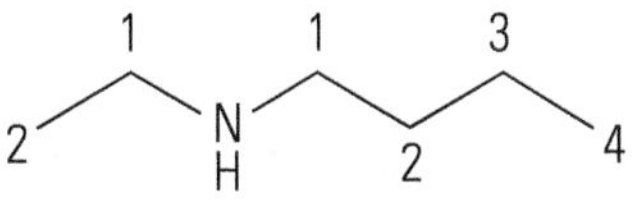

56. Draw the structure of dimethylamine.

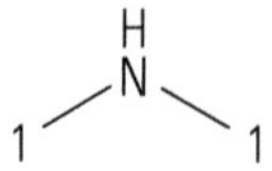

57. Draw the structure of diethylamine.

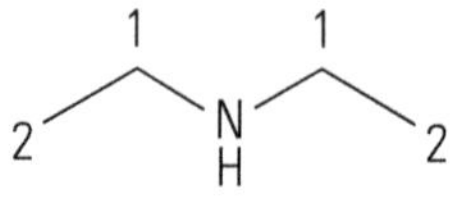

58. What are isomers?

Isomers are molecules that have the same molecular formula but different chemical structures.

59. What are the different types of isomers discussed in this chapter, and how are they different from one another?

Structural isomers (or constitutional isomers) are molecules that have the same chemical formula but different connectivity, while stereoisomers are molecules in which the atoms have the same connectivity but a different spatial arrangement. Stereoisomers can be further broken down into two other subcategories, geometric and optical isomers. Geometric isomers are two or more compounds which contain the same number and types of atoms and bonds but have different spatial arrangements. It is important to note that with this type of isomerism, the connectivity between atoms is the same. Optical isomers can be defined as compounds that also have the same connectivity, but are nonsuperimposable images of each other.

60. Which of the following structures is in fact an isomer (and not the same structure) of 3,5-dimethylheptane:

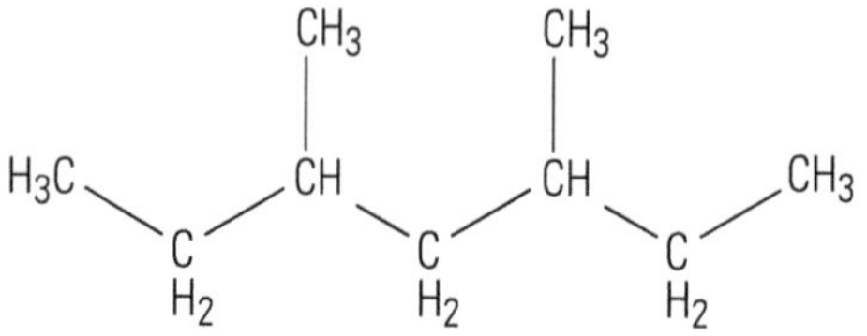

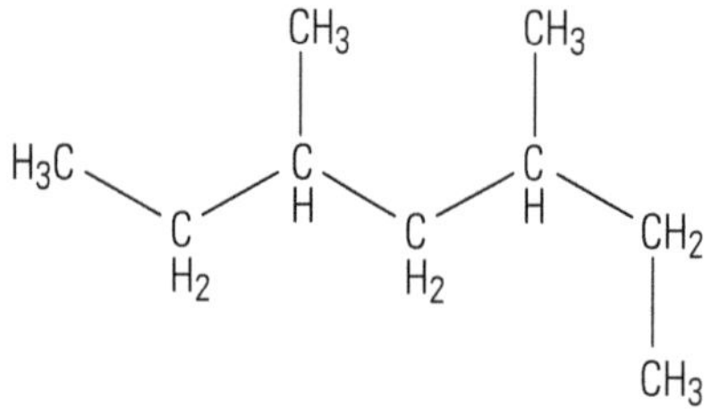

a.

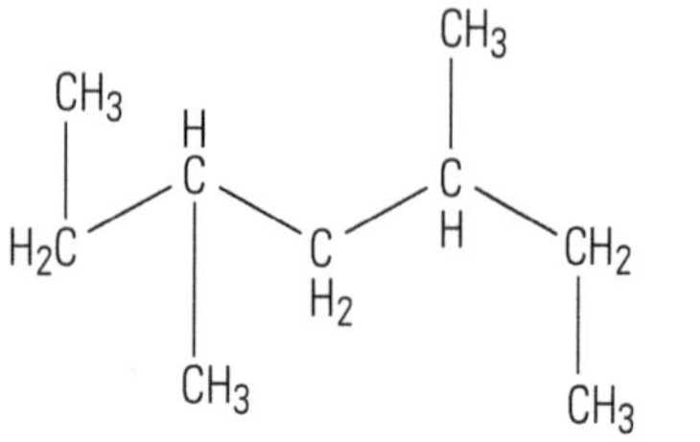

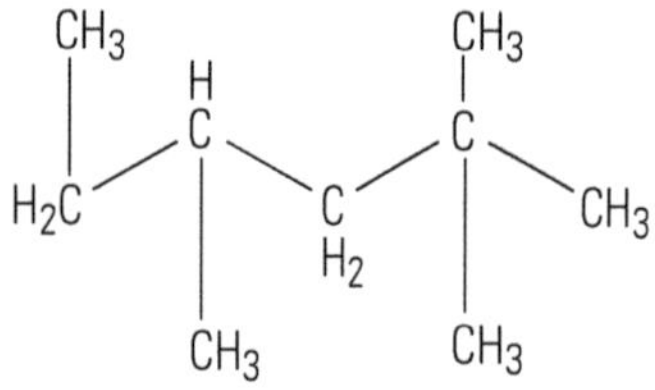

b.

c.

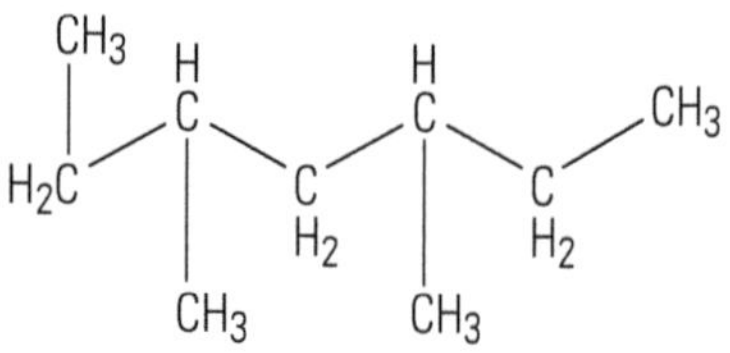

d.

The correct answer is b. All of the other structures are the same molecule 3,5-dimethylheptane. The isomer b. is 2,2,4-trimethylhexane.

61. Fill in the chart below:

Name of Hydrocarbon	Number of Carbons	Possible Structural Isomers
Methane	1	1
Ethane	2	1
Propane	3	1
Butane	4	2
Pentane	5	3
Hexane	6	5
Heptane	7	9
Octane	8	18
Nonane	9	35
Decane	10	75

62. Draw all the possible structural isomers for hexane.

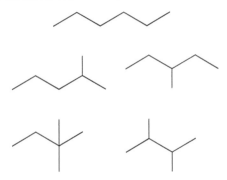

63. Which of the following molecules is *cis*-1,2-dichloroethene and which is *trans*-1,2-di-chloroethene? How can you tell?

trans-1,2-dichloroethene   *cis*-1,2-dichloroethene

The chlorine atoms are on the same side of the double bond (which we call *cis*-), or on opposite sides (which we call *trans*-).

64. What is a chiral molecule? How can you tell if a given carbon atom is chiral?

A chiral molecule exhibits optical isomerism. For a carbon atom to be chiral, it must be bonded to four different substituents.

65. What is a dextrorotary isomer (*d* isomer)?

The dextrorotary isomer (*d* isomer) rotates plane-polarized light clockwise.

66. What is a levorotatory isomer (*l* isomer)?

The levorotatory isomer (*l* isomer) rotates plane-polarized light counterclockwise.

67. What is a racemic mixture?

A racemic mixture is one that contains an equimolar amount of both isomers, which will not rotate plane-polarized light at all (i.e. they cancel each other out).

68. Would you expect the following molecule to be chiral and exhibit optical activity? Explain your answer.

$$H_3C - \overset{\overset{\displaystyle CH_3}{|}}{\underset{\underset{\displaystyle Cl}{|}}{C}} - \overset{\overset{\displaystyle H}{|}}{\underset{\underset{\displaystyle H}{|}}{C}} - CH_3$$

No, this molecule is not chiral and would not exhibit optical activity because it does not have a carbon atom with four different substituents bonded to it.

69. Would you expect the following molecule to be chiral and exhibit optical activity? Explain your answer.

$$H_3C - \overset{\overset{\displaystyle Br}{|}}{\underset{\underset{\displaystyle Cl}{|}}{C}} - \overset{\overset{\displaystyle H}{|}}{\underset{\underset{\displaystyle H}{|}}{C}} - CH_3$$

Yes, this molecule is chiral and would exhibit optical activity because the left carbon atom has four different substituents bonded to it.

70. What is an aromatic compound?

Aromatic compounds, or aryl compounds, contain a benzene ring.

71. Who is Friedrich August Kekulé and what is he most famous for?

The structure of benzene was determined in 1865 by Friedrich August Kekulé, who was one of the most prominent theoretical chemists in Europe in the mid to late 1800s. He claimed that he had determined the structure of benzene while day-dreaming of a snake seizing its own tail.

72. What is the correct name of the following molecule?

fluorobenzene (monsubstituted benzene ring).

73. What is the correct name of the following molecule?

tolene or methyl benzene (monsubstituted benzene ring).

74. What is the correct name of the following molecule?

1,4-dichlorobenzene or *para*-dichlorobenzene or *p*-dichlorobenzene (disubstituted benzene ring).

75. Draw the structure of 1-ethyl-3-propylbenzene.

76. Draw the structure of *m*-bromochlorobenzene.

77. Draw the structure of *ortho*-dibromobenzene.

KEY TERMS

Alcohols   Organic molecules that contain the –OH (hydroxyl) functional group, and have many uses.

Aldehydes   A carbonyl compound wherein the carbonyl carbon atom is bonded to a hydrogen and also an alkyl group (an exception is formaldehyde, CH_2O).

Aliphatic hydrocarbons   Saturated and unsaturated, nonaromatic hydrocarbons.

Alkanes   Fully saturated hydrocarbons that contain all single bonds.

Alkenes   Aliphatic hydrocarbons which contain at least one carbon-carbon double bond.

Alkynes   Aliphatic hydrocarbons which contain at least one carbon-carbon triple bond.

Amines   Nitrogen-containing organic compounds derived from ammonia.

Aromatic compounds   Organic compounds which are characterized by a cyclic (ring-like) structure which exhibits remarkable stability. These compounds are often described as containing (or derivative of) benzene rings. Many of these compounds have very pleasant aromas (i.e. vanilla, cinnamon etc.), and therefore are commonly referred to as aromatic.

Aryl compounds   See aromatic compounds.

Carbonyl group   A functional group consisting of a carbon-oxygen double bond.

Carboxylic acids   Organic compounds which contain a terminal carboxyl group ($R – COOH$).

Catenate   Catenate refers to carbon's ability to bond to itself to form long chains in more ways and combinations than any other element on the periodic table.

Chiral   From the Greek word "cheir", meaning hand, chiral compounds are those with optical isomers called enantiomers. Enantiomers are compounds which are identical chemically but are non-superimposable mirror images of each other, like your right and left hands.

Cis-trans isomerism   A type of stereoisomerism wherein functional groups are found on adjacent or opposite sides of a double bond.

Constitutional isomers   Molecules that have the same chemical formula but different structures (different connectivity).

Cyclic aliphatic compounds   Aliphatic hydrocarbons which exhibit a ring like structure.

Dextrorotary   The direction of rotation of plane-polarized light (clockwise) by one of two enantiomers or optical isomers.

Enantiomers   The stereoisomers (optical isomers) of a chiral compound.

Esters   Esters are derived from carboxylic acids in which at least one hydroxyl group (–OH) is replaced by an –O–alkyl group as follows ($R – COO – R$).

Ethers   Organic compounds which consist of an oxygen atom connected to two alkyl groups (or aryl groups).

Functional group   An atom, or group of atoms, which is primarily responsible for the chemical and physical properties of that particular molecule (hence the name "functional group", or to give "function to").

Geometric isomers Stereoisomers which contain the same number and types of atoms and bonds but have different spatial arrangements. It is important to note that with this type of isomerism, the connectivity between atoms is the same.

Heterocyclic compounds Cyclic compounds which contain more than one type of element in the ring structure (i.e. carbon and nitrogen).

Homocyclic compounds Cyclic compounds which contain only one type of element in the ring structure (i.e. carbon).

Hydrocarbons Organic compounds that contain only carbon and hydrogen.

Isomers Molecules that have the same molecular formula but different chemical structures.

Ketones Organic compounds which consist of a carbonyl group wherein the carbon atom is connected to two alkyl groups (or aryl groups).

Levorotary The direction of rotation of plane-polarized light (counterclockwise) by one of two enantiomers or optical isomers.

Monomers The repeating chemical units of which polymers are composed.

Optical isomers Compounds that also have the same connectivity but are non-superimposable images of each other. These isomers are also observed to rotate plane-polarized light.

Organic chemistry The study of carbon-containing compounds.

Polymers Large, high molecular weight compounds composed of many smaller chemical units called monomer, which are chemically linked together.

Racemic mixture A mixture of equimolar amounts of a pair of optical isomers (enantiomers), which will not rotate plane-polarized light at all (i.e. they cancel each other out).

Stereoisomers Molecules in which the atoms have the same connectivity but a different spatial arrangement.

Structural isomers See constitutional isomers.

16

Introduction to Biochemistry

KEY CONCEPTS

- Biochemistry
- Amino Acids, Peptides, and Proteins
- Carbohydrate Structure and Function
- Lipids Structure and Function
- Nucleic Acids Structure and Function

PROTEINS AND AMINO ACIDS

1. Define biochemistry.

    Biochemistry is the study of the chemical processes that take place within living organisms.

2. What are proteins and amino acids?

    Proteins are large biomolecules composed of individual building blocks called amino acids. Amino acids are defined as organic compounds that contain an amine and carboxyl functional groups, as well as a side-chain called the "R group". The side-chain is specific to each amino acid, and gives the individual amino acid its unique characteristics (i.e. polar, nonpolar, acidic, basic etc.).

3. What are amphoteric substances?

    Amphoteric substances can act as both an acid as well as a base. Amino acids are good examples of amphoteric substances.

4. What does it mean to be an essential or a nonessential amino acid? What are they?

    Essential amino acids must be obtained through our diet as we do not have the capabilities to make them ourselves, while we do have the ability to synthesize nonessential amino acids. Thus, there are 9 essential amino acids and 11 nonessential amino acids. The essential amino acids are valine, leucine, isoleucine, tryptophan, phenylalanine, methionine, threonine, lysine, and histidine. The nonessential amino acids are glycine, alanine, proline, serine, systeine, tyrosine, asparagine, glutamine, aspartic acid, glutamic acid, and arginine.

5. Are all of the 20 standard amino acids chiral? What designation (the D- *dextro*- or L- *levo*-designation) do we give the standard amino acids commonly found in the human body and does that mean that they all rotate plane-polarized light in the same direction?

    All of the 20 standard amino acids commonly found in the human body with the exception of glycine are chiral. These chiral amino acids are all of the L- designation, except glycine which is not chiral. However, about half of the chiral amino acids rotate plane-polarized light right, while the other half rotates plane-polarized light left. Thus, we can conclude that the D- *dextro*- or L- *levo*-designation used for the amino acids (and carbohydrates for that matter) has nothing to do with the rotation of plane-polarized light.

6. Draw all 20 standard amino acids as they appear at physiological pH (~7.2–7.4). Which ones are polar, nonpolar, acidic, or basic? What are their one-letter and three-letter designations?

    See Figure 16.1 and Table 16.1.

7. Which of the following structures is an amino acid?

a.

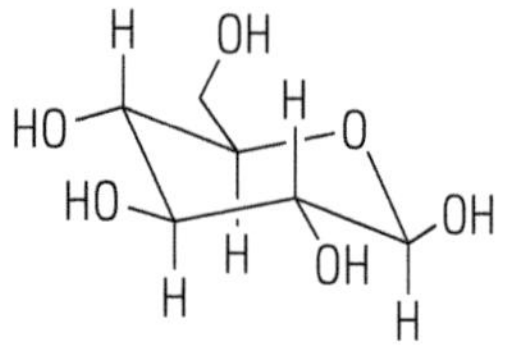

b.

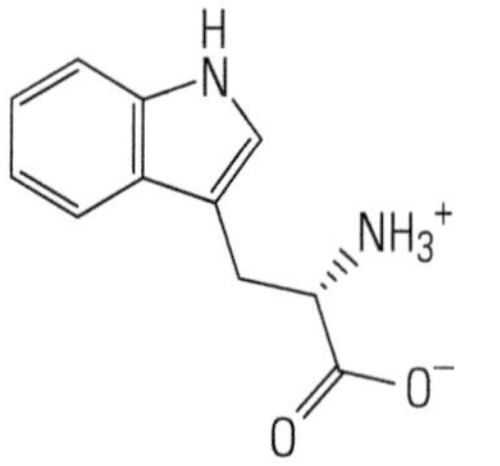

c.

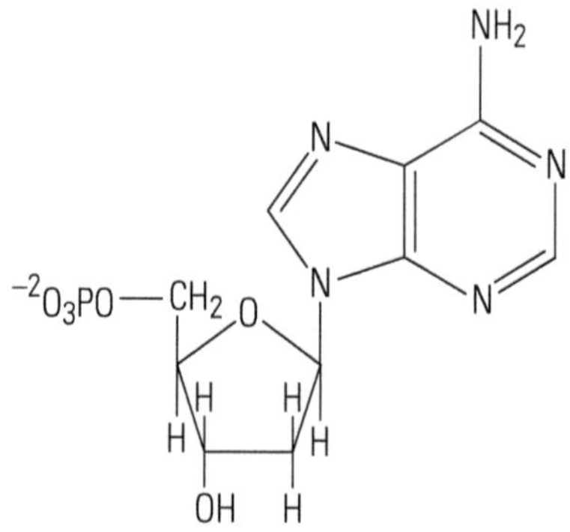

d.

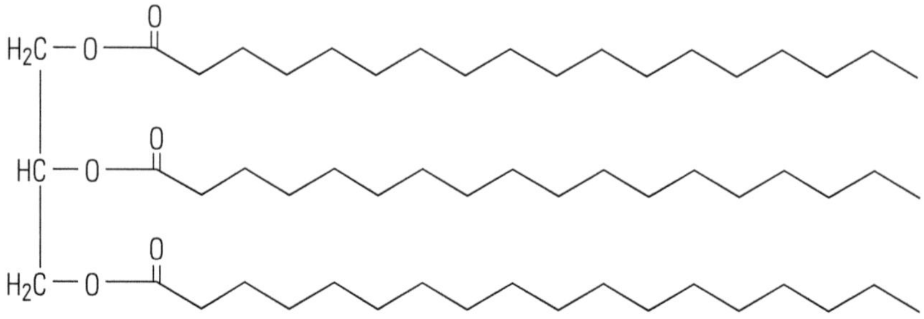

b. is an amino acid (tryptophan).

8. Determine the identities of each amino acid listed below based on their one-letter designation.
   a. G-Glycine
   b. W-Tryptophan
   c. N-Asparagine
   d. S-Serine

9. Determine the identities of each amino acid listed below based on their one-letter designation.
   a. L-Leucine
   b. Y-Tyrosine
   c. F-Phenylalanine
   d. R-Arginine

10. The type of bond that holds amino acids together is called a peptide bond, and is formed via a condensation reaction in which two amino acids combine to form a larger molecule with the loss of water.

11. A dipeptide consists of two amino acids, while a tripeptide would contain three amino acids.

12. By convention, peptides are written from left to right with the amine terminus on the left and the carboxylic acid terminus on the right.

13. Draw the structure of the dipeptide Leu-Ser at physiological pH (~7.2–7.4).

14. Draw the structure of the tripeptide Arg-Tyr-Ala at physiological pH (~7.2–7.4).

15. Describe what is meant by a particular protein's primary, secondary, tertiary, and quaternary structures.

A protein's primary structure (1°) is the amino acid sequence itself. The secondary structure (2°) results from regular polypeptide folding arrangements attributed to local interactions between individual amino acids, resulting in various geometric patterns such as α-helices and β-pleated sheets. A protein's tertiary structure (3°) and quaternary (4°) structures result from larger-scale interactions of the protein which can be held together by various intermolecular forces to include hydrophobic interactions between nonpolar amino acid side-chains, salt bridges between acidic and basic amino acids, as well hydrogen bonding. Furthermore, covalent bonds may in fact be involved in these types of structures such as disulfide bonds. Quaternary (4°) structures are generally thought of as the arrangements of various subunits being held together in the larger protein structure.

16. Explain the difference between fibrous and globular proteins. Give an example of each.

Keratins are good examples of fibrous proteins, which tend to be relatively simple linear structures and generally serve as structural proteins. On the other hand, hemoglobin is a good example of a globular protein—globular proteins are generally spherical in shape and usually have more complex structures. Enzymes are also good examples of globular proteins.

CARBOHYDRATES

17. What are carbohydrates?

Carbohydrates are also called sugars, and the term literally means carbon and water. Therefore, they often have the general formula $(CH_2O)n$. They are polyhydroxy molecules, meaning that they are molecules containing more than one hydroxyl group, derived from either aldehydes or ketones.

18. Define monosaccharides, disaccharides, and polysaccharides.

Monosaccharides are defined as the smallest carbohydrates, which can be derived from aldehydes (called aldoses) or ketones (called ketoses). Two monosaccharides can be joined together to form structures called disaccharides via a glycosidic bond, or several can be joined together to form more complex structures called polysaccharides.

19. What is a glycosidic bond?

A glycosidic bond is defined as a covalent bond that links a carbohydrate to another entity which may or may not also be a carbohydrate.

20. What designation (the D- dextro- or L- levo-designation) do we give most (not all) physiologically relevant sugars?

Most physiologically relevant sugars are of the D-designation; however there are in fact some that have the L-designation. Just remember that this designation should not be confused with the rotation of plane-polarized light as most sugars have multiple chiral carbons.

21. What is an aldose? What is a ketose?

Aldoses are sugars derived from aldehydes, while those derived from ketones are called ketoses.

22. Explain how we designate sugars as being either α- or β- during cyclization.

When the cyclic form of an aldose is generated (i.e. glucose), the alcohol group on the 5th carbon reacts with the 1st carbon containing the aldehyde group. Similarly, when a cyclic ketose forms (i.e. fructose), the alcohol group on the 5th carbon reacts with the 2nd carbon containing the ketone group. When this happens, the hydroxyl group on either the 1st carbon for glucose or the 2nd carbon for fructose will be on the opposite side of the CH_2OH group present at the 6th position which is designated as being the α-configuration, or it might be on the same side as the CH_2OH group at the 6th position, in which case it is designated as being the β-configuration.

23. What are complex carbohydrates?

Complex carbohydrates are polysaccharides made up of long and "complex" chains of sugar molecules.

24. What is cellulose? Discuss its structure.

Cellulose is the most abundant organic substance on earth and is a linear chain of several hundred and possibly thousands of glucose residues linked by β-glycosidic linkages. It has very rigid properties attributed primarily to the extensive hydrogen bonding that occurs in the molecule and can be found in plant cell walls.

25. What is starch? How is amylose and amylopectin different structurally?

    Starch is a complex carbohydrate primarily used for the main energy storage source for plants and is a mixture of both amylose and amylopectin. Amylose is a linear chain of many glucose residues similar to cellulose; however, the glucose residues here are connected by α-glycosidic linkages. Amylopectin is structurally similar to amylose but contains branching in the chains.

26. What is glycogen? How is it different structurally from amylopectin?

    Glycogen is complex carbohydrate and serves as a form of energy storage for animals. It is structurally similar to amylopectin but is even more highly branched.

27. Which of the following structures is a carbohydrate?

    a.

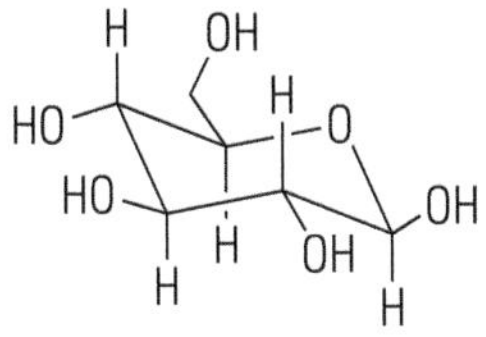

    b.

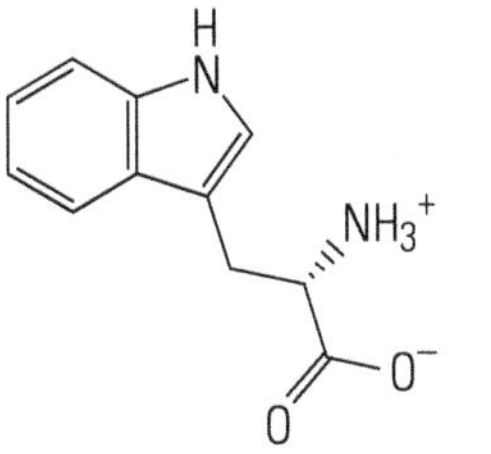

    c.

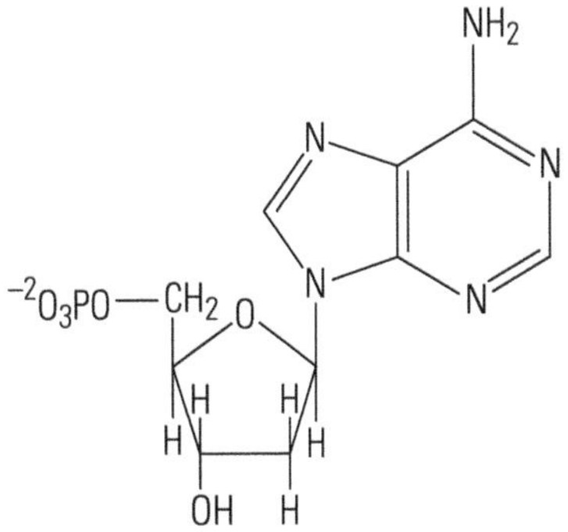

    d.

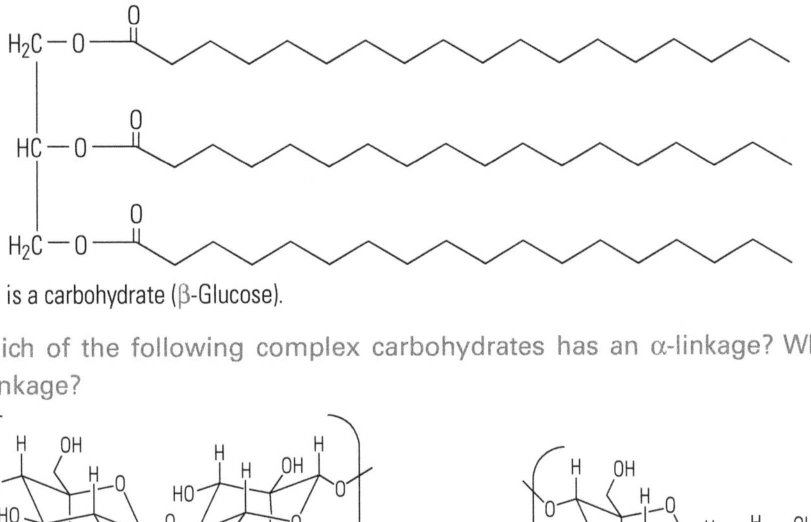

    a. is a carbohydrate (β-Glucose).

28. Which of the following complex carbohydrates has an α-linkage? Which one has a β-linkage?

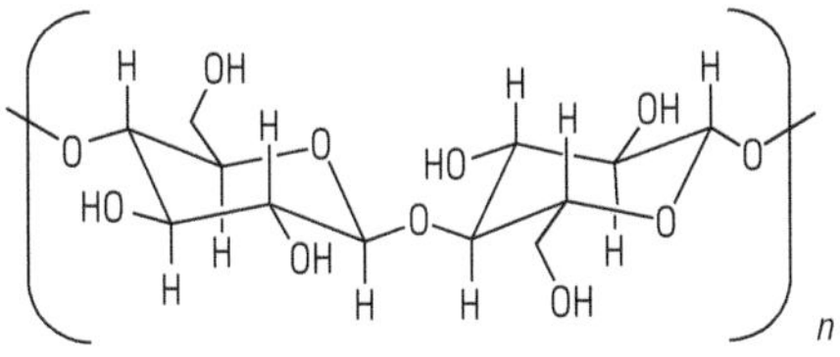

    β-linkage (i.e. Cellulose) 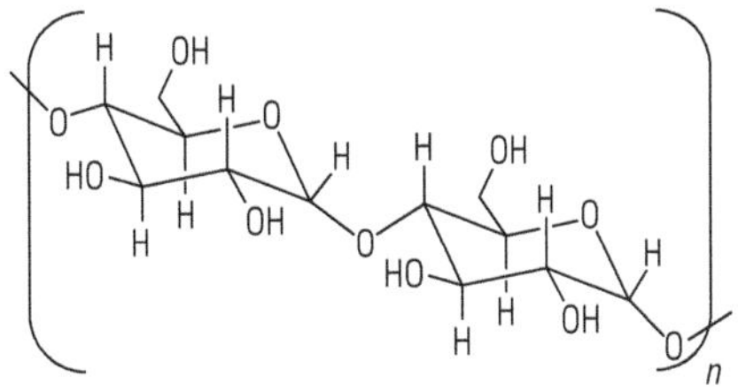   α-linkage (i.e Starch-Amylose)

LIPIDS

29. What are lipids?

The name lipids is derived from the Greek word "lipos" meaning fat, and lipids are therefore nonpolar molecules. They are a diverse family of molecules that have various biological functions to include energy storage and insulation, structural components of cell membranes, as well as cell signaling functions.

30. Define fatty acids.

Fatty acids are the simplest types of lipids, which are carboxylic acids that contain either saturated or unsaturated long aliphatic hydrocarbon tails. They are reactive and are generally found in nature as components of other larger types of lipids.

31. What is a saturated fatty acid? What is an unsaturated fatty acid? How does the presence of the double in unsaturated fatty acids affect the physical properties when compared to saturated fatty acids of comparable length?

A saturated fatty acid has no points of unsaturation along its aliphatic hydrocarbon tail, while an unsaturated fatty acid has at least one point of unsaturation (i.e double bond) in its tail group. The presence of the double bond in the tail changes the physical properties quite dramatically, as the double bond puts a "kink" in the tail, which prevents the entire chain from interacting with neighboring molecules via hydrophobic interactions. This can also influence membrane fluidity when unsaturated fatty acids are present in the phospholipid bilayers of cell membranes.

32. What is the name of the following fatty acid?

Myristic acid (C14:0)

33. What is the name of the following fatty acid?

Linoleic acid (C18:2)

34. What is the name of the following fatty acid?

Arachidic acid (C20:0)

35. Draw the structure of Lauric acid.

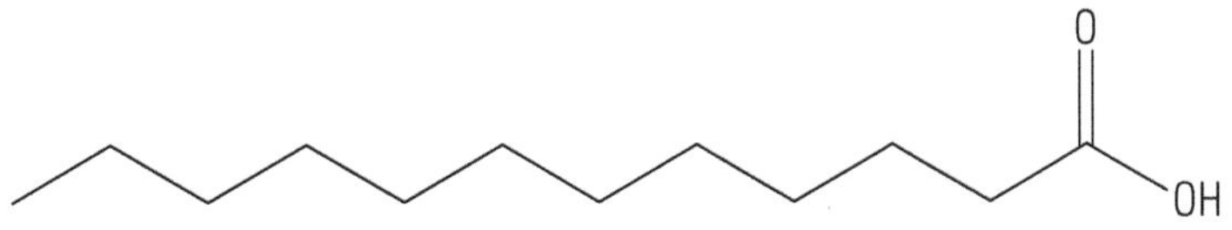

36. Draw the structure of Palmitoleic acid.

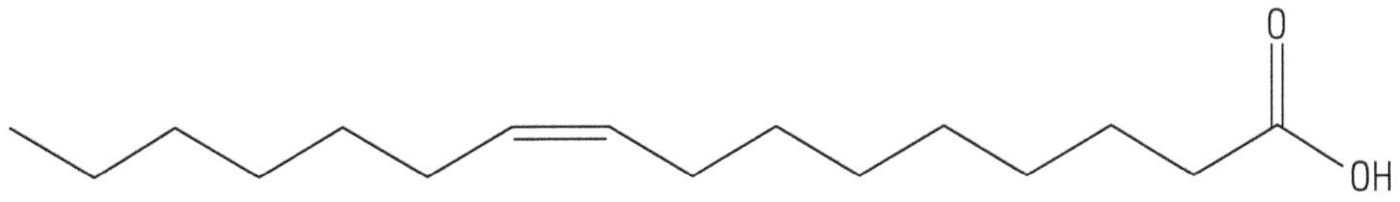

37. Draw the structure of Oleic acid.

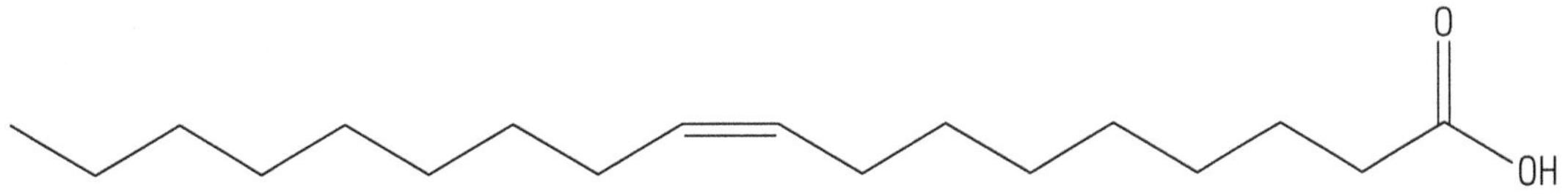

38. What are triglycerides?

Triglycerides are composed of a glycerol backbone to which three fatty acids are "esterfied." They are found in the body fat of humans and animals and are excellent sources of energy.

39. Which of the following structures is a triglyceride?

a.

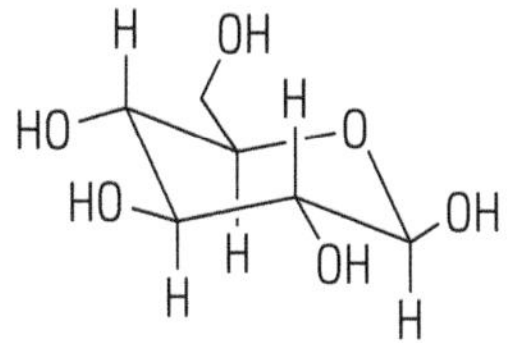

b.

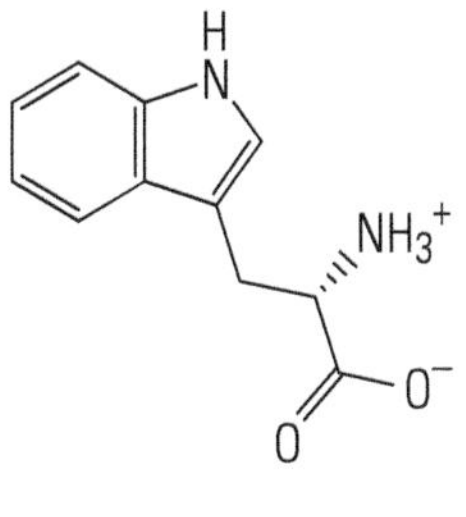

c.

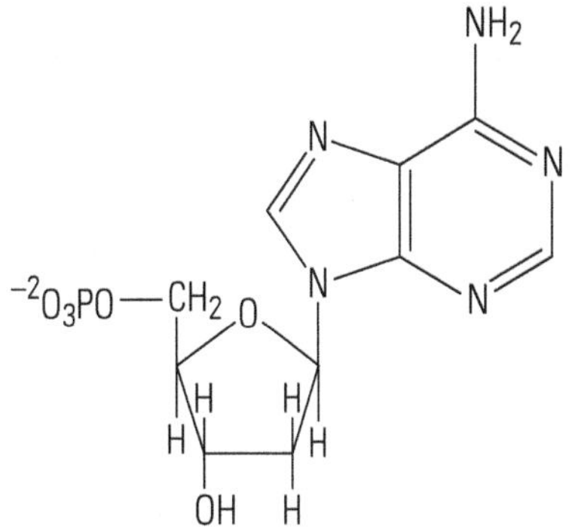

d.

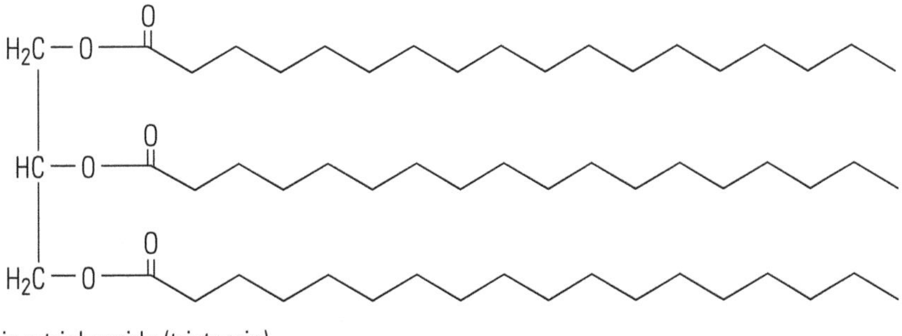

d.   is a triglyceride (tristearin).

40. Draw the structure of tristearin.

41. Explain why seals are a favorite meal source for polar bears.

By consuming the fat found in seals and storing high levels of triglycerides, polar bears can use them as an energy source during hibernation without having to get rid of excessive amounts of nitrogen through urination, which would otherwise be necessary with a high protein diet.

42. What are phospholipids and what are they primarily used for? Describe their general structure.

Phospholipids are another type of lipid which primarily functions as a major component of cell membranes rather than an energy source, but is similar in the structure to that of triglycerides in that both the first and second positions of the glycerol backbone contain fatty acids; however, the third position on the glycerol backbone is replaced by a phosphate group to which various head groups can be linked.

43. What are amphiphilic molecules?

Amphiphilic molecules possess both hydrophilic and hydrophobic properties (i.e. phospholipids are amphiphilic molecules).

44. Draw the characteristic four-ring structure found in steroids.

45. Cholesterol is the precursor to all other steroid hormones such as testosterone, which is the male sex hormone, and β-Estradiol, which is the female sex hormone.

NUCLEIC ACIDS

46. What are nucleic acids?

Nucleic acids are the means by which organisms can transfer genetic information between generations, and are necessary for all forms of known life. They are macromolecular biopolymers composed of monomeric units called nucleotides.

47. Johannes Friedrich Miescher was a Swiss physician and biologist who is most famously known for his discovery of nucleic acids in 1869.

48. What are nucleotides?

    Nucleotides have three parts to their overall structure, which include a five-carbon sugar, nitrogenous base, and phosphate group.

49. Which of the following structures is a nucleotide?

    a.

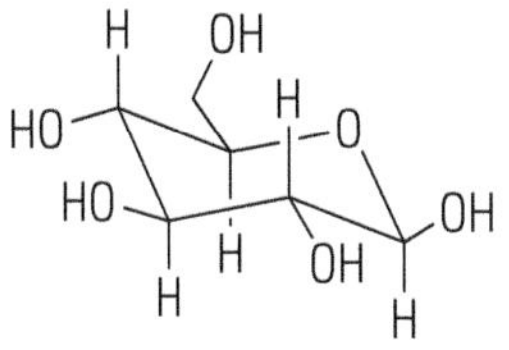

    b.

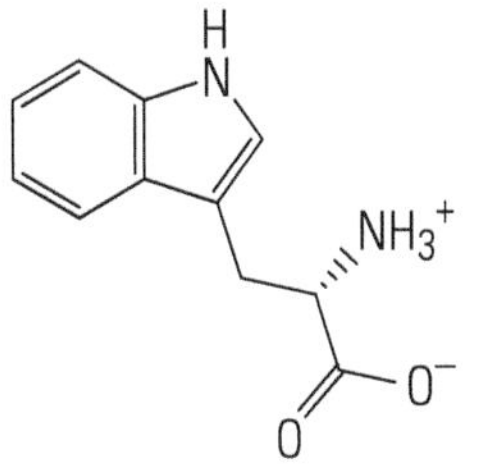

    c.

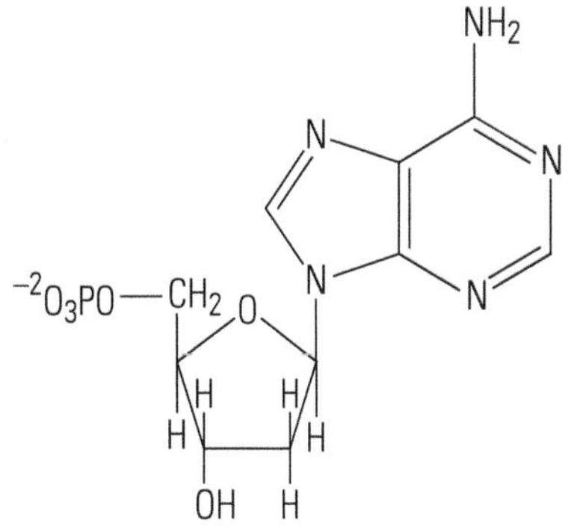

    d.

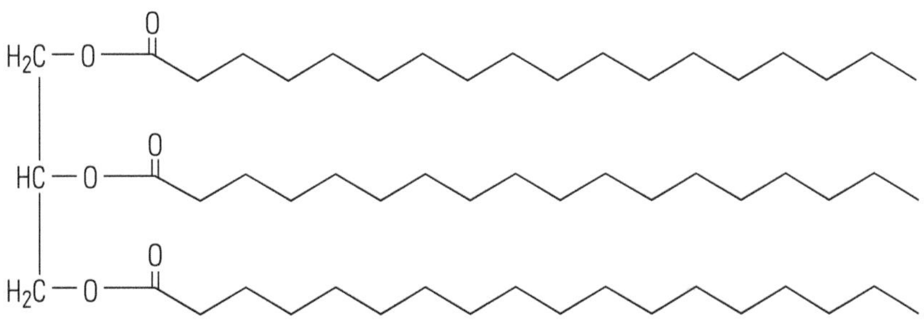

    c. is a nucleotide (nitrogenous base is adenine).

50. Discuss the numbering system commonly used with nucleotides to distinguish various positions found on the sugar versus the nitrogenous base.

    The prime system is used when describing the various positions on the sugar to distinguish it from the numbering pattern used on the nitrogenous base.

51. <u>RNA</u> is necessary for protein synthesis while <u>DNA</u> is the known genetic carrier of information.

52. Which of the following is a ribonucleotide and which is a deoxyribonucleotide? How can you tell?

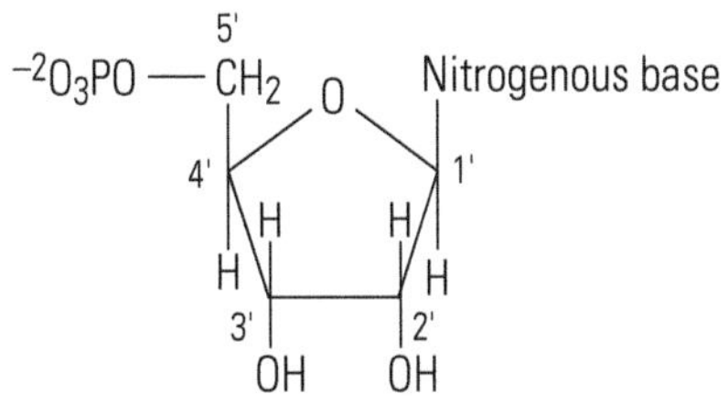

    Ribonucleotide 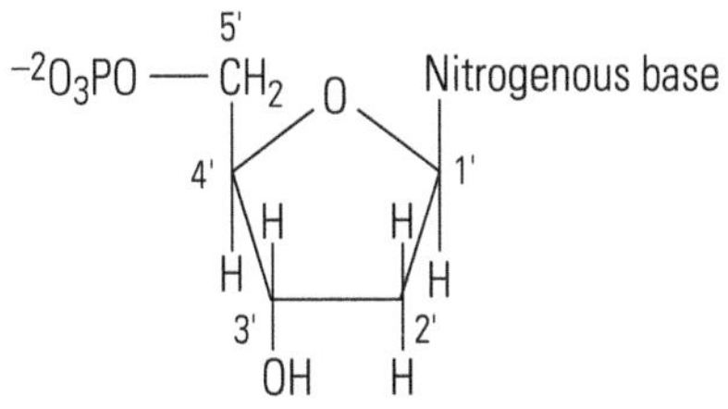   Deoxyribonucleotide

    The deoxyribonucleotides is missing a hydroxyl group at the 2' position on the sugar.

53. What is a nucleoside?

    A nucleoside is basically a nucleotide minus a phosphate group.

54. Draw the general structures of a purine and pyrimidine.

Purine   Pyrimidine

55. Which nitrogenous bases commonly found in DNA and RNA are derived from the purines?

Adenine and guanine are purines and found in both DNA and RNA.

56. Which nitrogenous bases commonly found in DNA and/or RNA are derived from the pyrimidines? Which ones are found in DNA? RNA?

Cytosine, thymine, and uracil are all pyrimidines. Cytosine and thymine are found in DNA, while cytosine and uracil are in RNA.

57. We now know that DNA is a double stranded helix held together by hydrogen bonding between base pairs thanks to work done by James Watson and Francis Crick in 1953.

58. In DNA, each adenine residue base pairs with thymine forming two hydrogen bonds, while each guanine residue base pairs with cytosine forming three hydrogen bonds.

59. In RNA, each adenine residue base pairs with uracil forming two hydrogen bonds, while each guanine residue base pairs with cytosine forming three hydrogen bonds.

60. In two polynucleotide strands that run antiparallel to each other in DNA held together by hydrogen bonding between base pairs, what is meant by the 5′ and 3′ ends of the molecule? Label each end of the following molecule:

The 5' end is the end where the 5' carbon does not have a neighboring nucleotide, while the 3' end is the end where the 3' carbon does not have a neighboring nucleotide. The two strands run antiparallel, such that the 5' end of one strand is aligned alongside the 3' strand of the other.

61. What is a codon?

Three bases to code for one amino acid, which we call a codon.

62. What is a gene?

A gene is defined as a sequence of codons present within a DNA molecule that encodes for a single protein.

63. Genes are contained on structures called <u>chromosomes</u>.

64. Most human cells have 23 pairs of chromosomes for a total of <u>46</u> chromosomes.

65. <u>Down syndrome</u> is one of the most common chromosome irregularities, and is caused by the presence of a third copy of either all or a portion of chromosome 21 (also called trisomy 21).

KEY TERMS

Adenine   One of the five nitrogenous nucleobases found on deoxyribonucleotides and ribonucleotide in DNA and RNA respectively. Its structure is complimentary to thymine in DNA and uracil in RNA.

Aldoses   Monosaccharides derived from aldehydes.

Amine terminus   Referring to peptide primary structure, this term is used to describe the amino acid with the free amine group on the main chain.

Amino acids   Organic compounds that contain amine and carboxyl functional groups, as well as a side-chain which we call the "R group". Amino acids are monomers in the structure of larger biopolymers called proteins.

Amphiphiles   Molecules that possess both hydrophilic and hydrophobic properties.

Amphoteric substances   Compounds that can act as both acids and bases.

Amylopectin   A branched chain of many glucose residues similar to cellulose; however, the glucose residues here are connected by α-glycosidic linkages.

Amylose   A linear chain of many glucose residues similar to cellulose; however, the glucose residues here are connected by α-glycosidic linkages.

Biochemistry   The study of the chemical processes that take place within living organisms.

Carboxylic acid terminus   Referring to peptide primary structure, this term is used to describe the amino acid with the free carboxyl group on the main chain.

Cellulose   The most abundant organic substance on earth, cellulose is a linear chain of several hundred and possibly thousands of glucose residues linked by β-glycosidic linkages. It has very rigid properties attributed primarily to the extensive hydrogen bonding that can take place between neighboring cellulose molecules, and is therefore an important structural component of cell walls found in plants.

Chromosomes   Structures within which genes are contained as sequences of codons in a DNA molecules.

Codon   A sequence of three nucleobases in DNA which encodes a single amino acid.

Complex carbohydrates   Polysaccharides comprised of a large complex number of sugars held together chemically by glycosidic linkages.

Condensation reactions   Reactions in which two amino acids combine to form a larger molecule with the loss of water.

Cytosine   One of the five nitrogenous nucleobases found on deoxyribonucleotides and ribonucleotide in DNA and RNA respectively. Its structure is complimentary to guanine.

Denatured protein   Often if a protein is heated (or there is a change in pH), a protein can be denatured in which it loses its secondary structure and can become random coils.

Deoxyribonucleic acids   Polymers composed of deoxyribonucleotides that are the known carrier of genetic information in biological systems.

Deoxyribonucleotides   The nucleotide (deoxyribose) sugars which are the building blocks of DNA.

Dipeptide   Two amino acids joined together by a single peptide bond.

Disaccharide   Two monosaccharides joined together by a single glycosidic bond.

Enzymes   Biological catalysts that increase the rates of biochemical reactions.

Essential amino acids   Essential amino acids must be obtained through diet as we do not have the capabilities to make them ourselves.

Fatty acids   Carboxylic acids that contain either saturated or unsaturated long aliphatic hydrocarbon tails.

Fibrous proteins   Proteins which tend to be relatively simple linear insoluble structures.

Gene   A sequence of codons present within a DNA molecule that encodes for a single protein.

Globular proteins   Distinct from fibrous proteins, these are generally spherical in shape and tend to be more complex structures.

Glycogen   A highly branched complex carbohydrate which serves as a form of energy storage for animals.

Glycosidic bond   A covalent bond that links a carbohydrate to another entity which may or may not also be a carbohydrate.

Guanine   One of the five nitrogenous nucleobases found on deoxyribonucleotides and ribonucleotide in DNA and RNA respectively. Its structure is complimentary to cytosine.

Hexose   A sugar with six carbons.

Hydrolysis   The splitting of a chemical bond by addition of water.

Ketoses   Monosaccharides derived from ketones.

Messenger RNA (mRNA)   In the process of protein synthesis, this is the RNA molecule that carries the DNA sequence necessary for a specific protein structure to the ribosome for translation.

Monosaccharides   The smallest possible carbohydrates.

Nucleic acids   The means by which organisms can transfer genetic information between generations, nucleic acids are necessary for all forms of known life. They are similar to proteins in that they are also macromolecular biopolymers composed of monomeric units, but in this case the individual monomeric units are called nucleotides rather than amino acids.

Nucleoside   A nucleotide without the phosphate group.

Nucleotides   Nucleotides have three parts to their overall structure, which include a five-carbon sugar, nitrogenous base, and phosphate group. The phosphate group is bound to the 5' carbon on the five-carbon sugar, which is then bound to the nitrogenous base through its 1' carbon (this resulting glycosidic bond is in the β-configuration if you recall our discussion regarding carbohydrates in Section 16.3).

Pentose   A sugar with five carbons.

Peptide backbone   The main chain (excluding R-groups) of a polypeptide.

Peptides   Short chains of amino acids.

Phospholipids   Phospholipids are similar in structure to triglycerides in that both the 1st and 2nd positions of the glycerol backbone contain fatty acids; however, the 3rd third position on the glycerol backbone is replaced by a phosphate group to which various head groups can be linked.

Polyhydroxy molecules   Molecules containing more than one hydroxyl group, derived from either aldehydes or ketones.

Polysaccharides   Oligomers and polymers composed of monosaccharides linked via a series of glycosidic bonds.

Primary protein structure   The amino acid order or sequence in a protein.

Proteins   Large biomolecules composed of individual building blocks called amino acids.

Purine   A heterocyclic, aromatic, organic compound which is the basic ring structure of the nucleobases adenine and guanine.

Pyrimidine   A heterocyclic, aromatic, organic compound which is the basic ring structure of the nucleobases thymine, uracil, and cytosine.

Quarternary protein structure   The number, arrangement, and orientation of two or more protein sub-units in a multi-protein complex, such as hemoglobin.

Random coil   An element of secondary protein structure, which is characterized by an irregular structure.

Ribonucleic acids   A polymer composed of ribonucleotides that is necessary for protein synthesis.

Ribonucleotides   The nucleotide (ribose) sugars which are the building blocks of RNA.

Ribosomes   Structures in the cytoplasm of the cell wherein protein synthesis occurs.

Secondary protein structure   Polypeptide folding arrangements attributed to local interactions between individual amino acids, resulting in various geometric patterns.

Starch   A mixture of both amylose and amylopectin, starch is another example of a complex carbohydrate primarily used for the main energy storage source for plants.

Tertiary protein structure   The global or long-range geometric shape of a single polypeptide.

Tetrose   A sugar with four carbons.

Thymine   One of the four nitrogenous nucleobases found on deoxyribonucleotides in DNA. Its structure is complimentary to adenine.

Transcription   In order to generate a protein, the DNA sequence is transcribed in a process called transcription into messenger RNA (mRNA) while in the nucleus.

Transfer RNA (tRNA)   In the process of protein synthesis, this is the RNA molecule that helps to decode the mRNA and ensures that the appropriate amino acid is added in the correct order to the growing end of the amino acid chain.

Translation   The synthesis of a protein with the aid of mRNA.

Triglycerides   Organic compounds which are composed of a glycerol backbone to which three fatty acids are "esterfied."

Triose   A sugar with three carbons.

Tripeptide   A molecule that consists of three amino acids connected via two peptide bonds.

Uracil   One of the four nitrogenous nucleobases found on ribonucleotides in RNA. Its structure is complimentary to adenine.

Zwitterions   An ion which contains separate positive and negative charges.

α-helix   An element of secondary protein structure, this is characterized by a coiled or spiraled conformation that can be formed due to hydrogen bond interactions between the backbone amine groups and carboxyl groups of amino acids approximately three to five residues apart along the main chain.

β-pleated sheets   An element of secondary protein structure, these are characterized by assemblies of multiple polypeptide chains aligned side-by-side which are held together primarily by hydrogen bonds between neighboring chains.

Lightning Source UK Ltd.
Milton Keynes UK
UKHW011845141021
392206UK00006B/253